Contents

PART II   FIBER FORMATION

PART III   FIBER PROPERTIES

Preface

Fiber science is the study of the formation, structure, and properties of fibers on various scales, ranging from the atomic to microscopic to macroscopic (large enough to be visible). It provides the fundamental knowledge for the industrial application of fibers in a wide range of areas, including apparel, home furnishing, nonowovens, composites, biomedical materials, energy storage and conversion, etc. Fiber science is, therefore, an essential part of the education of fiber scientists, engineers, and technologists in both academic and industry settings.

This book deals with the fundamental aspects of the formation, structure, and properties of fibers. It starts with the chemical and physical structures of polymer fibers, non-polymer fibers, and nanofibers, followed by their formation mechanisms. Properties of fibers are then discussed and correlated with their structure and formation mechanisms to establish the formation-structure-property relationships, enabling readers to advance to more complex engineering and design for numerous applications and to grasp the underlying concepts of fiber manufacturing techniques. Although the book is arranged to give a sense of direction to the readers to start from the beginning and proceed to the end, each chapter is self-contained and can be read independently.

This book covers both polymer and non-polymer fibers, as well as novel nanofibers. The book is not intended to provide a comprehensive review on all aspects of fibers. Instead, it is to provide the background of knowledge and understanding of fiber science, and to establish the foundation necessary to understand and contribute to the development of the subject in the 21st century. Hence, the book will be useful to all scientists and engineers involved in academic and industrial research related to different aspects of fiber science and to undergraduate and graduate students in the fields of fiber science, textiles, composites, polymer science and engineering, materials science and engineering, and chemical engineering.

Xiangwu Zhang
College of Textiles
North Carolina State University

CHAPTER 1

Introduction

Fibers are used for making materials for a wide range of applications, including apparel, home furnishing, nonwovens, composites, biomedical materials, energy storage and conversion, etc. The study of these materials begins with an understanding of the fibers from which they are made. Fiber science is the study of the formation, structure and properties of fibers on various scales, ranging from the atomic to microscopic to macroscopic (large enough to be visible). These three aspects are not independent from each other. Figure 1.1 shows the relationships among the formation, structure, and properties of fibers. Establishing quantitative and predictive relationships among the way fibers are formed, their structures and properties is fundamental to the study of fibers.

There are many different types of fibers. Most fibers have diameters greater than 1 micrometer, and they can be divided into polymer fibers and non-polymer fibers. Polymer fibers include synthetic polymer fibers and natural polymer fibers. Synthetic polymer fibers are made from polymers synthesized from raw

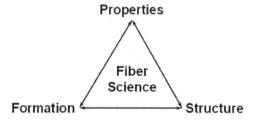

Figure 1.1. The triangle shows the interdependence of formation, structure, and properties of fibers.

materials, such as petroleum-based chemicals or petrochemicals. In general, synthetic polymer fibers are created by forcing, usually through extrusion, polymers through small holes (called spinnerets) into air or other mediums to form filaments. Natural polymer fibers include those produced by plants and animals. They are typically biodegradable and can be classified as natural cellulose fibers and natural protein fibers. Celluloses and proteins also can be modified and extruded into fibers using methods similar to those used in making synthetic polymer fibers. The resultant fibers are typically called manufactured cellulose and protein fibers. Non-polymer fibers are those that are not made from polymers, and include carbon, glass, ceramic, metal, and composite fibers, etc. In addition to traditional classifications, microscale polymer and non-polymer fibers, nanoscale fibers (i.e., nanofibers) have been developed using methods, such as electrospinning, centrifugal spinning, melt blowing, bicomponent fiber separation, phase separation, template synthesis, and self-assembly. Nanofibers also can be made of different materials and are typically intended for special applications. Figure 1.2 shows the fiber classification that is used in this book.

Part 1 of this book focuses on the chemical and physical structures of fibers, and it starts with synthetic polymer fibers. The fundamental knowledge on the chemical structure of synthetic polymer fibers is essential for understanding their physical structure and properties. The chemical structure, such as chain structure and configuration, of synthetic polymer fibers is determined when the polymer is synthesized. In general, the process for making the polymer into fibers does not change the chemical structure. The chemical structure of synthetic polymer fibers

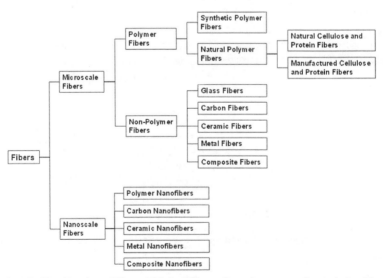

Figure 1.2. Classification of fibers. This is different from the commonly used classification of textile fibers. In the textile fiber classification, fibers are divided into natural fibers and man-made fibers.

does not depend on their shape or morphology, either. In addition to chemical structure, the physical structure of synthetic polymer fibers also is important in determining the fiber properties. Unlike chemical structure, the physical structure does depend on the processing and the final shape of the fibers. Chapters 2 and 3 deal with the chemical and physical structures of synthetic polymer fibers, respectively.

The chemical and physical structures of natural polymer fibers are more complex than those of synthetic polymer fibers. Two most important building units for natural polymer fibers are cellulose and protein. Natural cellulose fibers come from the "stringy" portions of plants ranging from the fine seed fibers of the cotton plant to the coarse pineapple leaf fibers. Natural protein fibers are hairs of animals, like the sheep and the delicate filaments spun by silkworms and insects. In addition to these natural fibers, manufactured cellulose and protein fibers also are based on natural biopolymers. Although these fibers are processed like synthetic polymer fibers, they are discussed in this book together with natural cellulose and protein fibers since they have similar chemical structures. The chemical and physical structures of natural polymer fibers are discussed in Chapters 4 and 5, respectively.

Chapter 6 addresses the structure of non-polymer fibers. A wide range of non-polymer fibers, such as carbon, glass, silicon carbide, boron, asbestos, and metal fibers, now is available commercially. Compared with polymer fibers, non-polymer fibers often are stronger, stiffer, more heat resistant, and nonflammable. However, except for metal fibers, non-polymer fibers also are characterized by their brittleness. These property characteristics are directly related to the atomic arrangement and the defect structure of non-polymer fibers. Chapter 6 discusses the structure of two most used non-polymer fibers: carbon and glass fibers.

Nanofibers are an important class of material that is useful in a variety of applications, including filtration, tissue engineering, protective clothing, composites, battery separators, energy storage, etc. Nanoscience is the study of atoms, molecules, and objects with sizes ranging from 1 to 100 nm. However, the term "nanofibers" has been traditionally used for fibers with diameters less than 1000 nm. Chapter 7 addresses the main structural characteristics of nanofibers.

In Part II, the formation of different fibers is discussed. Synthetic polymer fibers and manufactured natural polymer fibers can be produced by melt spinning, solution spinning, gel spinning, liquid crystal spinning, dispersion spinning, etc. To convert the polymer components into the desired fiber structures, it is important to understand the flow behavior of polymers. Chapter 8 describes the basic knowledge related to the flow behavior of polymers. The use of such knowledge in the formation of synthetic polymer fibers and manufactured cellulose and protein fibers is covered in Chapters 9 and 10, respectively. Chapter 10 also addresses the formation processes of natural cellulose and protein fibers, such as cotton, wool and silk, which are controlled by the genetic codes and are complex.

Non-polymer fibers can be produced by many different methods, depending on the type of materials used. For example, carbon fibers often are made by high temperature treatment of carbon precursors in an inert atmosphere. Glass fibers and some ceramic fibers can be directly spun from their melts. Ceramic fibers also can be obtained by the calcination of ceramic precursor fibers or by the chemical vapor deposition of precursor gas on a carbon fiber substrate. Chapter 11 focuses on the formation of carbon and glass fibers.

Electrospinning is the most reported method for producing nanofibers. Electrospinning uses an electrical charge to draw fine jets from a solution or melt. It has been combined with other methods to produce nanofibers of polymers, carbons, ceramics, metals, and composites. In addition to electrospinning, there are other methods that can be used to produce nanofibers. For example, centrifugal spinning utilizes the centrifugal force generated by a rotating spinneret to produce nanofibers. Melt blowing is typically used to produce fibers with diameters greater than 1 μm by using high-velocity air; however, it can produce nanofibers by using carefully selected materials and processing parameters. Bicomponent fiber separation, phase separation, template synthesis and self-assembly also are useful methods for fabricating nanofibers from different materials. Chapter 12 discusses the fiber formation process and processing-structure relationships of electrospinning. Other nanofiber formation methods are covered in Chapter 13.

Part III of the book discusses different properties of fibers. Fiber properties can be classified into primary and secondary properties. Primary properties are those that fibers must possess so they can be converted into useful products. Examples of primary properties are aspect ratio, strength, flexibility, cohesiveness, and uniformity. Secondary properties are those that are desirable and can improve consumer satisfaction with the end-products made from the fibers. Secondary properties include, but are not limited to physical shape, density, modulus, elongation, elastic recovery, resilience, thermal properties, electrical properties, color and optical properties, moisture regain, resistance to chemical and environmental conditions, resistance to biological organisms, and resistance to insects. Chapter 14 provides an introduction to these primary and secondary properties.

Among various properties, mechanical properties probably are the most important properties of fibers. There are many different types of mechanical properties, including tensile, torsional, bending, and compressional properties. Among them, tensile properties are the most intensively studied for fibers, probably because of their unique shape. However, other types of mechanical properties also are important. Chapter 15 first describes the basic definitions of Hooke's law, stress, strain, and tensile, bulk and shear moduli, and then gives more detailed discussion on the tensile, torsional, bending, and compressional properties of fibers.

Fibers often exhibit both viscous and elastic characteristics when undergoing deformation. As a matter of fact, all materials can exhibit elastic and viscous characteristics simultaneously if the time scale of observation is comparable to the relaxation times needed for large-scale atomic rearrangements in these materials.

However, the relaxation times of most non-polymer fibers are significantly greater than the time scale of normal observations, and hence it is hard to observe their viscoelastic behavior at room temperature. On the other hand, polymer fibers have relaxation times that are comparable to the time scale of observation, and they easily display viscoelastic behavior. Chapter 16, therefore, focuses on the viscoelastic properties of polymer fibers.

Thermal properties of fiber-based products are important in many applications. For example, the main function of textile fabrics is to protect the wearer from cold or heat, and to ensure appropriate heat transfer between the human body and the environment in order to maintain the physiological thermal balance of the wearer. Composites also need appropriate thermal properties so they can be useful in aerospace and space industries. The thermal properties of fibers are the starting point for understanding the final properties of these products, although many other factors also play important roles. Chapter 17 deals with the most basic thermal properties of fibers, including heat capacity, specific heat, thermal conductivity, thermal expansion and contraction, glass transition, melting, and degradation and decomposition.

The electrical behavior of non-polymer fibers is varied from excellent electrical conductors (e.g., carbon fibers) to good insulators (e.g., glass fibers). However, with only a few exceptions, pure polymer fibers are insulators with electrical conductivities in the order of 10^{-16} S cm^{-1}. Static charges can be easily generated and accumulated on the surface of polymer fibers. This could lead to serious consequences, such as handling problems during fiber processing, breaking down of sensitive electronic devices, ignition of flammable vapors and dusts in certain environments, and clinging tendency and annoying electrical shocks during consumer use. Chapter 18 focuses on the electrical conductivity and static charging of polymer fibers.

Frictional properties of fibers affect the processing, structure and properties of all fiber-based products. For example, friction is the force that holds the fibers together in yarns and fabrics. Without sufficient friction, the strength and structural integrity of yarns and fabrics will be lost. However, if the friction is too high, it could cause equipment failure, fiber surface damage, and even fiber breakage. Chapter 19 addresses the basic principles associated with the frictional properties of polymer fibers.

The transmission, reflection and absorption of light determine the visual appearance of an individual fiber. The appearance of fiber assemblies is then the result of the combined effects of individual fibers, although it also is affected by the arrangements of fibers. Optical properties of fibers also provide a convenient measure of many structural characteristics, especially the molecular orientation. Chapter 20 discusses the practical aspects of the optical properties of fibers.

PROBLEMS

(1) Read any scientific or engineering paper in fiber science written in the last five years, and discuss how it advances the field. Provide exact reference: author, title, journal, volume, page, and year.

(2) Pick at least one type of fiber from the list: polyester, nylon, acrylic, olefin, cotton, wool, silk, and glass fibers. Then, carry out a literature search to find out the production and consumption of that fiber in the United States and in the world.

PART I

Fiber Structure

CHAPTER 2

Chemical Structure of Synthetic Polymer Fibers

The fundamental knowledge on the chemical structure of synthetic polymer fibers (or simply synthetic fibers) is essential for understanding their physical structure and properties. The chemical structure, such as chain structure and configuration, of synthetic fibers is determined when the polymer is synthesized. The process of making the polymer into fibers typically does not change the chemical structure. The chemical structure of synthetic fibers does not depend on their shape or morphology, either. In addition to chemical structure, the physical structure of synthetic fibers also is important in determining the fiber properties. Unlike chemical structure, the physical structure does depend on the processing and the final shape of the fibers. The physical structure of synthetic fibers also is influenced by their chemical structure. This chapter focuses on the chemical structure of synthetic fibers, and the next chapter deals with the physical structure.

2.1 REPEATING UNITS

2.1.1 CONCEPT OF REPEATING UNIT

One essential concept to define the chemical structure of synthetic fibers is the repeating unit. The term repeating unit denotes an elementary unit whose repetition would produce the entire polymer chain, except for the chain ends. Basically, a polymer chain is constructed by connecting the repeat units together successively along the main chain, like the beads of a necklace (Figure 2.1). A repeating unit is not to be confused with the term monomer, which refers to the small molecule, from which a polymer is synthesized. Another important term for describing the chemical structure is monomeric unit, which is a structural unit, defined by the monomer, constituting part of the repeating unit.

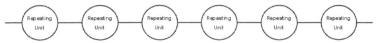

Figure 2.1. Repeating units connect together successively forming a linear polymer chain.

Repeating unit, monomer and monomeric unit are three different concepts. They can be coincident, but in many cases, they are different from each other. Table 2.1 shows three different cases. In some polymers, such as polyethylene and polypropylene, the monomers do not lose any atoms during the synthesis process, and the repeating and monomeric units keep the same composition and structure with the monomers (Case 1). In some other polymers, the monomers lose atoms during the synthesis process, and the repeating and monomer units differ from the monomers by a limited number of atoms in the chemical formula (Case 2). One such example is polyamide 6 (nylon 6), which can be synthesized from monomer ε-aminocaproic acid. During the synthesis of nylon 6, water molecules are lost and the resultant repeating and monomeric units have fewer atoms than the corresponding monomer structure. There are also polymers, in which the repeating unit, monomer and monomeric unit are all different from each other (Case 3). For example, polyamide 6,6 (nylon 6,6) can be synthesized by alternate combination of two different monomers hexamethylenediamine and adipic acid. As a result, the repeating unit of nylon 6,6 is formed by two monomeric units, which also are different from the monomer structures due to the loss of water molecules.

2.1.2 REPEATING UNITS OF SYNTHETIC FIBERS

The physical structure and properties of synthetic fibers are largely determined by the repeating units. Polymers with all kinds of repeating units have been developed for different applications. However, only a few of these polymers have been made into synthetic fibers. This is because to make useful fibers, the polymers have to meet certain structure requirements, which will be discussed later. Table 2.2 shows the repeating units for some important polymers that can be made into synthetic fibers.

Table 2.1. Comparison of monomers, monomeric units, and repeating units.

Polymer	Monomer	Monomeric Unit	Repeating Unit	Polymer Structure
Case 1: Monomer = Monomeric Unit = Repeating Unit				
Polyethylene (PE)	$H_2C=CH_2$	$-CH_2-CH_2-$	$-CH_2-CH_2-$	$-[CH_2-CH_2]_n-$
Polypropylene (PP)	$H_2C=CH$ $\quad CH_3$	$-CH_2-CH-$ $\quad CH_3$	$-CH_2-CH-$ $\quad CH_3$	$-[CH_2-CH]_n-$ $\quad CH_3$
Case 2: Monomer ≠ Monomeric Unit = Repeating Unit				
Polyamide 6 (Nylon 6)				
Case 3: Monomer ≠ Monomeric Unit ≠ Repeating Unit				
Polyamide 6,6 (Nylon 6,6)				

Table 2.2. Repeating units of some important polymers.

Type	Polymer Name	Repeating Unit
Polyolefins	Polyethylene (PE)	$-CH_2-CH_2-$
	Polypropylene (PP)	$-CH_2-CH-$ with CH_3
Vinyl Polymers	Polyvinyl chloride (PVC)	$-CH_2-CH-$ with Cl
	Polyvinylidene chloride (PVDC)	$-CH_2-C-$ with Cl, Cl
	Polyvinylidene fluoride (PVDF)	$-CH_2-C-$ with F, F
	Polytetrafluoroethylene (PTFE)	$-C-C-$ with F, F, F, F
	Polyvinyl alcohol (PVA)	$-CH_2-CH-$ with OH
	Polystyrene (PS)	$-CH_2-CH-$ with phenyl
	Polyacrylonitrile (PAN)	$-CH_2-CH-$ with $C\equiv N$
	Polyvinylidene dinitrile	$-CH_2-C-$ with $C\equiv N$, $C\equiv N$
Polyesters	Polyethylene terephthalate (PET)	
	Polytrimethylene terephthalate (PTT)	
	Polybutylene terephthalate (PBT)	
	Polyethylene naphthalate (PEN)	
	Poly-1,4-cyclohexylene -dimethylene terephthalate (PCDT)	
Polyamides	Nylon 6	$-N(CH_2)_5C-$ with H, O
	Nylon 6,6	$-N(CH_2)_6N-C(CH_2)_4C-$ with H, H, O, O
	Nylon 11	$-N(CH_2)_{10}C-$ with H, O
	Nylon 6,10	$-N(CH_2)_6N-C(CH_2)_8C-$ with H, H, O, O
Aramids	Polyparaphenylene terephthalamide (Kevlar®)	
	Polymetaphenylene isophthalamide (Normax®)	

Type	Polymer Name	Repeating Unit
Others	Polyphenylene sulfide (PPS)	
	Polycarbonate (PC)	
	Polybenzimidazole (PBI)	
	Polyparaphenylene benzobisoxazole (PBO)	
	Polyparaphenylene benzobisthiazole (PBT)	
	Polyhydroquinone-diimidazopyridine (M-5)	

2.2   MOLECULAR WEIGHT

The size of polymer chains can be characterized by measuring the molecular weight (M). Typically, the size of polymer chains increases with increase in molecular weight. The molecular weight of a polymer is determined by the degree of polymerization (N), i.e., the number of repeating units in the polymer chain, by the following equation:

$$M = NM_0 \qquad (2.1)$$

where M_0 is the molecular weight of the repeating unit.

2.2.1   AVERAGE MOLECULAR WEIGHTS

With very few exceptions, the molecular weight of a polymer does not have a single value because different polymer chains can have different lengths. Hence, there is a distribution of molecular weights. The molecular weight distribution is typically shown graphically by plotting the number of polymer chains against the molecular weight, as exemplified in Figure 2.2.

The distribution curve of molecular weights is essential for some applications. However, in most practical uses of polymers, it is more convenient to characterize the distribution in terms of average molecular weights. Since the molecular weight of a polymer changes in intervals of M_0, the distribution of molecular weights is actually discontinuous. As a result, the average molecular weights are defined by assuming the polymer chains exist in discrete fractions i containing N_i molecules of molecular weight M_i.

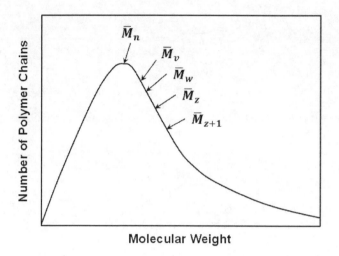

Figure 2.2. A distribution of molecular weight along with various average molecular weights.

Average molecular weights can be defined several different ways. Among them, the two most important ones are number average molecular weight ($\bar{M}_n$) and weight average molecular weight ($\bar{M}_w$). The number average molecular weight is defined as the total weight of the polymer divided by the total number of the molecules, *i.e.*,

$$\bar{M}_n = \frac{\text{Total Weight}}{\text{Total Number}} = \frac{\sum_{i=1}^{\infty} N_i M_i}{\sum_{i=1}^{\infty} N_i} \tag{2.2}$$

Here, the term $N_i / \sum_{i=0}^{\infty} N_i$ is physically the number fraction (x_i) of polymer chains with molecular weight M_i. Therefore, Equation 2.2 can be rewritten as:

$$\bar{M}_n = \sum_{i=1}^{\infty} x_i M_i \tag{2.3}$$

Many polymer properties are not just dependent on the number of polymer chains, but on the size or weight of each polymer chain. In addition, many molecular weight measurements, such as light scatting and ultracentrifuge methods, are based on the contributions of polymer chains according to their sizes. For these cases, we need to use the weight average molecular weight, which can be described as:

$$\bar{M}_w = \frac{\sum_{i=1}^{\infty} N_i M_i^2}{\sum_{i=1}^{\infty} N_i M_i} \tag{2.4}$$

In Equation 2.4, $N_i M_i / \sum_{i=1}^{\infty} N_i M_i$ is the weight fraction (w_i) of polymer chains with molecular weight M_i. Hence, an alternative form for the weight average molecular weight is:

$$\bar{M}_w = \sum_{i=1}^{\infty} w_i M_i \tag{2.5}$$

Comparing Equations 2.3 and 2.5, it is clear that $\bar{M}_n$ is the average M_i weighed according to the number fraction and $\bar{M}_w$ is the average M_i weighed according to the weight fraction.

In addition to $\bar{M}_n$ and $\bar{M}_w$, higher molecular weight averages are also used. For example, $\bar{M}_w$ can be derived from $\bar{M}_n$ simply by replacing N_i with $N_i M_i$ in Equation 2.2. This process can be generalized to replace N_i by $N_i M_i^k$ to obtain an average molecular weight denoted as $\bar{M}_k$:

$$\bar{M}_k = \frac{\sum_{i=1}^{\infty} N_i M_i^{k+1}}{\sum_{i=1}^{\infty} N_i M_i^k} \tag{2.6}$$

From Equation 2.6, it is seen that $\bar{M}_n = \bar{M}_0$ and $\bar{M}_w = \bar{M}_1$. When k is greater than 1, z average molecular weight $\bar{M}_z$ and z+1 average molecular weight $\bar{M}_{z+1}$ can be defined as:

$$\bar{M}_z = \bar{M}_2 = \frac{\sum_{i=1}^{\infty} N_i M_i^3}{\sum_{i=1}^{\infty} N_i M_i^2} \tag{2.7}$$

and

$$\bar{M}_{z+1} = \bar{M}_3 = \frac{\sum_{i=1}^{\infty} N_i M_i^4}{\sum_{i=1}^{\infty} N_i M_i^3} \tag{2.8}$$

which often are used in ultracentrifugation experiments.

One average molecular weight that often is used, but does not fit into the form of $\bar{M}_k$ is the viscosity average molecular weight $\bar{M}_v$:

$$\bar{M}_v = \left(\frac{\sum_{i=1}^{\infty} N_i M_i^{1+\alpha}}{\sum_{i=1}^{\infty} N_i M_i} \right)^{\frac{1}{\alpha}}$$ (2.9)

where α is a constant that is determined by the polymer/solvent system used during the viscosity measurements.

The relationship between various average molecular weights is shown in Figure 2.2. It is seen that, the average molecular weights rank in the order:

$$\bar{M}_n \leq \bar{M}_v \leq \bar{M}_w \leq \bar{M}_z \leq \bar{M}_{z+1}$$ (2.10)

The equalities hold only for monodisperse polymers, *i.e.*, only when all polymer chains have the same molecular weight. As discussed previously, most polymers are polydisperse since different polymer chains can have different lengths. Hence, the different average molecular weights are all different from each other, and they rank in the order shown in Equation 2.10. Therefore, the difference between the average molecular weights is a good indication of the distribution of molecular weight. For example, the ratio of the weight average molecular weight to the number average molecular weight is known as the polydispersity index (*PDI*).

$$PDI = \frac{\bar{M}_w}{\bar{M}_n}$$ (2.11)

The polydispersity index is always greater than or equal to one. It is equal to one only if the polymer is monodisperse. For polydisperse polymers, the polydispersity index is greater than one. A larger polydispersity index indicates a broader distribution of molecular weights.

2.2.2 EFFECT OF MOLECULAR WEIGHT

Properties of synthetic fibers are closely related to their molecular weight. To obtain useful fibers, the molecular weight of a polymer must exceed a critical value. Below the critical molecular weight, the polymer does not have the physical properties needed for fiber application. Beyond the critical molecular weight, the mechanical strength of the resultant fibers increases rapidly with increases in molecular weight. However, the increase of mechanical strength becomes lower at high molecular weights, and the strength eventually becomes relatively constant. In addition to mechanical strength, many other physical properties, such as modulus and glass transition temperature, have the same trend. Figure 2.3 shows the effect of molecular weight on fiber properties.

Although higher molecular weight leads to better fiber properties, synthetic fibers are not always made from polymers that have very high molecular weights. With increase in molecular weight, the polymer chains tend to entangle more, which significantly increases the viscosity of polymer melt or solution. Eventually, the viscosity of the polymer melt or solution becomes so high and the formation of fibers is no longer possible or economic. Therefore, there is a certain molecular weight range that is suitable for fiber application, as shown in Figure 2.3.

2.3 CONFIGURATIONS

Although there are many different polymers, not all of them can be made into useful fibers. To be made into useful fibers, the polymer chains must be linear and the molecular weight needs to be high enough for mechanical stability, but low enough for dissolving or melting for forming fibers. The polymer chains also must have the appropriate configuration. Configuration refers to the permanent geometry resulted from the spatial arrangement of bonds in a polymer chain. Only polymer chains with certain configuration can form fibers with desirable physical structure and properties.

2.3.1 HEAD-TO-HEAD AND HEAD-TO-TAIL

One simple but important configuration type is the head-to-head or head-to-tail placement of repeating units along the polymer chain. Figure 2.4 show the

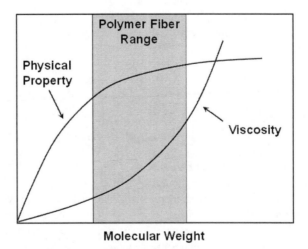

Figure 2.3. Effects of molecular weight on the property of synthetic fibers and the viscosity of polymer melt or solution.

head-to-head and head-to-tail configurations of polypropylene, in which the α carbon connected to the methyl group is considered as the head and β carbon as the tail.

The head-to-tail configuration is the thermodynamically and spatially preferred structure for most polymers that contain side groups. However, it is possible to deliberately design the synthesis process to obtain polymer chains with head-to-head configuration. Polymers with head-to-tail and head-to-head configurations have different properties. For example, poly-isobutylene with the head-to-tail configuration has a glass transition temperature of −61°C and a melting temperature of 5°C; it is an excellent rubber material. On the other hand, poly-isobutylene with the head-to-head configuration has a glass transition temperature of 87°C and a melting temperature of 187°C; it cannot be used as a rubber. In fiber application, synthetic fibers are typically made from polymers with the head-to-tail configuration.

2.3.2 TACTICITY

Tacticity is the relative stereochemistry of adjacent chiral centers within a polymer chain. The term chiral here is used to describe a structure that is not superimposable on its mirror image. Figure 2.5 shows an example of a chiral center and shows that the chemical structures on both sides of the mirror have identical chemical composition, but they represent different spatial configurations since they are nonsuperimposable. The cause of the two different configurations is the asymmetric carbon in the center of the structure, known as the chiral center.

For a carbon atom to become a chiral center, it must be linked to four different atoms or groups. Figure 2.6 shows a typical chiral center in a polymer chain. If the C* atom is not in the middle of the polymer chain, the two chain segments on each side are of unequal length and can be considered to be different groups. As

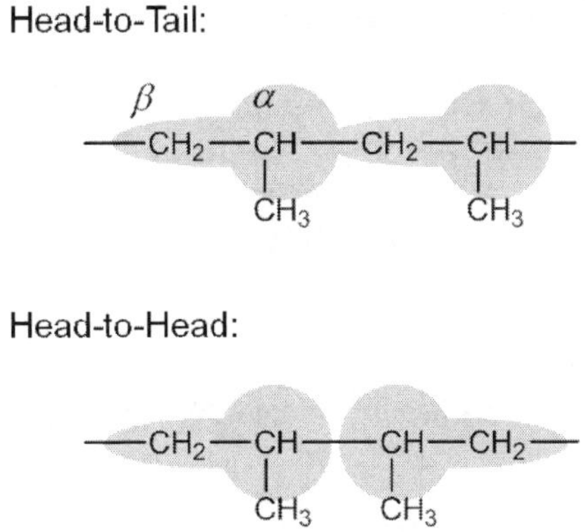

Head-to-Tail:

Head-to-Head:

Figure 2.4. Head-to-tail and head-to-head configurations of polypropylene.

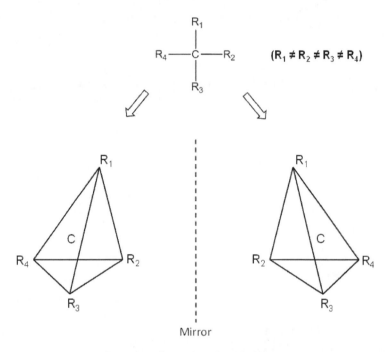

Figure 2.5. Illustration of a chiral center.

a result, the C* atom becomes a chiral center if the R group is different from the H atom. For polymers with chiral centers, the different spatial arrangements lead to their tacticity.

Many polymers, such as polypropylene, polyvinyl chloride, and polyacrylonitrile, have R groups on every other carbon atom. If the chiral centers connected to all these R groups have the same configuration, the polymer is called isotactic. If the chiral centers alternate in configuration, the polymer is called syndiotactic. The polymer becomes atactic if the chiral centers have random order in configuration (Figure 2.7).

Figure 2.7 illustrates the three-dimensional structure of isotactic, syndiotactic and atactic configurations. The differences between these configurations also can be presented in two dimensions (Figure 2.8). The two-dimensional illustration is made by using Fisher projections, in which the R groups are placed either up or down. All up or all down represent the isotactic configuration. Alternating up and down represents syndiotactic configuration. The atactic configuration is shown as random up and down.

The tacticity of polymers has important effects on their physical structure and properties. Atactic polymers usually are amorphous unless the side group is extremely polar and allows some crystallinity. On the other hand, both isotactic and syndiotactic structures can crystalize due to their regularity along the polymer

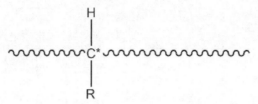

Figure 2.6. A chiral center (C*) in a polymer chain.

Isotactic:

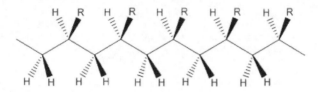

Syndiotactic:

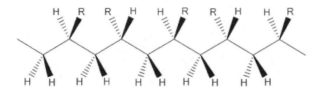

Atactic:

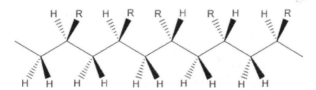

Figure 2.7. Three-dimensional illustration of isotactic, syndiotactic and atactic configurations. The triangular and dotted lines indicate bonds to atoms or groups above or below the plane of the carbon-carbon backbone, respectively.

chains. However, their unit cells and melting temperatures are different. As a result, to make synthetic fibers, it is important to select polymers with appropriate tacticity. For example, polypropylene fibers typically are made from the isotactic structure, which is highly crystalline and has a melting point of at least 160°C due to the closely packed regular chains. Syndiotactic or atactic polypropylene is not

Isotactic:

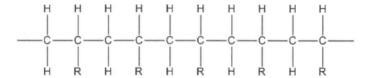

Syndiotactic:

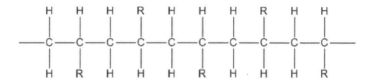

Atactic:

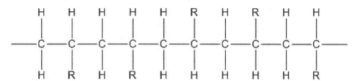

Figure 2.8. Two-dimensional illustration of isotactic, syndiotactic and atactic configurations.

being made into synthetic fibers since they either have low degree of crystallinity or are completely amorphous.

2.3.3 SKELETAL STRUCTURE

There are many different skeletal structures. Figure 2.9 shows three most important skeletal structures: linear, branched, and network. In linear polymers, repeating units are arranged in a chainlike fashion with no branches or bridges between the chains. On the other hand, branched polymers have side chains, i.e., branches, of significant length that are bonded to the main chains. Network polymers contain branches that connect different polymer chains into a "network".

Synthetic fibers typically are made from linear polymers since they can be aligned and packed closely during fiber formation to achieve the desired physical structure and properties. Branched polymer chains are hard to pack and hence they are seldom made into synthetic fibers. Network polymers do not melt or

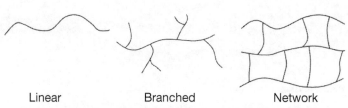

| Linear | Branched | Network |

Figure 2.9. Linear, branched and network skeletal structures.

dissolve, and they cannot be spun into fibers. However, after linear polymers are made into fibers, they can be crosslinked to form a network structure to alter the fiber properties by using chemical crosslinkers or radiation.

2.3.4 COPOLYMERS

The polymers discussed so far in this chapter are all homopolymers that are composed of a single type of repeating unit. However, a large and growing number of commercial polymers actually are composed of different types of repeating units. These polymers are called copolymers. It is an important strategy for fiber engineers to manipulate the formation and properties of synthetic fibers by using copolymers. This is because it is time consuming and expensive to develop a new homopolymer for a specific application. However, it is much more time and cost effective to obtain a copolymer with desired properties by simply introducing a second repeating unit to an existing homopolymer.

There are different types of copolymers, depending on the particular arrangement of the repeating units along the polymer chain. Figure 2.10 shows four different types of copolymers:

- Random copolymers, in which the distribution of repeating units is random;
- Alternating copolymers with two types of repeating units arranged alternately along the polymer chain;
- Block copolymers, in which the repeating units exist only in long sequences, i.e., blocks, of the same type;
- Graft copolymers, a special type of branched polymers in which the branches are composed of repeating units that are different from those in the backbone.

Random and alternating copolymers typically exhibit properties that are between those of the corresponding homopolymers. Therefore, they often are developed to combine the properties of homopolymers into a single fiber. This is difficult to achieve by simply blending the homopolymers because most polymers are immiscible with each other. For example, fibers of polyacrylonitrile homopolymer have been used in hot gas filtration systems, outdoor fabrics, and precursors for carbon fibers. However, many commercial acrylic fibers actually are made

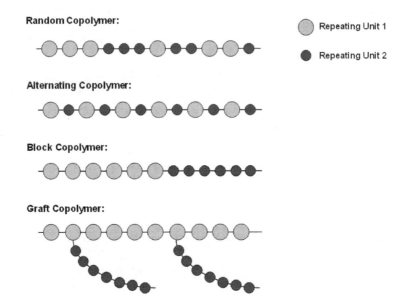

Figure 2.10. Random, alternating, block and graft copolymers.

of copolymers that contain at least 85% acrylonitrile repeating units. During the synthesis of these copolymers, either neutral and/or ionic co-monomers are added to change the fiber morphology, provide dye sites, or improve water sorption.

Block and graft copolymers often show the characteristic of each of the homopolymers, and they also may have some unique new properties caused by the chemical bonds between the homopolymer segments. Block and graft copolymers often are used to make synthetic fibers for special applications. For example, polypropylene fibers are mechanically strong and are a good reinforcement for polymer composites. However, polypropylene is inert and does not form strong intermolecular interaction with the matrix, which could lead to the failure of the composite. One approach to address this problem is to add different monomers during the melt spinning of polypropylene fibers to form a graft copolymer, which can have good intermolecular interaction with the matrix. Composites using these polypropylene-based copolymer fibers are significantly stronger and more durable than those made of polypropylene homopolymer fibers.

2.4 CONFORMATIONS

Polymer chains shown from Figure 2.7 to 2.10 are all static representations of real chains. Static representations do not show an important aspect of real polymer chains, i.e., their oscillation and movement caused by the thermal vibrations of the polymer chain structure. With an increase in temperature, the motions of polymer chains increase in both frequency and amplitude. There are many different motions of the polymer chain structure, and among them the most important one probably is the rotation of single bonds. Double and triple bonds are rigid and cannot rotate without being broken. Only single bonds can rotate, which lead to the movement of adjacent atoms. Conformation can, therefore, be defined as the order that arises from the rotation of molecules around the single bonds.

Conformation and configuration are two diffrent concepts. The configuration of a polymer cannot be altered unless chemical bonds are broken and reformed. When a polymer changes its configuration, it turns into a different polymer. However, the conformation of a polymer can be changed by rotating around the single bonds, during which no bonds are broken or formed. Hence, the polymer remains the same when its conformation changes.

During the rotation of single bonds, there are preferred low-energy conformations. Using a simple molecule of *n*-butane as an example, Figure 2.11 shows the potential energies related to different conformations. The *n*-butane molecule consists of four carbon atoms linked together in a linear chain with the hydrogen atoms along the periphery. When the adjacent hydrogen atoms are aligned, there will be considerable interference among them, leading to the high-energy eclipsed conformation, which is not desirable. The interference can be significantly lowered when they rotate around their axis to a staggered conformation (Figure 2.11A). By rotating the single bond connecting the two central carbon atoms, it is seen that there are two positions where the outer carbon atoms can be located to lower the interference. One position where the outer carbons are in opposite direction is called the *trans* conformation, and the other where they are adjacent is called the *gauche* conformation (Figure 2.11B). Depending on the rotational angle, there is one *trans* conformation for a single bond in the center of *n*-butane molecule, but two possible *gauche* conformations, named as *gauche* (-) and g*auche* (+). From Figure 2.11C, it is clear from the *n*-butane model that the *trans* conformation has lower energy than both *gauche* (-) and g*auche* (+) conformations.

As compared with small molecules such as *n*-butane, polymer chains have many more single bonds on the backbone. Each single bond can have one *trans* and two *gauche* conformations, and hence a polymer chain with N bonds on the backbone can have 3^N different conformations. For example, a polyethylene chain with 10,000 bonds can have $3^{10,000}$ (= $10^{4,800}$) different conformations. When a polymer chain changes the conformation, its size and shape also change. As a result, the ability of polymers to change their conformations leads to an internal degree of freedom that is not available to small molecules.

Synthetic fibers typically are semicrystalline. During the fiber formation process, the polymer chains change their conformations to form the crystalline phase. After the fiber formation, the polymer chains in the crystalline phase are largely in *trans* conformations, which remain unchanged until the crystalline structure is damaged or altered. However, in the amorphous phase, the polymer chains still can change their conformations after the fiber formation. For example, the

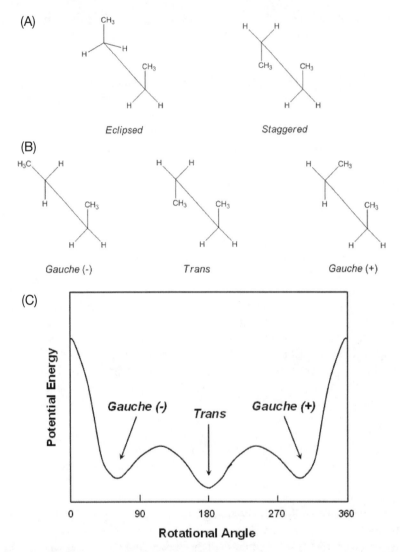

Figure 2.11. (A) Eclipsed and staggered conformations, (B) trans and gauche conformations, and (C) potential energy of n-butane molecule.

drawing of a synthetic fiber can change some singe bonds from *gauche* to *trans*
conformation, leading to a better aligned structure.

In the amorphous phase of synthetic fibers, the ratio (N_{gauche}/N_{trans}) of *gauche*
and *trans* conformations can be estimated by

$$\frac{N_{gauche}}{N_{trans}} = 2exp\left(-\frac{\Delta E}{kT}\right)$$ (2.12)

where ΔE is the energy difference between the two conformations, k the Boltzmann constant, and T the absolute temperature. It is seen that with increase in temperature, the N_{gauche}/N_{trans} ratio increases. The result is the polymer chains tend to contract in size at elevated temperatures and change to a less ordered structure.

Many properties of synthetic fibers are related to how many possible conformations the polymer chains can have. However, not all polymer chains have the same number of possible conformations even if they have the same chain length. Figure 2.12 compares a rigid rod-like polymer chain and a flexible random coil polymer chain. Rigid rod-like polymer chains typically assume more extended conformations than flexible polymer chains, and as a result, fibers made from rigid polymers are generally stiffer and have a higher glass transition temperature. One example of a rigid rod-like polymer fiber is Kevlar®.

2.5 BONDING

Repeating units are the smallest building blocks discussed so far in this chapter. Repeating units are formed by atoms, which are held together by bonds. In polymer fibers, there are two categories of bonds, i.e., primary and secondary (Figure 2.13). Primary bonds link the atoms together to form repeating units and eventually the polymer chains. Secondary bonds, also called intermolecular interactions or intermolecular bonds, are significantly weaker than preliminary bonds, but they are critical for binding the polymer chains into fibers. In polymer fibers, all primary bonds are covalent. However, there are many different types of secondary bonds, including ionic secondary bond, hydrogen bond, dipole-dipole force, aromatic ring association, and van der Waals force.

2.5.1 PRELIMINARY BONDING

Primary bonds are the attractive forces that hold atoms together to form polymer chains. The breaking of primary bonds leads to the degradation or even decomposition of the polymer. In synthetic fibers, the primary bonds typically are covalent bonds, which are formed by the sharing of pairs of electrons between atoms. The electrons being shared are called valence electrons and are in the highest energy

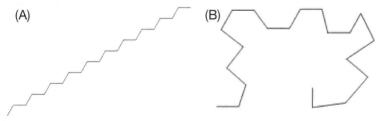

(A)   (B)

Figure 2.12. (A) Rigid rod-like polymer chain, and (B) flexible random coil polymer chain.

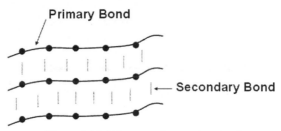

Figure 2.13. Primary and secondary bonds.

level of the atom, i.e., outer shell. The number of valence electrons of an atom is the same as the group number in the periodic table. Table 2.3 shows the group numbers and valence electrons of the atoms that often are seen in synthetic fibers, including hydrogen, carbon, nitrogen, oxygen, sulfur, fluorine, and chlorine. During the formation of covalent bonds, these atoms share the valence electrons in a way that enables them to acquire a stable electronic configuration, i.e., full valence shell. This means that these atoms tend to have eight electrons at the outer shell (except H, which tends to have two electrons) by sharing electrons. To acquire the stable electronic configuration, two atoms can share two electrons to form a single bond. It also is possible for two atoms to form double bonds by sharing four electros, or triple bonds by sharing six electrons.

The number of covalent bonds that an atom can form is determined by how many valence electrons it has. For example, hydrogen can form one bond, carbon can form four, nitrogen three, oxygen two, etc. Figure 2.14 shows the formation of covalent bonds in a small molecule: methane. It is seen that each carbon atom provides four valence electrons to be combined with the four electrons from four different hydrogen atoms. In the resultant methane molecule, the carbon atom shares eight electrons on its outer shell while each hydrogen shares two electrons. Thus, all atoms in methane achieve their stable electronic configuration. The ethane structure is the result of the formation of seven covalent bonds by sharing fourteen valence electrons among two carbon and six hydrogen atoms, while polyethylene

Table 2.3. Group numbers and valence electrons of atoms that often are seen in synthetic fibers.

Atom	Group Number	Valence Electron
Hydrogen (H)	Group I	1 valence electrons: $1s^1$
Carbon (C)	Group IV	4 valence electrons: $2s^2, 2p^2$
Nitrogen (N)	Group V	5 valence electrons: $2s^2, 2p^3$
Oxygen (O)	Group VI	6 valence electrons: $2s^2, 2p^4$
Sulfur (S)	Group VI	6 valence electrons: $3s^2, 3p^4$
Fluorine (F)	Group VII	7 valence electrons: $2s^2, 2p^5$
Chlorine (Cl)	Group VII	7 valence electrons: $3s^2, 3p^5$

has $3n + 1$ covalent bonds formed by the sharing of $6n + 2$ electrons among n carbon and $2n + 2$ hydrogen atoms (Figure 2.15).

Two important characteristics of covalent bonds are length and strength. Bond length is defined as the distance between the centers of two bonded atoms, while bond strength is the amount of energy required to break a bond. The length and strength of covalent bonds depend on many factors, e.g., electron affinities, sizes and electronegativity of atoms. However, the length and strength of the same bond in various molecules are consistent. Table 2.4 compares the lengths and strengths of the covalent bonds that are commonly seen in synthetic fibers.

The strength of covalent bonds is directional. Hence, the bonds in a molecule have the tendency to maximize their separation in space. Figure 2.16 shows the possible geometry of the covalent bonding of methane and polyethylene. In methane, the four covalent bonds maximize their separation by forming a tetrahedral geometry. The bond angles are 109.5°. In the case of polyethylene, the maximization of bond separation theoretically gives the polymer chain a three-dimensional zigzag geometry. However, since the polymer chain can change its conformation by rotating the single bonds, it has many other geometries, but the bond separation is always maximized.

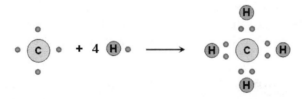

Figure 2.14. Formation of covalent bonds in methane.

Ethane:

Polyethylene:

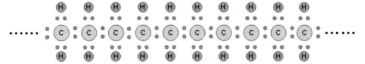

Figure 2.15. Covalent bonds in ethane and polyethylene.

Table 2.4. Bond lengths and bond strengths of covalent bonds in synthetic fibers.

Bond	Length (pm)	Strength (kJ/mol)
C-C	154	348
C-H	109	413
C-N	147	308
C-O	143	360
C-F	135	488
C-Cl	177	330
C=O	122	745
C≡N	115	890
N-H	101	391
O-H	96	366

2.5.2 SECONDARY BONDING

Secondary bonds are the attractive forces that hold polymer chains together to form fibers. Secondary bonds also are called intermolecular interactions or intermolecular bonds. In fibers, the polymer chains can change their conformation by breaking and reforming secondary bonds. The melting of synthetic fibers is in part determined by the total strength of secondary bonds. There are different types of secondary bonds, and the most important ones are ionic secondary bond, hydrogen bond, dipole-dipole force, aromatic ring association, and van der Waals force. The bond lengths of secondary bonds are longer than those of primary bonds, and they are in the order of 300–500 pm. The bond strengths of secondary bonds are

Methane:

Polyethylene:

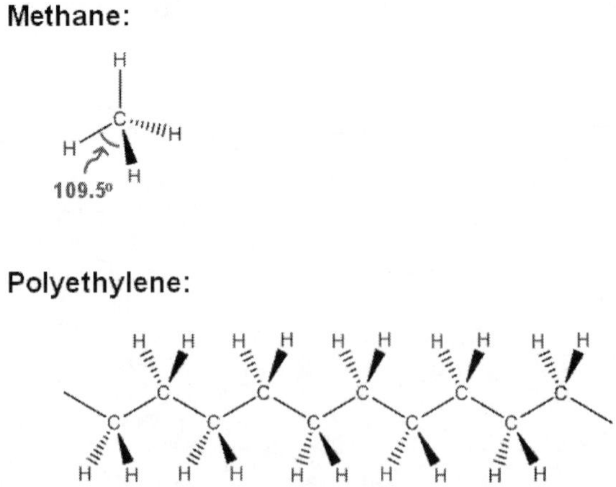

Figure 2.16. Geometry of covalent bonding in methane and polyethylene with all-*trans* conformation.

Table 2.5. Bond strengths of primary and secondary bonds.

Bond	Strength (kJ/mol)
Covalent Bond	300–400
Ionic Secondary Bond	100–350
Hydrogen Bond	10–60
Dipole-Dipole Force	5–30
Aromatic Ring Association	5–30
Van der Waals force	< 5

weaker than those of primary bonds. Table 2.5 compares the bond strengths of primary and secondary bonds.

Among all secondary bonds, ionic bond is the strongest, with the bond strength ranging from 100 to 350 kJ/mol. An ionic secondary bond is a type of chemical bond formed through an electrostatic attraction between two oppositely charged atoms on two neighboring polymer chains (Figure 2.17). Unlike in a covalent bond where two atoms acquire the stable electronic configuration by sharing electrons at the outer shells, the atoms involved in an ionic secondary bond have very different electronegativities and one of the atoms lose its electron(s) to the other atom. Therefore, the formation of ionic secondary bonds results from the transfer of electrons between atoms on adjacent polymer chains. Ionic secondary bonds are just slightly weaker than covalent primary bonds. Ionic secondary bonds can be found in natural polymer fibers, e.g., wool. However, ionic secondary bonds are not common in synthetic polymer fibers.

The next strongest secondary bond is hydrogen bond. Hydrogen bond is the attractive intermolecular interaction between a hydrogen atom and an electronegative atom, such as nitrogen, oxygen, or fluorine. Not all hydrogen atoms can form hydrogen bonds. For a hydrogen bond to be formed, the hydrogen atom also must be linked to an electronegative atom of oxygen, nitrogen or fluorine, which is called the hydrogen-bond donor. This hydrogen-bond donor attracts the electrons shared with the hydrogen atom and leaves the hydrogen a positive partial charge. The positive partial charge then attracts a lone pair of electrons on the hydrogen-bond acceptor to form a hydrogen bond. In synthetic fibers, hydrogen bonds are mainly formed between OH groups (e.g., polyvinyl alcohol) and between >C=O

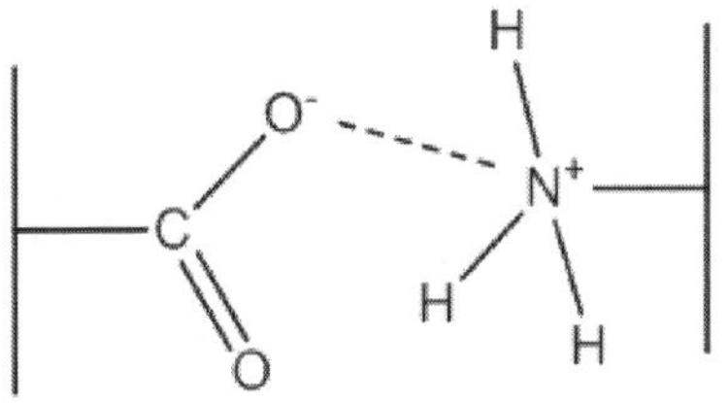

Figure 2.17. Example of ionic secondary bonding between polymer chains.

and NH groups (e.g., nylon). Figure 2.18 shows the formation of hydrogen bonds in polyvinyl alcohol and nylon. The bond strengths of hydrogen bonds are between 10–60 kJ/mol. The formation of hydrogen bonds affects the crystallization process and mechanical properties of synthetic fibers. In addition, synthetic fibers that can form hydrogen bonds tend to have better moisture absorption properties.

A third type of relatively strong secondary bond is dipole-dipole force, which is the attractive interaction between the positive end of a polar group and the negative end of another polar group. Dipoles occur due to the unequal sharing of electrons between atoms in polar groups. In a polar group, the atom that is more electronegative than others pull the electrons closer to itself to form a dipole, in which one side of the group possesses a partially negative charge and the other side a partially positive charge. For example, in polyacrylonitrile, the -C≡N group is a polar group, in which the carbon atom is partially positive and the nitrogen is partially negative. When two -C≡N get close enough, the dipole-dipole force is formed by the attraction of the partially positive carbon and partially negative nitrogen in two groups (Figure 2.19). The strengths of dipole-dipole forces are weaker than those of hydrogen bonds, and typically are in the range of 5–30 kJ/mol.

Another type of secondary bond that has similar strength with dipole-dipole force is aromatic ring association. The aromatic ring association, also called π-π stacking, is the attraction interaction between two aromatic rings. The delocalized π electrons on aromatic rings are somewhat mobile. The shifting of these delocalized π electrons leads to the formation of attraction interaction between two neighboring aromatic rings. The aromatic ring association can be found in the

Figure 2.18. Hydrogen bonds in polyvinyl alcohol (left) and nylon (right).

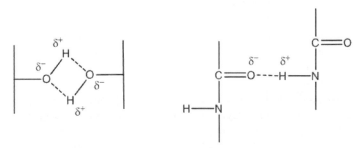

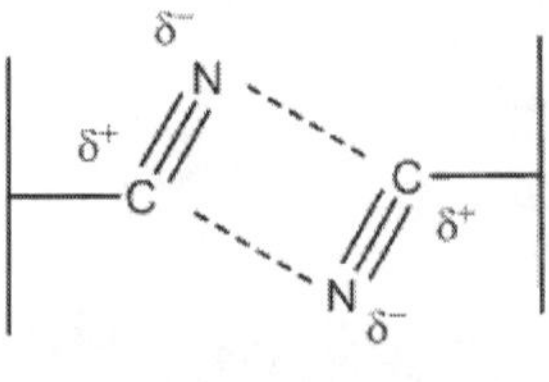

Figure 2.19. Dipole-dipole force in polyacrylonitrile.

crystallization region of some synthetic fibers, such as polyethylene terephthalate (PET), where the aromatic rings stack regularly on each other. Figure 2.20 shows the aromatic ring association between two aromatic rings in two adjacent PET polymer chains.

The weakest secondary bond is the van der Waals force. The formation of van der Waals force lies in the instantaneously induced dipoles generated by the momentary shifting of electrons surrounding the nucleus of electrically neutral atoms. Unlike other types of secondary bonds, which occur between certain atoms or groups, the var der Waals force always exists as long as two atoms or groups are close enough to each other (Figure 2.21). Therefore, although the van der Waals force is the weakest secondary bond, the sum of van der Waals forces between two neighboring polymer chains is significant. Both the melting and dissolving processes are closely related to the van der Waals force between polymer chains.

In addition to the five secondary bonds mentioned above, there are other types of interactions existing between polymer chains. Examples include ion-dipole force, ion-aromatic ring interaction, and ion-induced dipole force. These secondary bonds are formed between an ionic group with a dipole, aromatic ring, and induced dipole, respectively. Ion-dipole force and ion-aromatic have similar strength, and they are weaker than ionic secondary bonding, but may be slightly stronger than dipole-dipole force or aromatic ring association.

REFERENCES

[1]   Bower, D.I., *An Introduction to Polymer Physics*, Gambridge University Press, 2002.

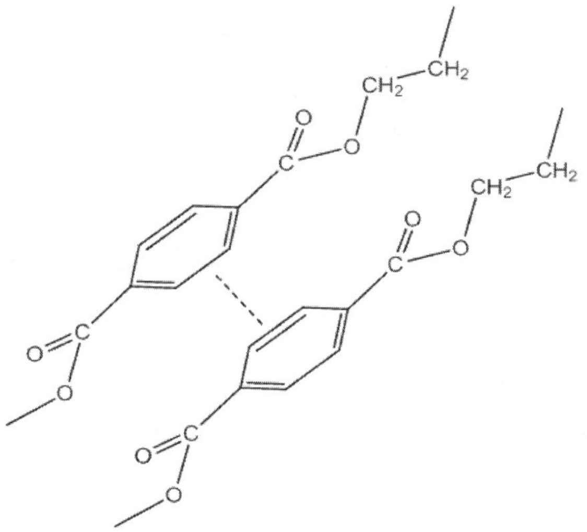

Figure 2.20. Aromatic ring association in PET.

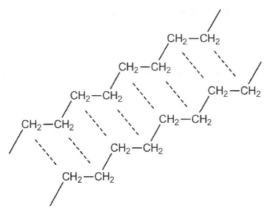

Figure 2.21. Van der Waals force in polyethylene.

[2] Callister, W.D., *Materials Science and Engineering: An Introduction*, Seventh Edition, John Wiley & Sons, 2007.

[3] Carey, F.A., and Sundberg, R.J., *Advanced Organic Chemistry, Part A: Structure and Mechanisms*, Fifth Edition, Springer, 2007.

[4] Cook, J.G., *Handbook of Textile Fibers, Vol. II. Man-Made Fibers*, Fifth Edition, Woodhead Publishing Limited, 1984.

[5] Flory, P.J., *Principles of Polymer Chemistry*, Cornell University Press, 1953.

[6] Grosberg, A.Y., and Khokhlov, A.R., *Giant Molecules: Here, There, and Everywhere*, Academic Press, 1997.

[7] Hearle, J.W.S., "Fibre Structure: Its Formation and Relation to Performance", in *Handbook of Textile Fibre Structure. Volume I: Fundamentals and Manufactured Polymer Fibers*, editors Eichhorn, S.J., Hearle, J.W.S., Jaffe, M., and Kikutani, T., Woodhead Publishing Limited, 2009.

[8] Israelachvili, J.N., *Intermolecular and Surface Forces*, Third Edition, Academic Press, 2011.

[9] Mark, J.E., Eisenberg, A., Graessley, W.W., Mandelkern, L. Samulski, E.T., Koenig, J.L. and Wignall, G.D., *Physical Properties of Polymers*, Second Edition, American Chemical Society, 1993.

[10] Painter, P.C., and Coleman, M.M., *Fundamentals of Polymer Science: An Introductory Text*, Second Edition, Technomic, 1997.

[11] Peebles, L.H., *Molecular Weight Distributions in Polymers*, Wiley, 1971.

[12] Rubinstein, M., and Colby, R.H., *Polymer Physics*, Oxford University Press, 2003.

[13] Rudin, A., and Choi, P., *The Elements of Polymer Science & Engineering*, Third Edition, Academic Press, 1982.

[14] Sperling, L.H., *Introduction to Physical Polymer Science*, 4th Edition, John Wiley & Sons, Inc., 2006

[15] Tonelli, A.E., *Polymers From the Inside Out—An Introduction to Macromolecules*, John Wiley & Sons, Inc., 2001.

[16] Warner, S.B., *Fiber Science*, Prentice Hall, 1995.

PROBLEMS

(1) Both polyethylene fiber and wax are essentially $-CH_2-$. How does a polyethylene fiber differ from wax?

(2) Natural fibers can have very long chains but polymers used for synthetic fibers typically have shorter chain lengths. Why?

(3) Consider a nylon 6,6 fiber having the following distribution of polymer chains:

20 chains of degree of polymerization 20

120 chains of degree of polymerization 60

200 chains of degree of polymerization 80

100 chains of degree of polymerization 100

30 chains of degree of polymerization 500

 (i)   Calculate the number average molecular weight.
 (ii) Calculate the weight average molecular weight.
 (iii) Calculate the polydispersity.

(4) Write the chemical structures of polyethylene, polypropylene, nylon 6, nylon 6,6, polyester, polyacrylonitrile, and Kevlar® fibers.

(5) Different polypropylenes may be described as isotactic, syndiotactic, or atactic. What does this mean? Which polypropylene is used to make commercial textile fibers?

(6) What is the difference between a block and a graft copolymer? What are the possible applications for fibers made from block and graft copolymers?

(7)   A polyester fiber is described as having a polydispersity of 1.07. What does this mean?

(8)   Name the most prevalent primary bond found in polymer fibers. Describe its electronic structure or mention what causes it to be formed between two atoms.

(9)   What are the main characteristics of covalent bonds?

(10) What kind of secondary bonds can be found in polypropylene, nylon, polyester, and polyacrylonitrile fibers, respectively?

(11) Describe how ionic secondary bond, hydrogen bond, dipole-dipole force and aromatic ring association are formed.

(12) All fibers have van der Waals force. Describe what causes the van der Waals force to form.

CHAPTER 3

Physical Structure of Synthetic Polymer Fibers

The chemical structure of synthetic fibers deals with how the atoms and repeating units are arranged in polymer chains, while the physical structure addresses how the polymer chains are assembled to form fibers. In general, the chemical structure determines the maximum potential a fiber can achieve. However, the physical structure determines how well the potential actually is achieved in practice. The chemical structure affects the physical structure of synthetic fibers. This chapter focuses on the physical structure of synthetic fibers.

3.1 SOLID PHASES

States of matter are the distinct forms, in which different phases of matter exist. Three most commonly seen states of matter are solid, liquid, and gas. Figure 3.1 shows these three states of small molecule compounds. In the solid state, the molecules are packed closely together. The secondary bonds between the molecules are strong enough so the molecules cannot move freely; they can only vibrate. There are two types of solids: crystalline and amorphous. The molecules in crystalline solids are packed in a three-dimensionally ordered, repeating pattern, while those in amorphous solids are distributed randomly. When the temperature increases, the molecules become more excited and active, and the material can change from the solid state to liquid. In the liquid state, the secondary bonds are weakened due to the increased intermolecular distance. The molecules have enough energy to have translational movement and the structure is mobile. As a result, the shape of the liquid is not definite but is determined by its container. When the temperature continues to increase, the molecules eventually can have enough energy to completely break all secondary bonds, leading to the transition from the liquid state to gas. In the gas state, the distance between adjacent

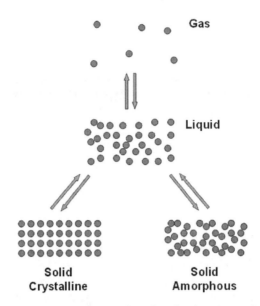

Figure 3.1. Three states of small molecule compounds.

molecules is much greater than the molecular size, and the material has no definite shape or volume. The molecules in the gas state keep their translational movement until they hit each other or the wall of the container.

Figure 3.2 shows the states of polymers. Polymers do not exhibit a gas state because of the presence of secondary bonds. To change polymers to a gas state, all secondary bonds must be completely broken to separate polymer chains from each other. Although an individual secondary bond is weaker than a primary bond, the sum of secondary bonds is significant due to the extremely long length of polymer chains. Therefore, it is impossible to break all secondary bonds without damaging the primary bonds, i.e., the decomposition of polymers. Therefore, polymers only have liquid and solid states. The liquid state of polymers has significantly higher viscosity than that of small molecular compounds. The behavior of polymer liquids is essential for the formation of synthetic fibers and will be discussed in Chapter 8. This chapter focusses on the solid state.

As shown in Figure 3.2, polymers also have two types of solid states: crystalline and amorphous. In reality, solid-state synthetic fibers are typically semi-crystalline, which means both the amorphous and crystalline phases co-exist in synthetic fibers. In the amorphous phase, the arrangement of polymer chains is disordered. However, in the crystalline phase, the polymer chains are assembled in a three-dimensionally ordered manner. The crystalline phase has higher mechanical strength than the amorphous one. During the fiber formation, an important task is to manipulate the spinning parameters to achieve a high degree of crystallization. Due to the extremely long length of polymer chains, it is almost impossible to

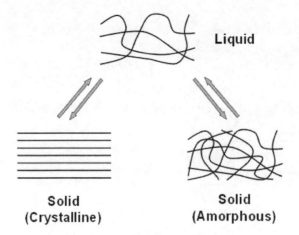

Figure 3.2. States of polymers.

assemble them in a completely ordered structure in most practical fiber formation processes. Therefore, synthetic fibers are typically semi-crystalline.

3.2 UNIT CELLS

3.2.1 *CONCEPT OF UNIT CELL*

The crystalline phase is composed of smaller units, called unit cells. A unit cell is basically a small set of atoms, ions, or molecules that are arranged in a particular way, which is periodically repeated in three dimensions on a lattice. Unit cells are the building block of the crystallites. The entire crystallite structure can be constructed by pure translational repetition of unit cells. The overall properties of a crystallite structure also can be calculated, at least theoretically, by considering an individual unit cell.

There are totally 14 different types of unit cells, which meet the following criteria:

- The unit cell is the simplest repeating unit in the crystal.
- Opposite faces of a unit cell are parallel.
- The edge of the unit cell connects equivalent points.

These fourteen unit cells belong to seven categories, which differ in the three edge lengths (a, b, and c) and three internal angles (a, β, and γ). Figure 3.3 shows the fourteen different unit cells, and Table 3.1 shows their edge lengths and internal angles.

In a real crystallite, each unit cell contains a few atoms, ions or molecules, depending on the type of the material. For example, cesium chloride (CsCl) has a

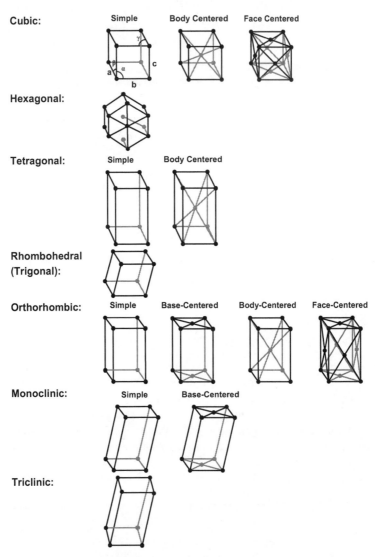

Figure 3.3. Fourteen types of unit cells.

body-centered cubic unit cell structure (Figure 3.4). In a CsCl unit cell, the Cl⁻ is located in the body center and the Cs^+ ion in the corner. In Figure 3.4, it looks like the unit cell has eight Cs^+ ions since it has eight corners. However, on each corner, the Cs^+ is shared by eight neighboring unit cells, and hence each unit cell only contains $8 \times 1/8 = 1$ Cs^+ ion. As a result, each unit cell of CsCl contains two ions: one Cl⁻ ion and one Cs^+ ion.

Table 3.1. Edge lengths and internal angles of the seven categories of unit cells.

Category	Edge lengths	Internal angles
Cubic	$a = b = c$	$\alpha = \beta = \gamma = 90°$
Hexagonal	$a = b \neq c$	$\alpha = 120°, \beta = \gamma = 90°$
Tetragonal	$a = b \neq c$	$\alpha = \beta = \gamma = 90°$
Rhombohedral (Trigonal)	$a = b = c$	$\alpha = \beta = \gamma \neq 90°$
Orthorhombic	$a \neq b \neq c$	$\alpha = \beta = \gamma = 90°$
Monoclinic	$a \neq b \neq c$	$\alpha \neq 90°, \beta = \gamma = 90°$
Triclinic	$a \neq b \neq c$	$\alpha \neq \beta \neq \gamma \neq 90°$

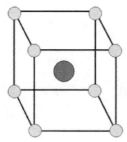

Figure 3.4. Unit cell structure of CsCl.

3.2.2 UNIT CELLS OF SYNTHETIC POLYMERS

Synthetic fibers are composed of long polymer chains. Research shows the edge lengths of unit cells of polymers are in the same order of magnitude as the co-valent bond lengths. Hence, it is impossible for an entire polymer chain to be included in a single unit cell. Instead, each polymer chain passes through many unit cells. The long length and entanglement of polymer chains impede the chain motion and leave regions that are amorphous. This is the main reason why most synthetic fibers are not 100% crystalline. The following discusses the unit struc-tures of several important fiber-forming synthetic polymers.

Polyethylene is a polymer with the simplest repeating unit structure. The crys-talline phase of polyethylene typically is composed of orthorhombic unit cells, with edge lengths of $a = 0.740$ nm, $b = 0.493$ nm, and $c = 0.254$ nm. In the crystal-line phase, the chains of polyethylene are in all-*trans* conformation and have a lin-ear zigzag conformation. Figure 3.5 shows the unit cell structure of polyethylene. It is seen that each unit cell contains two repeating units.

Vinyl polymers have side groups on their backbones, and only isotactic or syn-diotactic vinyl polymers can crystallize. Due to the substantial steric hindrance from the side groups, vinyl polymers adopt a helical conformation during crystal-lization, where the extra side groups are accommodated on the outside of the helix

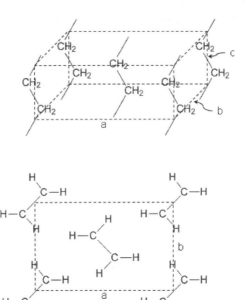

Figure 3.5. Unit cell structure of polyethylene.

by twisting of the entire polymer chain. For example, isotactic polypropylene crystallized at normal conditions can have either hexagonal or monoclinic unit cell. In either case, the polypropylene forms a helix that makes one complete turn for every three repeating units. Figure 3.6 compares the zigzag conformation of polyethylene and the helix conformation of polypropylene. Of course, both left- and right-handed helices are possible. Figure 3.7 shows that left- and right-handed helices of polypropylene face each other, leading to a closer packing of polymer chains in the crystalline phase. Other vinyl polymers also form helical conformation in the crystalline phase, but they may require different numbers of repeating units for making a complete turn.

The polymers discussed above are nonpolar and van der Waals force is the only type of secondary bond that holds the polymer chains together in the crystalline phase. When polymers have other types of stronger secondary bonds, the crystallite structure tends to be affected by these bonds. Figure 3.8 shows the effect of hydrogen bonding on the chain arrangement in the crystalline phase of nylon 6,6. The unit cell structure of nylon 6,6 is triclinic, with the edge lengths of $a = 0.49$ nm, $b = 0.54$ nm, and $c = 1.73$ nm, and internal angles of $\alpha = 48°, \beta = 77°$, and $\gamma = 63°$. To maximize the number of hydrogen bonds, the nylon 6,6 chains tend to form a fully extended, planar zigzag conformation.

The crystalline phase of polyethylene terephthalate (PET) also has a unit cell structure of triclinic. The edge lengths are: $a = 0.456$ nm, $b = 0.594$ nm, and $c = 1.075$ nm, and internal angles are: $\alpha = 98.5°, \beta = 118°$, and $\gamma = 112°$. Figure 3.9

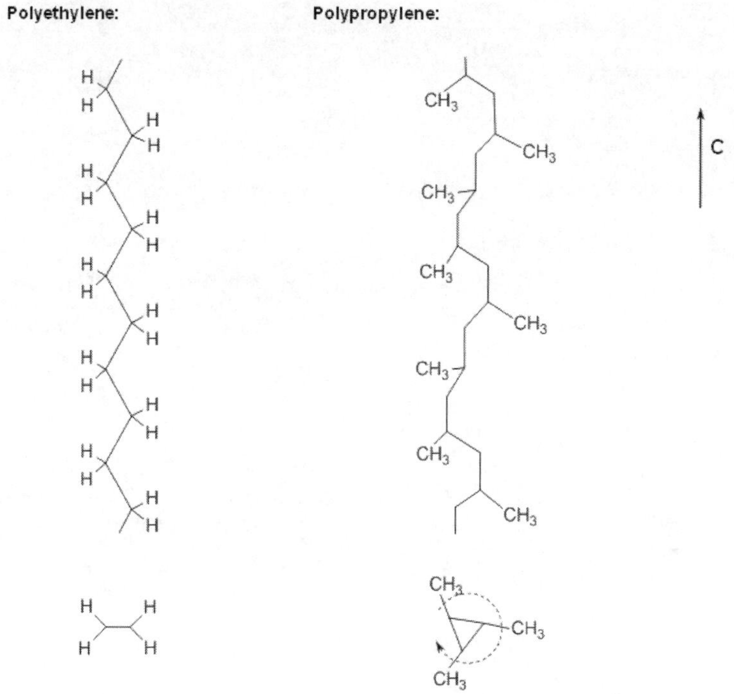

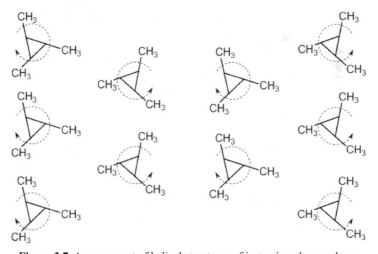

Polyethylene: **Polypropylene:**

Figure 3.6. Zigzag structure of polyethylene and helical structure of polypropylene.

Figure 3.7. Arrangement of helical structures of isotactic polypropylene.

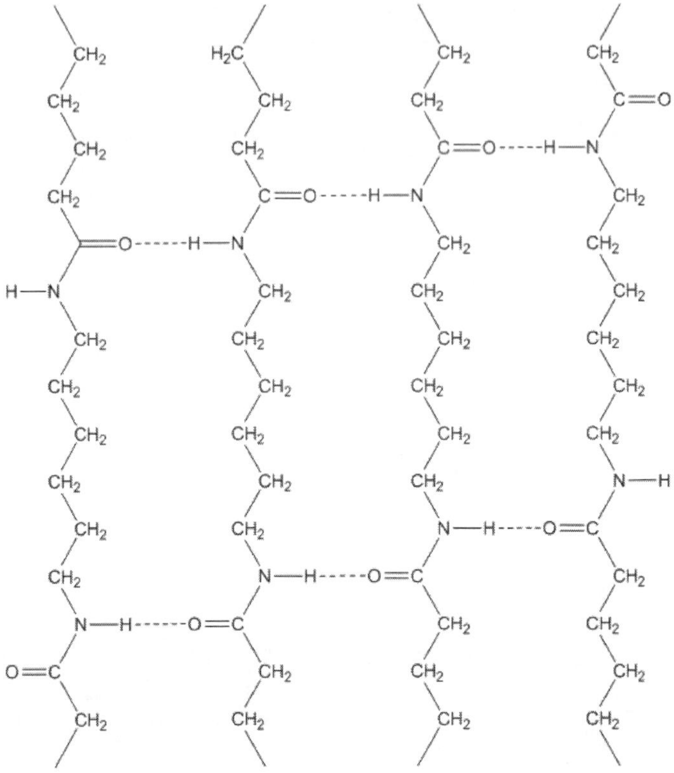

Figure 3.8. Planar zigzag structure of nylon 6,6.

shows the effect of aromatic ring association on the arrangement of polymer chains in PET crystalline phase. The aromatic rings tend to be stacked together to maximize the secondary bonding (aromatic ring association), leading to the formation a planar zigzag structure (Figure 3.9). Both nylon 6,6 and PET fibers have relatively high melting temperatures (around 260°C) due to the hydrogen bonding in the former case and the aromatic ring association in the latter case. It must be mentioned that in the case of PET, the polymer chain is relatively stiff, which also contributes to its planar zigzag conformation and high melting temperature.

3.3 CRYSTALLINE MODELS

Synthetic fibers are semicrystalline. The unit cell structure deals with how the polymer chains are organized inside the crystalline phase. However, it does not tell how the crystallites look like in semicrystalline synthetic fibers. To address this, several crystalline models have been developed.

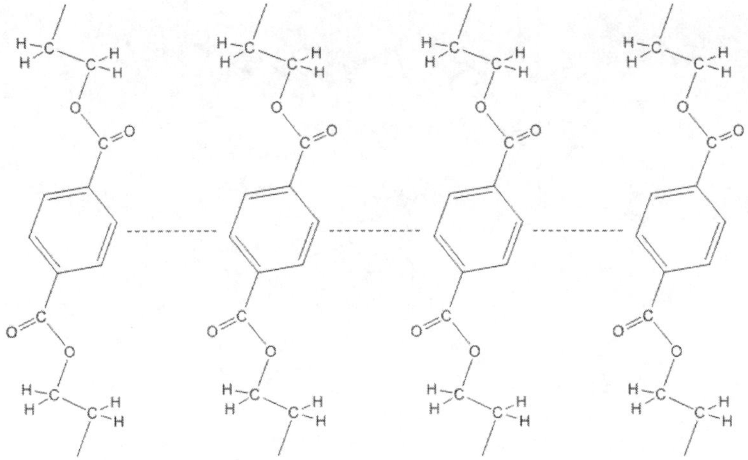

Figure 3.9. Planar zigzag structure of PET.

3.3.1 FRINGED MICELLE MODEL

It has been discussed that the polymer chains pass through many unit cells in the crystalline phase. Due to the large molecular weights, the polymer chains are calculated to be even longer than the crystallites. Hence, it is believed the polymer chains also pass in and out of many crystallites. This leads to the fringed micelle model (Figure 3.10). According to the fringed micelle model, the polymer chains wander from the amorphous phase through a crystallite, and then back out into the amorphous phase. Because of the polymer chains' length, they pass through several crystallites to bind them together. This model is successful in explaining the good tensile strength and flexible nature of semicrystalline synthetic fibers.

3.3.2 FOLDED-CHAIN MODEL AND SWITCHBOARD MODEL

One important feature of the fringed micelle model is that all the polymer chains run continuously between the crystalline and amorphous phases without folding back. This view changed when single crystals of polyethylene were prepared by Keller in 1957. These single crystals were made by precipitation from dilute solutions of hot xylene, and they typically have diamond shape, with thicknesses ranging from 10 to 20 nm. To explain the structure of polyethylene single crystals, a folded-chain model was developed (Figure 3.11). The folded-chain model explains the chain-folding phenomenon, which is not captured in the fringed micelle model. However, the folded-chain model can only be used to explain special crystalline structure, such as single crystals. This is because the folded-chain model requires large-scale, long-range reorganization of all polymer chains. Due to the long length and entanglement of polymer chains, this is difficult during the fiber formation process. Therefore, a switchboard model also has been developed.

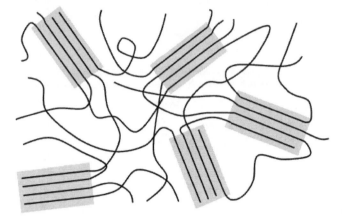

Figure 3.10. Fringed micelle model with the crystalline phase shadowed.

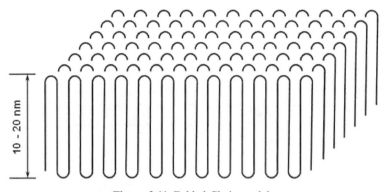

10 - 20 nm

Figure 3.11. Folded-Chain model.

Figure 3.12 compares the chain re-entry in folded-chain and switchboard models. In the folded-chain model, the polymer chains reenter the crystalline phase right next to where they left. On the other hand, in the switchboard model, the polymer chains do not have to follow adjacent re-entry. Instead, they can re-enter the crystalline phase randomly. The switchboard model requires minimum movement and re-organization of polymer chains.

3.3.3 *Modified Fringed Micelle Model and Fringed Fibril Model*

Considering the fact that polymer chains can fold back and re-enter the crystallites, the fringed micelle model has been modified. Figure 3.13 shows the modified fringed micelle model. At the ends of the crystallites in a modified fringed micelle model, there is a mixture of chain folding and fringing into tie-molecules, leading to other crystallites. The modified fringed micelle model is being widely used to explain the crystalline structure of polymers.

Folded-Chain Model   **Switchboard Model**

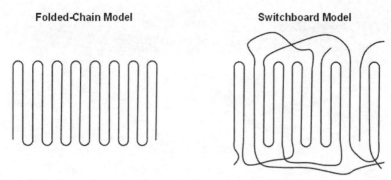

Figure 3.12. Comparison of polymer chain re-entry in folded-chain and switchboard models.

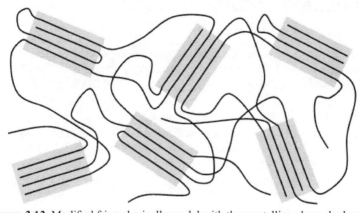

Figure 3.13. Modified fringed micelle model with the crystalline phase shadowed.

In synthetic fibers, the micelles are different from those in many other polymer products. The micelles in synthetic fibers often have the fibril shape, with diameters ranging from several nm to 100 nm. The lengths of fibrils depend on the polymer type and the processing conditions. This leads to a fringed fibril model. Figure 3.14 shows a basic fringed fibril model. The bonding between fibrils is relatively weak, and hence fibrils actually can be observed in fracture studies of some synthetic fibers.

The actual crystalline structure of synthetic fibers is largely affected by the polymer type and the fiber formation conditions. The models discussed above cannot explain all the crystalline structures that have been found in synthetic fibers. Hence, other models also have been developed, and many of them are modified versions of above-mentioned models so they can better explain the structure and properties of different synthetic fibers.

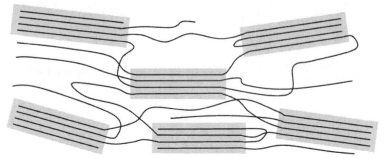

Figure 3.14. Fringed fibril model with the crystalline phase shadowed.

3.4 MORPHOLOGY OF CRYSTALLITES

3.4.1 SPHERULITIC MORPHOLOGY

Under quiescent conditions, the crystallization of polymers begins at numerous nucleation points and the crystalline phase grows outward (spherically) from these centers to form shperulites. Spherulites can be observed in polarized optical microscope, which produces a Maltese Cross appearance for the individual spherulites. Figure 3.15 shows both a polarized light microscopy image of spherulites and a sketch of the spherulite structure. Spherulites contain both crystalline and amorphous phases. In spherulites, polymer chains are oriented normal to the radial direction. The crystals in the spherulites are called lamellar crystals and often are described using the switchboard model. The diameters of spherulites grow linearly with time until they impinge on each other. Eventually, the spherulites can pervade the entire space of the material.

3.4.2 FIBRILLAR MORPHOLOGY

Spherulites are formed under quiescent conditions (no flow and no large-scale molecular orientation). However, synthetic fibers are formed by using different spinning techniques. Polymer chains and crystallites can orient themselves during the fiber spinning processes. To enhance the mechanical properties, spun fibers also are drawn or stretched to further increase the orientation. As a result, the spherulitic structure gives away to the fibrillar morphology. For many synthetic fibers, fibrils are formed directly by oriented polymer chains during spinning processes and the fibrillar morphology is enhanced by drawing. However, some polymers have high crystallization rate and may form some spherulites in as-spun fibers under certain spinning conditions. In this case, the shperulites are stretched during drawing and some folded polymer chains slip, twist or even unfold to form fibrils. As a result, spherulites are not common in commercial synthetic fibers.

Figure 3.16 shows an example of the fibrillar morphology. It is seen the orientation direction of fibrils is the same as that of the polymer chains in the crystalline phase. In synthetic fibers, the diameters of fibrils can range from tens of nanometers to several micrometers. Each fibril also may contain both crystalline and amorphous phases. The fibrillar morphology of synthetic fibers can be described using the fringed fibril model (Figure 3.14) or its modified version with higher degrees of crystallinity and orientation.

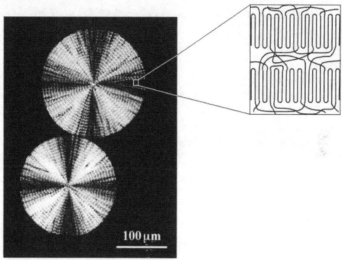

Figure 3.15. Appearance and structure of spherulites. (Lotz, B., et. al., *Polymer*, 46, 577–610, 2005.)

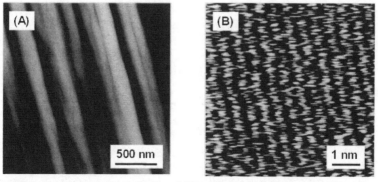

Figure 3.16. AFM images of (A) fibrils and (B) polymer chains in the crystalline phase for stretched polyethylene. (Snetivy, D., et. al., *Journal of Materials Chemistry*, 2, 891–892, 1992.)

3.4.3 OTHER MORPHOLOGIES

Compared with the spherulitic structure, the fibrillar morphology is more desirable for synthetic fibers. During the formation of oriented fibrils, the polymer chains are arranged in a way that allows alignment of more primary bonds along the fiber axis direction. This leads to increased mechanical properties for synthetic fibers. However, as shown in the fringed fibril model (Figure 3.14), a significant amount of polymer chains still are folded rather than extended. As a result, the actual strength and modulus of most synthetic fibers are only a small fraction of the theoretical values that perfectly aligned polymer chains can achieve. The key to maximize the mechanical properties of synthetic fibers is to fully extend the polymer chains and align them along the fiber axis. Such structure could be achieved by high-speed spinning of fibers, spinning fibers directly from liquid crystalline polymers, and gel spinning. Figure 3.17 shows a model for polyester fibers made by high-speed spinning. Figure 3.18 shows a model for Kevlar® fibers spun from the liquid crystalline state and Spectra® polyethylene fibers made by gel spinning.

The structures discussed above are just examples that can be found in many synthetic fibers. Fiber scientists now can manipulate the fiber formation processes to obtain a wide range of structures for different applications. Therefore, other crystalline morphologies and models exist for synthetic fibers.

3.5 MORPHOLOGY OF SYNTHETIC FIBERS

3.5.1 CROSS-SECTIONAL MORPHOLOGY

The cross-sectional shape of synthetic fibers is largely determined by the spinneret profiles used during fiber spinning. Circular cross-sectional shape is the simplest and it can be produced with spinnerets with circular holes. However, the cross-sectional shapes also are affected by the spinning method used. For example, when fibers are spun from polymer solutions, the fiber skin is the first region to be solidified during the removal of solvent. With the continuous removal of solvent after the solidification of the skin, the fiber diameter decreases and the skin has to be deformed to accommodate the diameter change. As a result, fibers spun from solutions are not round. Instead, they may present crenulated, bilobal, trilobal, or other cross-sectional shapes (Figure 3.19).

Non-circular synthetic fibers also can be obtained by using different spinneret profiles. Figure 3.20 shows several different spinneret hole shapes. While producing synthetic fibers with different cross-sectional shapes, it is important to consider the unique properties of polymer melts or solutions. For example, polymers swell when they exit the spinneret holes, and the swelling is uneven from non-circular spinneret holes. Typically, the swelling at corners is less significant than at other locations. Therefore, to produce square or triangle fibers, the spinneret holes need have stretched corners (Figures 3.20A and B).

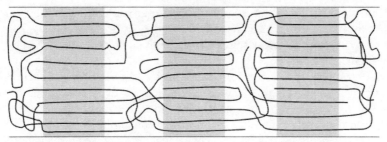

Figure 3.17. Model for polyester fibers made by high-speed spinning.

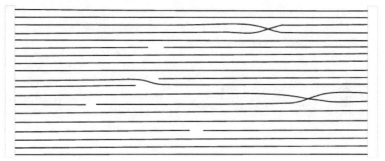

Figure 3.18. Model for Kevlar® fibers spun from the liquid crystalline state and Spectra® polyethylene fibers made by gel spinning.

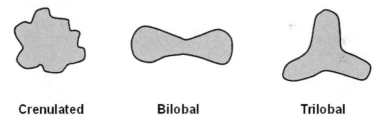

Crenulated   **Bilobal**   **Trilobal**

Figure 3.19. Crenulated, bilobal and trilobal cross-sectional shapes of synthetic fibers.

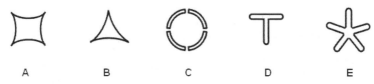

A   B   C   D   E

Figure 3.20. Examples of spinneret holes for making fibers with different cross-sections of (a) square, (b) triangle, (c) hollow, (d) T, and (e) star shapes.

Some synthetic fibers consist of two polymers arranged in separated phases on the cross-section. These bicomponent fibers typically are produced by spinning two polymers from the same spinneret with both polymers contained within the same filament. Side-by-side, segmented pie, core-sheath and islands-in-the-sea are examples of the cross-sectional structures for bicomponent fibers (Figure 3.21). Bicomponent fibers can have a number of advantages over single-component fibers. For example, in some bicomponent fibers, the second component can serve as a reinforcing agent to enhance the mechanical properties of the fibers. In some other bicomponent fibers, the second component can improve the dyeing capability of the fibers. Some bicomponent fibers also are used as self-crimping fibers. In addition, some bicomponent fibers are designed to make special fibers that are not easy to produce using regular spinning method. For example, islands-in-sea bicomponent fibers often are used to make micro/nanofibers or hollow fibers by dissolving one of the two components.

3.5.2 *Longitudinal Morphology*

As-spun synthetic fibers are typically straight. However, some synthetic fibers possess a wavy, undulating structure, which is called crimp. Crimped fibers can be produced by different methods. The most straightforward method is to introduce crimp by thermomechanical means. In this method, straight fibers are mechanically deformed into a crimped structure, followed by heat setting.

An alternative approach is to produce self-crimped fibers by using the bicomponent fiber structures discussed in section 3.5.1. The two components in the fibers can be different polymers or the same polymer but with different average molecular weights, different molecular weight distributions, different additives, or other structural differences. The key to introduce self-crimp is to design structural asymmetry across the fiber cross-section.

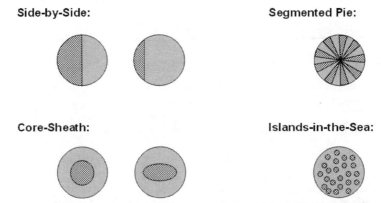

Figure 3.21. Side-by-side, segmented pie, core-sheath and islands-in-the-sea structures of bicomponent fibers.

REFERENCES

[1] Callister, W.D., *Materials Science and Engineering: An Introduction*, Seventh Edition, John Wiley & Sons, 2007.

[2] Cook, J.G., *Handbook of Textile Fibers, Vol. II. Man-Made Fibers*, Fifth Edition, Woodhead Publishing Limited, 1984.

[3] Geil, P.H., *Polymer Single Crystals*, Interscience, 1963.

[4] Grosberg, A.Y., and Khokhlov, A.R., *Giant Molecules: Here, There, and Everywhere*, Academic Press, 1997.

[5] Hearle, J.W.S., "Fibre Structure: Its Formation and Relation to Performance", in *Handbook of Textile Fibre Structure, Volume I: Fundamentals and Manufactured Polymer Fibers*, editors Eichhorn, S.J., Hearle, J.W.S., Jaffe, M., and Kikutani, T., Woodhead Publishing Limited, 2009.

[6] Kikutani, I., Radhakrishnan, J., Arikawa, S., Takaku, A., Okui, N., Jin, N., Niwa, F., and Kudo, Y., "High-Speed Melt Spinning of Bicomponent Fibers: Mechanism of Fiber Structure Development in Poly(ethylene terephthalate)/Propylene System", *Journal of Applied Polymer Science*, 62, 1913–1924, 1996.

[7] Lotz, B., and Cheng, Z.D., "A Critical Assessment of Unbalanced Surface Stresses as the Mechanical Origin of Twisting and Scrolling of Polymer Crystals", *Polymer*, 46, 577–610, 2005.

[8] Mark, J.E., Eisenberg, A., Graessley, W.W., Mandelkern, L. Samulski, E.T., Koenig, J.L. and Wignall, G.D., *Physical Properties of Polymers*, Second Edition, American Chemical Society, 1993.

[9] Mather, R.R., "The Structure of Polyolefin Fibers", in *Handbook of Textile Fibre Structure, Volume I: Fundamentals and Manufactured Polymer Fibers*, editors Eichhorn, S.J., Hearle, J.W.S., Jaffe, M., and Kikutani, T., Woodhead Publishing Limited, 2009.

[10] Painter, P.C., and Coleman, M.M., *Fundamentals of Polymer Science: An Introductory Text*, Second Edition, Technomic, 1997.

[11] Rudin, A., and Choi, P., *The Elements of Polymer Science & Engineering*, Third Edition, Academic Press, 1982.

[12] Salem, D.R., *Structure Formation in Polymer Fibers*, Hanser Publishers, 2001.

[13] Snetivy, D., Yang, H., and Julius Vancso, G., "Imaging of Different Crystal Planes in Oriented Polyethylene by Atomic Force Microscopy", *Journal of Materials Chemistry*, 2, 891–892, 1992.

[14] Sperling, L.H., *Introduction to Physical Polymer Science*, 4th Edition, John Wiley & Sons, Inc., 2006.

[15] Tonelli, A.E. *Polymers From the Inside Out—An Introduction to Macromolecules*, John Wiley & Sons, Inc., 2001.

[16] Warner, S.B., *Fiber Science*, Prentice Hall, 1995.

PROBLEMS

(1) Explain why polymer does not have a gas state.

(2) Why are some polymers transparent? Others are not?

(3) The lengths of polymer chains are significantly greater than the edge lengths of unit cells. How can polymer chains crystallize in fibers by forming unit cells?

(4) What are the common conformations found in the crystalline phase of polymer fibers?

(5) How does the hydrogen bonding affect the crystalline structure of nylon fibers?

(6) Spherulites are commonly seen in many polymer products. However, spherulites should be avoided during the formation of synthetic fibers. Why?

(7) The crystallites in many polymer fibers have fibrillar morphology. How does the drawing process affect the fibrillar morphology?

(8) What are the possible routes for making high-performance synthetic fibers?

(9) What determines the cross-sectional shape of melt-spun fibers?

(10) What are the typical cross-sectional shapes of solution-spun fibers?

CHAPTER 4

Chemical Structure of Natural Polymer Fibers

The chemical structure of natural polymer fibers is more complex than that of synthetic fibers. Two most important building units for natural polymer fibers are cellulose and protein. Natural cellulose fibers come from the "stringy" portions of plants, ranging from the fine seed fibers from the cotton plant to the coarse pineapple leaf fibers. Natural protein fibers are hairs of animals like the sheep and the delicate filaments spun by silkworms and insects. In addition to these natural fibers, manufactured cellulose and protein fibers also are important fibers that are based on natural biopolymers, but are processed like synthetic polymer fibers.

4.1 NATURAL CELLULOSE FIBERS

Natural cellulose fibers also are called plant fibers or vegetable fibers. Natural cellulose fibers include cotton together with flax, jute, jute, ramie and other fibers produced by plants. Natural cellulose fibers can be classified to seed, bast, leaf, and fruit fibers. Figure 4.1 shows the classification of natural cellulose fibers.

4.1.1 CELLULOSE

The basic building unit of natural cellulose fibers is cellulose, the most abundant biopolymer in nature. Figure 4.2 shows the chemical structure of cellulose, which basically is a polysaccharide consisting of a linear chain of several hundred to more than ten thousand β-linked glucose units. The glucose unit has a ring structure of one oxygen -O- atom and five -CH- groups. Three hydroxyl (–OH) side groups also are connected to the ring structure. Among them, two -OH groups are linked directly to the -CH- group on the ring while the other -OH group is linked to -CH- through a -CH$_2$- group. The remaining two -CH- groups on the ring

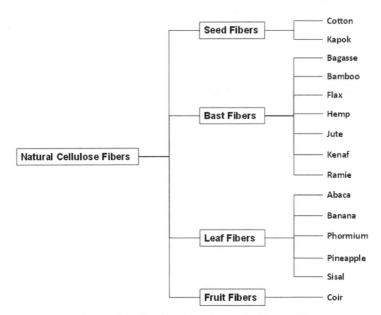

Figure 4.1. Classification of natural cellulose fibers.

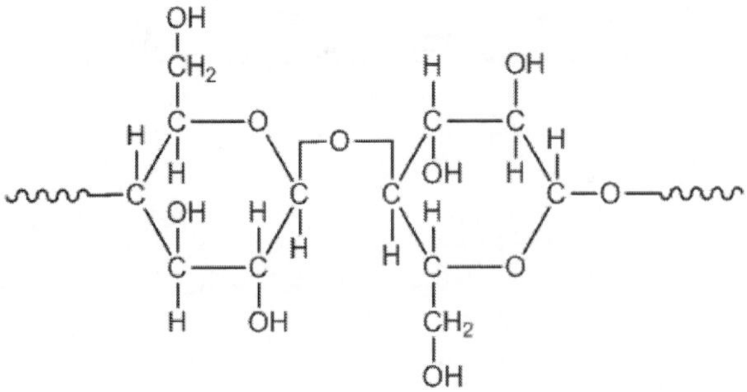

Figure 4.2. Chemical structure of cellulose.

structure are connected by -O- atoms to neighboring glucose units on the linear polymer chain.

Two important features of the chemical structure of cellulose are the glucose ring structure and –OH side groups. The glucose ring structure provides stiffness to the polymer chain and the –OH groups can form hydrogen bonds. These features define many important properties of natural cellulose fibers.

Starch is another important biopolymer that is found in plants and has a similar structure to cellulose. Like cellulose, starch also consists of glucose units. However, the glucose units in cellulose and starch are connected with different types of linkages, and the resultant polymer chains have different configurations. Figure 4.3 compares the polymer chains of starch and cellulose. The glucose units

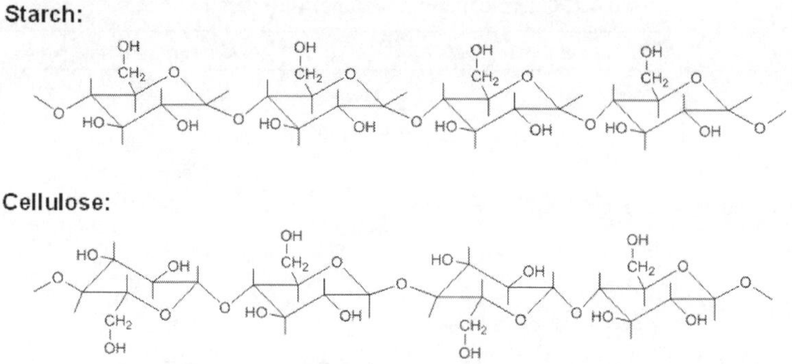

Starch:

Cellulose:

Figure 4.3. Comparison of starch and cellulose.

in starch are connected with α linkages and the polymer chain has a α configuration, i.e., all –CH_2-OH groups on the same side of the polymer chain. However, the glucose units in cellulose are connected by β linkages, and the polymer chain has a β configuration. In the β configuration, each successive glucose unit is rotated around the axis of the polymer chain, and -CH_2-OH groups on neighboring rings are on the alternative sides of the polymer chain. This small difference in the chemical structures of starch and cellulose has significant impacts on their properties. For example, starch is soluble in water when heated and is used by plants to store energy in their carbon-hydrogen bonds. However, cellulose does not dissolve in water and is strong enough to form usable fibers.

4.1.2 COTTON AND OTHER NATURAL CELLULOSE FIBERS

Cotton fibers are the most important natural cellulose fibers. Cotton fibers are one of the purest sources of cellulose. The cellulose content in cotton fibers is in the range of 88.0% – 96.0%. The noncellulosic components of cotton fibers include proteins, pectic substances, sugars, wax, and organic acids. Table 4.1 shows the contents of different components in dried cotton fibers. The actual contents of different components may vary, depending on the variety and maturity of cotton and environmental conditions such as climate, soil, water source, farming method, etc. Treatments can remove most of the noncellulosic components, and the cellulose content of the treated cotton fibers could be more than 99%.

In addition to cotton fibers, they are many other types of natural cellulose fibers. One major difference between cotton and other natural cellulose fibers is the cellulose content. Cotton fibers are the purest and other natural cellulose fibers have significantly lower content of cellulose. For example, both cotton and kapok are seed fibers, but cotton has the highest cellulose content and kapok has the lowest (13 wt%). The cellulose contents of other natural cellulose fibers are in the range of 40%–90%. Table 4.2 shows the cellulose contents of several natural cellulose fibers.

Table 4.1. Chemical composition of dried cotton fibers.

Component	Content (wt %)
Cellulose	88.0–96.0
Protein	1.1–1.9
Ash	0.7–1.6
Pectic substances	0.7–1.2
Organic acids	0.5–1.0
Wax	0.4–1.0
Sugars	0.1–1.0
Others	—

Source: Wakelyn, P.J., et al., *Cotton Fiber Chemistry and Technology*, CRC press, 2007.

Table 4.2. Cellulose contents of different natural cellulose fibers.

Cellulose Fiber	Plant Origin	Content (wt %)
Cotton	Seed	88–96
Kapok	Seed	13
Hemp	Bast	70–92
Ramie	Bast	68–76
Flax	Bast	60–81
Jute	Bast	51–84
Kenaf	Bast	44–57
Bagasse	Bast	32–48
Bamboo	Bast	26–43
Phormium	Leaf	67
Pineapple	Leaf	70–82
Abaca	Leaf	61–64
Banana	Leaf	60–65
Sisal	Leaf	43–78
Coir	Fruit	43–46

Source: Mwaikambo, L.Y., *African Journal of Science and Technology*, 7, 120–133, 2006.

4.2   MANUFACTURED CELLULOSE FIBERS

Manufactured cellulose fibers are man-made fibers. To make manufactured cellulose fibers, the cellulose component of the plant is dissolved in a solvent, which then is spun into fibers in the same ways that synthetic polymer fibers are made. Examples of manufactured cellulose fibers are rayon, acetate, triacetate, Lyocell, and Cupro.

Manufactured cellulose fibers can be made by both derivative and direct methods. In derivative methods, cellulose is chemically modified to form a cellulose derivative, which is spun into a coagulation bath to produce manufactured cellulose fibers. Rayon is the first manufactured cellulose fiber produced by the derivative approach, and the process used is called viscose process. In this process, cellulose in the form of wood pump is treated with sodium hydroxide and carbon disulfide to form cellulose xanthate. The cellulose xanthate is extruded into an acid bath, where the xanthate groups are removed from the polymer chains to regenerate the cellulose in the fiber form, called rayon (Figure 4.4). However, the cellulose derivative is not always regenerated back into cellulose. For example, acetate and triacetate fibers are produced by acetylation with acetic acid and acetic anhydride with the presence of sulfuric acid. The acetylation converts hydroxyl groups in cellulose to acetate groups (Figure 4.5), which render the cellulose polymer much more soluble in organic solvents. After the fiber formation, the cellulose derivative is not converted back into cellulose. The difference between acetate and triacetate fibers lies in the degree of acetylation. In acetate fibers, less than 92% but at least 74% of the –OH groups are acetylated. In triacetate fibers, at least 92% of the hydroxyl groups are acetylated.

In the direct methods, cellulose is dissolved and spun into fibers by using special solvent systems without chemical modification of the polymer structure. For example, Lyocell fibers are produced by using an organic solvent, N-methylmorpholine N-oxide, to dissolve cellulose. Cupro fibers are manufactured by dissolving cellulose in a mixed solution of copper salts and ammonia. (Some researchers consider Cupro fibers to be produced by a derivative method because interaction is formed between cellulose and the cuprammonium ions in the solution, as discussed in Chapter 10.) More recently, researchers also are using ionic liquids as the solvent to fabricate manufactured cellulose fibers.

The fabrication methods and chemical structures of manufactured cellulose fibers are summarized in Table 4.3.

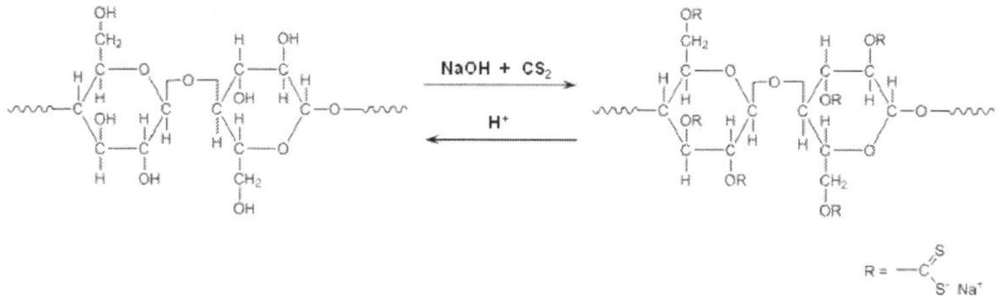

Figure 4.4. Chemical modifications involved in the viscose process of Rayon.

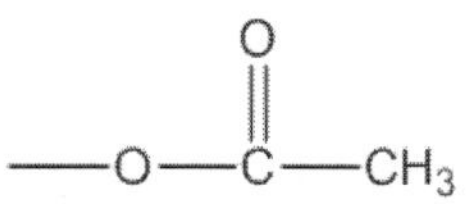

Figure 4.5. Acetate group.

Table 4.3. Fabrication methods, main characteristics, and chemical structures of manufactured cellulose fibers.

Fiber Name	Fabrication Method	Main Characteristics	Fiber Structure
Rayon	Derivative method	Produced by the viscose process	Cellulose:
Acetate	Derivative method	Less than 92% but at least 74% of the hydroxyl groups are acetylated	Cellulose acetate: $X = -H$ or $-C\overset{O}{\underset{CH_3}{}}$
Triacetate	Derivative method	At least 92% of the hydroxyl groups are acetylated	Cellulose triacetate: $X = -H$ or $-C\overset{O}{\underset{CH_3}{}}$
Lyocell	Direct method	Produced by using an organic solvent, N-methylmorpholine N-oxide	Cellulose:
Cupro	Direct method*	Processed by using a mixed solution of copper salts and ammonia	Cellulose:

*Some researchers consider Cupro fibers to be produced by a derivative method because interaction is formed between cellulose and the cuprammonium ions in the solution.

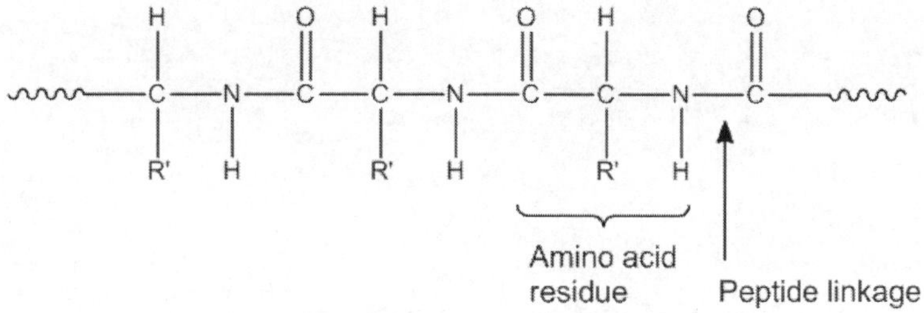

Figure 4.6. Structure of a polypeptide chain.

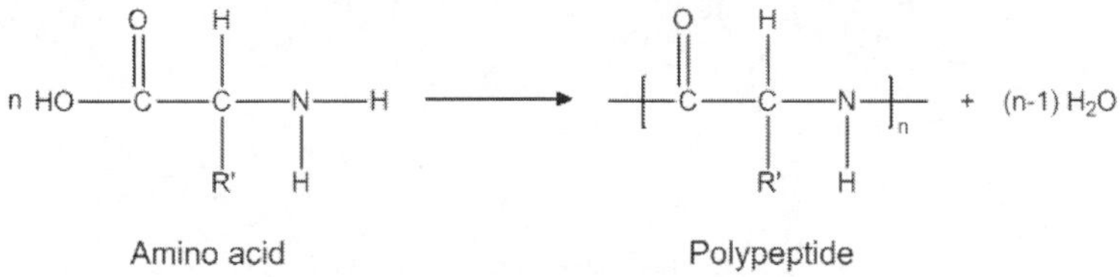

Figure 4.7. Reaction of amino acids to form a polypeptide.

4.3 NATURAL PROTEIN FIBERS

Natural protein fibers can be classified into two basics groups, animal hair fibers and extruded protein fibers. Animal hair fibers include but are not limited to wool (from sheep), cashmere, mohair, yak, and alpaca. All animal hair fibers have similar chemical structure. Extruded protein fibers are spun by silkworm, spider, etc., and they also have similar chemical structure. In this section, the discussion on natural protein fibers will focus on wool and silk (by silkworm).

4.3.1 PROTEIN

Among all fibers, protein fibers have the most complex chemical structure. Proteins consist of one or more polypeptides folded together. A polypeptide is a single linear polymer chain of amino acids bonded together by peptide linkages between the carboxyl and amino groups of adjacent amino acid residues. Figure 4.6 shows a linear polypeptide chain, and Figure 4.7 shows the reaction of amino acids to form a polypeptide.

There are twenty different types of amino acids, which are distinguished by their different side (-R') groups (Figure 4.8). The sequences of different amino acid residues in proteins are defined by the genetic codes, and the different sequences represent the different biological functions of proteins. Twenty different amino acids lead to an enormous list of possible sequences that make proteins the most versatile biopolymers. In the case of wool and other hair fibers, the genetic codes trigger the production of different proteins with different compositions and sequences of amino acid residues when the fibers grow out of hair follicles. The

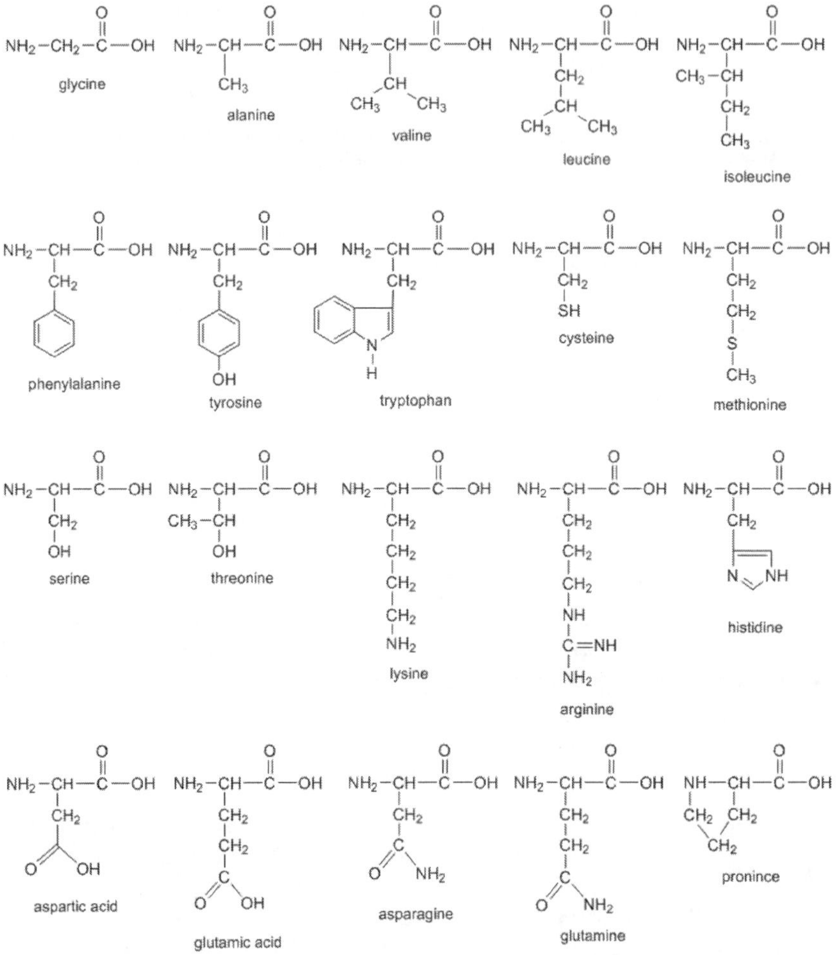

Figure 4.8. Chemical structures of twenty amino acids.

formation process of silk filaments also is affected by the protein properties, which are determined by the compositions and sequences of the amino acid residues.

4.3.2 WOOL AND SILK

Table 4.4 shows typical contents of different amino acid residues in the proteins of wool and silk fibers. The contents of amino acid residues vary with breed, diet and other factors. For example, wool fibers from different sources could have differences of up to 20% in the contents of some amino acid residues.

Table 4.4. Amino acid residue contents of wool and silk fibers.

Type	Side Group	Amino Acid	Amino Acid Residue Content (wt %)	
			Wool	**Silk**
Inert	-H	Glycine	6.5	43.8
	$-CH_3$	Alanine	4.1	26.4
	$-CH(CH_3)_2$	Valine	5.5	3.2
	$-CH_2CH(CH_3)_2$	Leucine	9.7	0.8
	$-CH(CH_3)CH_2CH_3$	Isoleucine	—	1.37
	$-CH_2C_6H_5$	Phenylalanine	1.6	1.5
Acidic	$-CH_2COOH$	Aspartic acid	7.27	3.0
	$-CH_2CH_2COOH$	Glutamic acid	16.0	2.03
Basic	$-(CH_2)_4NH_2$	Lysine	2.5	0.88
	$-(CH_2)_3NHC(NH)NH_2$	Arginine	8.6	1.05
	$-CH_2$—[imidazole ring]	Histidine	0.7	0.47
Hydroxyl	$-CH_2OH$	Serine	9.5	12.6
	$-CH(OH)CH_3$	Threonine	6.6	1.5
	$-CH_2C_6H_4OH$	Tyrosine	6.1	10.6
Ring	[cyclic $-CH_2$ / CH_2 / $-CH_2$]	Proline	7.2	1.5
Double	$-CH_2-S-S-CH_2-$	Cystine	11.8	—
Other	$-CH_2CH_2-S-CH_3$	Methionine	0.35	—
	$-CH_2$—[indole ring]	Tryptophan	0.7	—

Source: Harris, M., *Handbook of Textile Fibers*, Harris Research Laboratories, 1954.

Due to the large amount of functional side groups and the >C=O and >N-H groups on the polymer main chains, many different types of intermolecular bonds can be formed in wool and silk fibers:

- Hydrogen bonds can be formed between >C=O and >N-H groups on the main chains and between the hydroxyl and amide side groups.
- Ionic secondary bonds occur between acidic and basic side groups.
- Aromatic ring association can be formed between the aromatic rings in some of the side groups.

- Covalent amide bonds can be formed between polymer chains during to the presence of –COOH and –NH$_2$ groups, which is not common in synthetic polymer fibers.
- Covalent disulfide bonds also can occur between polymer chains due to the presence of cysteine (-CH$_2$-SH). During protein synthesis, cysteine is oxidized to cystine, -CH$_2$-S-S-CH$_2$-, which provides the disulfide bonds.

In wool and silk fibers, intermolecular bonds are so extensive that the polymers cannot melt. When heated, the primary bonds on the main chains break before all intermolecular bonds can be damaged. As a result, both wool and silk behave like thermosetting polymers. However, the ability for wool and silk fibers to form intermolecular bonds is different. As shown in Table 4.4, the chemical structure of silk is relatively simple and contains mainly residues of four types of amino acids: glycine, alanine, serine, and tyrosine. Wool has a more complex chemical structure and consists of many different types of amino acid residues. As a result, more types of intermolecular bonds can be found in wool fibers.

4.4 MANUFACTURED PROTEIN FIBERS

Manufactured protein fibers, often called azlons, are man-made fibers produced from animal or plant proteins. Examples of protein sources are milk, chicken feathers, soy beans, peanuts, corns, etc. Traditionally, most manufactured protein fibers were made directly from proteins dissolved in solvents. Recent trends in the research and development of manufactured protein fibers include the use of biochemistry to modify the source proteins and the introduction of synthetic polymers such as polyvinyl alcohol and polyacrylonitrile to improve the fiber mechanical properties. Antibacterial agents are often being added during the fiber formation process to provide health benefits to the manufactured protein fibers. As a result, the chemical structure of manufactured protein fibers is becoming more complex.

Currently, the market share of manufactured protein fibers is smaller than most other types of fibers. However, advances in manufacturing process and structure modification in the latest manufactured protein fibers indicate they may have a chance to increase the public acceptance.

REFERENCES

[1]   Brooks, M.M., "Regenerated Protein Fibres: a Preliminary Review", in *Handbook of Textile Fibre Structure, Volume II: Natural, Regenerated, Inorganic and Specialist Fibres*, editors Eichhorn, S.J., Hearle, J.W.S., Jaffe, M., and Kikutani, T., Woodhead Publishing Limited, 2009.

[2]   Choudhury, A.K.P., *Textile Preparation and Dying*, Science Publishers, 2006.

[3] Cook, J.G., *Handbook of Textile Fibres, Volume I—Natural Fibres*, Woodhead Publishing Limited, 2001.

[4] Ciechanska, D., Wesolowska, E., Wawro, D., "An Introduction to Cellulosic Fibres", in *Handbook of Textile Fibre Structure, Volume II: Natural, Regenerated, Inorganic and Specialist Fibres*, editors Eichhorn, S.J., Hearle, J.W.S., Jaffe, M., and Kikutani, T., Woodhead Publishing Limited, 2009.

[5] Dyer J., Daul, G., "Rayon Fibers", in *Handbook of Fibre Science and Technology, Volume IV. Fibre Chemistry*, editors Lewin, M., Pearce, E.M., Marcel Dekker, 1985.

[6] Ganster, J., Pink, H.P., "The Structure of Man-Made Cellulosic Fibres", in *Handbook of Textile Fibre Structure, Volume II: Natural, Regenerated, Inorganic and Specialist Fibres*, editors Eichhorn, S.J., Hearle, J.W.S., Jaffe, M., and Kikutani, T., Woodhead Publishing Limited, 2009.

[7] Harris, M., *Handbook of Textile Fibers*, Harris Research Laboratories, 1954.

[8] Hearle, J.W.S., "An Introduction to Protein Fibres", in *Handbook of Textile Fibre Structure, Volume II: Natural, Regenerated, Inorganic and Specialist Fibres*, editors Eichhorn, S.J., Hearle, J.W.S., Jaffe, M., and Kikutani, T., Woodhead Publishing Limited, 2009.

[9] Hsieh, Y.L., "Chemical Structure and Properties of Cotton", in *Cotton: Science and Technology*, editors Gordon S., and Hsieh, Y.L., Woodhead Publishing Limited, 2007.

[10] Kosan, B., Michels, C., and Meister, F., "Dissolution and Forming of Cellulose with Ionic Liquid", *Cellulose*, 15, 59–66, 2008.

[11] Mwaikambo, L.Y., "Review of the History, Properties and Application of Plant Fibres", *African Journal of Science and Technology*, 7, 120–133, 2006.

[12] Wakelyn, P.J., Edwards, J.V., Bertoniere, N.R., Triplett, B.A., Hunter, L., French, A.D., Rousselle, M.A., McAlister, D.D., Thibodeaux, D.P., Goynes, W.R. Jr., and Gamble, G.R., *Cotton Fiber Chemistry and Technology*, Taylor & Francis Group, 2007.

[13] Warner, S.B., *Fiber Science*, Prentice Hall, 1995.

PROBLEMS

(1) What are the four main types of natural cellulose fibers?

(2) Describe the repeating unit of cellulose.

(3) How do the hydroxyl groups affect the properties of natural cellulose fibers?

(4) What is the major difference between the chemical compositions of cotton and other natural cellulose fibers?

(5) What are the two methods for making manufactured cellulose fibers? Describe their major difference.

(6) How does triacetate differ from acetate?

(7) Describe the chemical structure of natural protein fibers.

(8) Describe the main differences (chain structure, side groups, and morphology, whatever are applicable) between the structures of wool and silk.

(9) What are the secondary bonds that can be found in wool and silk fibers?

(10) Why do wool and silk give different smells in the burning test?

CHAPTER 5

Physical Structure of Natural Polymer Fibers

The physical structure of natural cellulose and protein fibers is determined by the genetic codes. Human can only have limited influence on the physical structure of natural cellulose and protein fibers by selecting the species being raised and the environmental conditions such as soil, water source, farming method, etc. However, the physical structure of manufactured cellulose and protein fibers can be manipulated by controlling the chemical structure and processing conditions.

5.1 NATURAL CELLULOSE FIBERS

5.1.1 COTTON

As discussed in Chapter 4, cellulose is by far the major component in cotton fibers, but its precise content depends on the growth environment, geographical location and maturity of the plant. The glucose rings are not flat but bent in a chair configuration and each successive ring is rotated by 180° with respect to the polymer main chain. The hydroxyl groups attached to the ring units can form hydrogen bonds with each other and link cellulose chains into thin sheets (Figure 5.1). These sheets are hold together by van der Waals forces to form crystallites. Figure 5.2 shows a unit cell structure of the cellulose in cotton, with 1.030 nm for two glucose units along the polymer chain axis, 0.835 nm for spacing between adjacent chains in the sheets, and 0.790 nm between sheets. The crystal lattice in cotton is known as Cellulose I, which is different from the Cellulose II structure in manufactured cellulose fibers. When cellulose is dissolved and regenerated to the fiber form, the parallel arrangement of cellulose chains is altered and the resultant manufactured cellulose fibers will have a Cellulose II structure with anti-parallel chains.

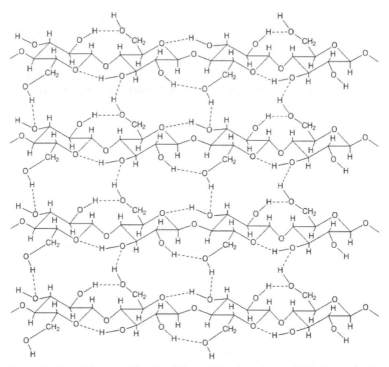

Figure 5.1. Possible assembly of cellulose chains in a sheet with hydrogen bonds.

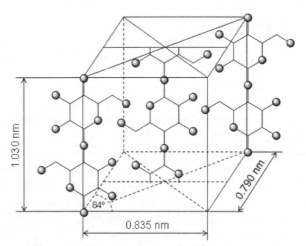

Figure 5.2. Unit cell structure of cellulose in cotton.

Cellulose in cotton is synthesized by the condensation of glucose monomers at enzyme complexes. Each enzyme complex produces 30 cellulose chains, which lie in the same direction to crystallize into long microfibrils. The microfibrils have an average diameter of several nanometers. From this aspect, the cellulose in cotton is considered to be 100% crystalline since all cellulose chains contribute to the formation of microfibrils. However, the density of cotton is lower than the crystal density, and experimental measurements using diffraction, spectroscopic, thermal and other techniques show cotton is about 60% crystalline. This can be explained by the imperfect packing when the microfibrils are formed. Microfibrils consisting of aligned cellulose chains are the main structural components of cotton fibers.

Figure 5.3 shows the cellular structure of a cotton fiber. A cotton fiber basically is a large single cell. During the fiber formation, the cell first grows to the full length of the fiber by stacking microfibrils to form a primary wall. The microfibrils in the primary wall are randomly oriented. After the formation of the primary wall, secondary walls are deposited in daily growth rings inside the primary wall, leaving a small lumen at the center. Secondary walls include parallel microfibrils aligned with helix angles ranging from 20°–30°. In addition, there is also a cuticle layer outside the primary wall. The cuticle is a waxy protective barrier that provides water resistance to the fibers as they grow. During wet processing of cotton fibers, the cuticle is typically removed.

The lumen is a hollow tube and it is filled with fluid when the cotton fibers are growing. Fresh cotton fibers have a circular cross-sectional structure. However, when cotton fibers are dried, the lumen losses its fluid and collapses (Figure 5.4). The collapse of the lumen leads to the kidney-bean cross-sectional shape and flat, twisted longitudinal structure of dried cotton fibers (Figure 5.5).

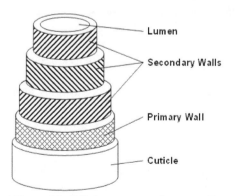

Figure 5.3. Cellular structure of a cotton fiber.

Figure 5.4. The collapse of lumen in a cotton fiber.

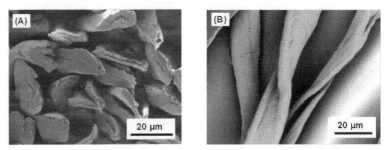

Figure 5.5. SEM images of cotton fibers with (A) cross-sectional and (B) longitudinal views.

5.1.2 *OTHER NATURAL CELLULOSE FIBERS*

Like in cotton, cellulose chains in other natural cellulose fibers also crystallize by forming the same unit cell structure as shown in Figure 5.2. Cellulose chains stack together to form microfibrils. The diameters of microfibrils in most natural cellulose fibers are in the same range, but the internal structure of the microfibrils show different degrees of crystallinity. In addition, the helix angles of microfibrils are different in different natural cellulose fibers (Table 5.1). Except coir, all other natural cellulose fibers have lower helix angles than cotton when microfibrils stack together to form the walls. Smaller spiral angles result in higher tensile moduli for these fibers.

Another major difference among different natural cellulose fibers is their morphology. Kapok fibers are obtained from the seed pods of the tropical kapok tree. Like cotton, kapok fibers are unicellular fibers. However, kapok fibers do not collapse and twist after dried (Figure 5.6). Dried kapok fibers have circular, hollow (lumen) cross-sectional structure with total wall thicknesses of around 2 μm and fiber diameters ranging from 15 to 35 μm. As a result, kapok fibers have lower densities (0.31–0.38 g/cm^3) than most other natural cellulose fibers.

Many other natural cellulose fibers form bundles. For example, short flax fibers (27–36 mm) overlap each other and are held together by a mixture of non-cellulosic polymers, including hemicellulose, lignin, and pectins (Figure 5.7). The resultant fiber bundles have irregular shapes and contain multiple lumens. Individual flax fibers have an average diameter of around 20 μm, but the bundle

Table 5.1. Helix angles of natural cellulose fibers.

Cellulose Fiber	Plant Origin	Helix Angle (°)
Cotton	Seed	20–30
Kapok	Seed	—
Hemp	Bast	6.2
Ramie	Bast	—
Flax	Bast	5
Jute	Bast	8.1
Kenaf	Bast	—
Bagasse	Bast	—
Bamboo	Bast	—
Phormium	Leaf	—
Pineapple	Leaf	6–14
Abaca	Leaf	—
Banana	Leaf	11–12
Sisal	Leaf	10–22
Coir	Fruit	39–49

Source: Mwaikambo, L.Y., *African Journal of Science and Technology*, 7, 120–133, 2006.

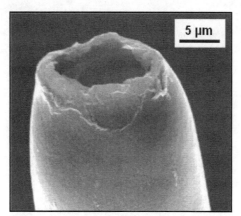

Figure 5.6. SEM image of a kapok fiber. (Abdullah, M.A., et. al., *Journal of Hazardous Materials*, 177, 683–691, 2010.)

size varies considerably. Figure 5.8 through Figure 5.10 show SEM images of bundle structures formed by kenaf, hemp, and sisal fibers, respectively.

The sizes and densities of natural cellulose fibers vary considerably. Table 5.2 shows the typically lengths, diameters, and densities of natural cellulose fibers. The actual sizes and densities are affected by the farming technique, growth environment, geographical location and maturity of the plant.

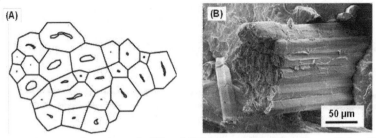

Figure 5.7. Cross-section schematic (A) and SEM image (B) of flax fibers. (Baley, C., et. al., *Materials Letters*, 60, 2984–2987, 2006.)

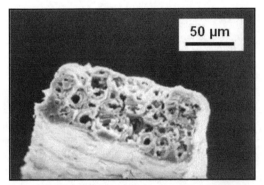

Figure 5.8. SEM image of kenaf fibers. (Shibata, S., et. al., *Polymer Testing*, 24, 1005–1011, 2005.)

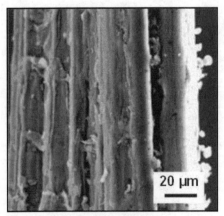

Figure 5.9. SEM image (longitudinal) of hemp fibers. (Troëdec, M.L., et. al., *Journal of the European Ceramic Society*, 29, 1861–1868, 2009.)

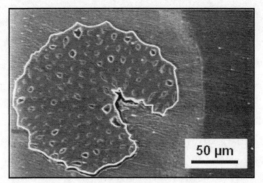

Figure 5.10. SEM image of sisal fibers. (Thomason, J.L., et. al., *Composites Science and Technology*, 71, 1008–1015, 2011.)

5.2 MANUFACTURED CELLULOSE FIBERS

Manufactured cellulose fibers have a very different physical structure from natural cellulose fibers. The crystal lattice formed by native cellulose chains in natural cellulose fibers is called Cellulose I (Figure 5.2). When cellulose is dissolved and spun into fibers, the crystal lattice changes to Cellulose II. Table 5.3 compares the unit cell parameters and crystal densities of Cellulose I and Cellulose II. The

Table 5.2. Lengths, diameters and densities of natural cellulose fibers.

Cellulose Fiber	Plant Origin	Fiber Length (mm)	Fiber Diameter (μm)	Bulk Density (g/cm³)
Cotton	Seed	20–64	11.5–17	1.55
Kapok	Seed	8–32	15–35	0.31–0.38
Hemp	Bast	8.3–14	17–23	1.40–1.50
Ramie	Bast	60–250	28.1–35	1.55
Flax	Bast	27–36	17.8–21.6	1.40–1.50
Jute	Bast	1.9–3.2	15.9–20.7	1.30–1.50
Kenaf	Bast	—	17.7–21.9	1.22–1.40
Bagasse	Bast	1.7	20	0.550–1.35
Bamboo	Bast	2.7	10–40	1.50
Phormium	Leaf	5.0–5.7	15.4–16.4	
Pineapple	Leaf	—	20–80	1.44–1.56
Abaca	Leaf	4.6–5.2	17–21.4	1.50
Banana	Leaf	2–3.8	—	1.30–1.35
Sisal	Leaf	1.8–3.1	18.3–23.7	1.30–1.55
Coir	Fruit	0.9–1.2	16.2–19.5	1.15–1.25

Source: Mwaikambo, L.Y., *African Journal of Science and Technology*, 7, 120–133, 2006.

Table 5.3. Edge lengths, internal angles and crystal
densities of Cellulose I and Cellulose II.

Crystal Type	Edge Lengths (nm)			Internal Angle β (o)	Crystal Density (g/cm3)
	a	b	c		
Cellulose I	0.835	1.030	0.790	84	1.625
Cellulose II	0.802	1.030	0.903	63	1.620

unit cell size of Cellulose II is slightly larger than that of Cellulose I, leading to a lower crystal density.

Another important difference between Cellulose I and Cellulose II is the orientation of cellulose chains. In Cellulose I, all cellulose chains are aligned in the same parallel direction, while those in Cellulose II have anti-parallel directions. In some manufactured cellulose fibers, the chemical structure of cellulose chains is altered by replacing the hydroxyl groups. Acetate and triacetate fibers are the most important examples of such fibers. In acetate and triacetate fibers, the polymer chains also have anti-parallel arrangement when they crystallize. However, both acetate and triacetate fibers do not have sufficient hydroxyl groups to form a huge amount of hydrogen bonds between adjacent chains, and hence their degrees of crystallinity and bulk densities are relatively low.

The crystallite morphology of manufactured cellulose fibers is similar to that of synthetic polymer fibers since both are man-made spun fibers. Two basic models often are used for manufactured cellulose fibers: fringed micelle model and fringed fibril model. In both cases, polymer chains are more or less aligned along the fiber axis. The fringed fibril model with fringe chains connecting the crystallites is the more appropriate model for most manufactured cellulose fibers. Figure 5.11 shows a fringed fibril model proposed by Fink and his coworker for describing the crystalline structure of manufactured cellulose fibers. Although thfringed fibril model is more desirable, the fringed micelle model still is suitable for a few manufactured cellulose fibers such as rayon.

Manufactured cellulose fibers are spun from solutions. During fiber formation, the fiber skin is solidified first and the sequence solidification of the fiber core reduces the fiber diameter and deforms the fiber skin. As a result, manufactured cellulose fibers typically have an irregular, crenulated cross-sectional shape. Figure 5.12 shows a transmission electron microscopy (TEM) image of a rayon fiber. Due to the different solidification rates of the fiber skin and core, this particular rayon fiber has a skin-core morphology, in which the core has voids in the order of 20 –150 nm and the skin is a densified layer of about 1.5–2.5 μm thick. The crystalline structures in the skin and core also are different. Figure 5.13 shows schematically the crystallite orientations in skin and core regions. The cross-sectional collapse occurred during fiber formation leads to a radial orientation of crystallites in the skin, but the core has more disordered orientation.

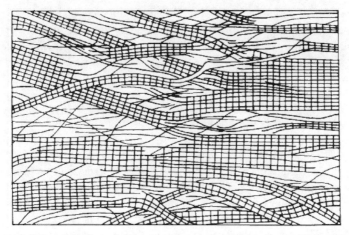

Figure 5.11. Fringed fibril model for manufactured cellulose fibers. (Fink, H.P., et. al., *Journal of Applied Polymer Science*, 30, 3779–3790, 1985.)

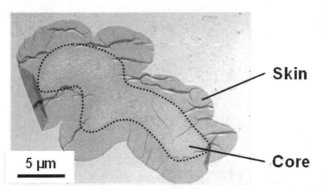

Figure 5.12. TEM image of a rayon fiber. (Fink, H.P., at. al., *Progress in Polymer Science*, 26, 1473–1524, 2001.)

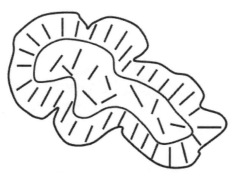

Figure 5.13. Crystallite orientation in skin and core of a rayon fiber.

Manufactured cellulose fibers with other morphologies can be obtained by using non-circular spinneret holes to achieve different cross-sectional shapes, or by injecting a gas into the spinning solution to produce inflated fibers. In addition, the "all-skin" morphology also is obtained in fibers used for tire yarns by adding dimethylamine or dimethylformamide.

5.3   NATURAL PROTEIN FIBERS

5.3.1   WOOL

The physical structure of wool is complex. The cross-section of wool is circular, or slightly elliptical in shape. The diameter of wool fibers is in the range of 20–40 μm. Figure 5.14 shows a schematic of the cross-section of a wool fiber, which consists of three major components, cuticle, cortex, and medulla.

Mechanically, the most important component of wool fibers is the cortex. Figure 5.15 shows the structure of the cortex in a wool fiber. The protein in wool fibers is called keratin. Three keratin chains in wool form helices with helix angles ranging from 30° to 35°. Three helix chains twist compactly together to form a protofibril with a diameter of around 2 nm. Eleven protofibrils assemble to form a microfibril with a diameter of 7–8 nm. Microfibrils also are called intermediate filaments and they helically wind together into a macrofibril with a diameter of

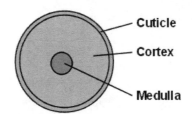

Figure 5.14. Cross-section structure of a wool fiber.

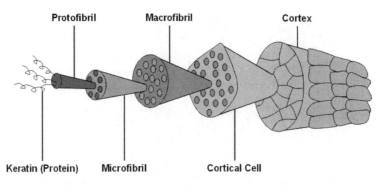

Figure 5.15. Structure of the cortex in a wool fiber.

about 0.4–0.5 μm. Macrofibrils are aligned to form a cortical cell. Cortical cells assemble to form the cortex component of the wool fiber.

Wool fibers contain three types of cortical cells, called *ortho-*, *meso-* and *para-*cortical cells. Figure 5.16 shows the distribution of these three types of cells in a wool fiber. Cortical cells are separated from each other by a cell membrane complex (CMC) with a thickness of around 25 nm. Most wool fibers mainly contain *ortho-* and *para-*cortical cells, which are arranged bilaterally. In *ortho-*cortical cells, the macrofibrils are discrete and twisted along their long axis, with microfibrils forming a whorl pattern due to the twisting of the peripheral microfibrils around the cell core. In *para-*cortical cells, the macrofibrls are fused together around the cell periphery and the microfibrils are all parallel to the fiber axis. In addition, *para-*cortical cells contain more sulfur-containing cysteine groups than *ortho-*cortical cells. Due to the structural differences between *ortho-* and *para-*cortical cells, wool fibers typically have a natural helical crimp with the *para-*cortical cells on the inside.

The cuticle also is an important component of wool fibers. Figure 5.17 shows a SEM image of a wool fiber. It is seen that the cuticle is an overlapping scale structure covering the cortex of wool fibers. The thicknesses of the cuticle and the scale are both 1–2 μm, indicating the scales are just overlapped slightly to provide a covering for the fiber with the thickness of one or two layers of scales. The scale structure leads to a directional friction effect, with the fibers being smoother in the growth direction. Unlike the cortex, in which the keratin chains crystallize by forming helices, the cuticle cells are largely amorphous.

The third component is the medulla, which may be empty or may contain a group of open cell walls. The cells in medulla do not contain sulfur in their

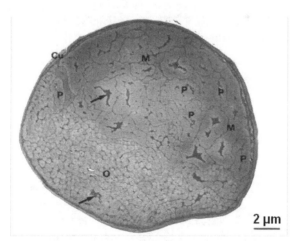

Figure 5.16. TEM image of the cross-section of a wool fiber. *Ortho-*cortical (O), *meso-*cortical (M) and *para-*cortical (P) cells and the cuticle (Cu) are indicated. (Marshall, R.C., et. al., *Electron Microscopy Reviews*, 4, 47–83, 1991.)

Figure 5.17. SEM image of a wool fiber.

proteins. Mechanically, the medulla represents empty space. The medulla can be easily observed in coarse wool fibers, but it may not be present in some finer fibers.

In addition to wool fibers obtained from sheep, there are many other animal hair fibers. These animal hair fibers differ from each other mainly in fiber diameter, length, number of scales in the cuticle, and natural color. For example, Mohair comes from Angora goat, and it possesses little crimp and has flat scales. Camel hair is the hair fiber of the two-humped camels of Mongolia, Tibet and other areas of Asia. Camel hair has poorly defined scales and it does not felt like wool. Cashmere is an extremely fine and soft fiber from Asian Cashmere goat. Alpaca fiber is a hair fiber from the alpaca of South America, and it is durable, silky, and lustrous. Vicuna, from the vicuna of South America, is lightweight and has fine scales that result in a smooth hand and high luster.

5.3.2 *Silk*

Silk has a simpler structure than wool. The protein in silk is called fibroin and it mainly has four types of simple side groups: -H, $-CH_3$, $-CH_2OH$, and $-CH_2C_6H_5OH$. Sulfur-containing cystine groups and other side groups are in small quantities. The intermolecular bonds between polymer chains are hence mostly the hydrogen bonds between $>C=O$ and $>N-H$ groups on the main chains, and a few hydrogen bonds and ionic secondary bonds between side groups.

The fibroin chains are held together by hydrogen bonds and are aligned along the fiber axis to form β-pleated sheets, leading to the formation of partially extended chain crystallites (Figure 5.18). However, the bulky side groups are undesirable for forming crystallites. Hence, the sections of the fibroin chains that contain bulky side groups tend to be distributed in the amorphous phase.

In addition to fibroin protein, the as-spun silk produced by silkworm has another component, called sericin, which also is a protein. The un-degummed silk has around 75% fibroin and 25% sericin. Figure 5.19 shows a schematic of un-degummed silk. It is seen that two fibroin fibers are held together with sericin coating. Fibroin is insoluble in water, but sericin can be removed by boiling with soap water, i.e., the degumming process. Figure 5.20 shows a degummed silk fiber, which has a triangle cross-section.

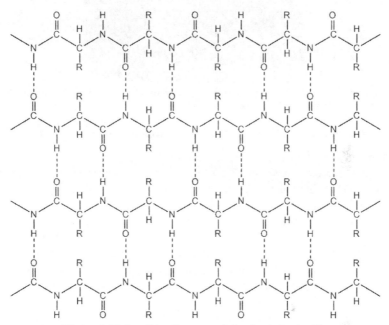

Figure 5.18. Possible alignment of fibroin chains in silk.

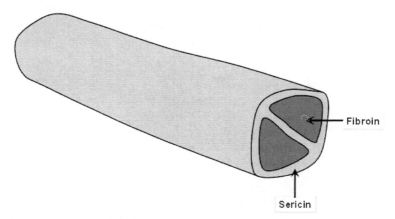

Figure 5.19. Schematic of un-degummed silk.

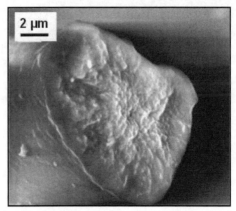

Figure 5.20. SEM image of degummed silk. (Zhang, K., et. al., *Acta Biomaterialia*, 6, 2165–2171, 2010.)

5.4   MANUFACTURED PROTEIN FIBERS

Manufactured protein fibers typically are made from proteins of milk, peanut, corn, soybean, etc. These proteins often are coiled into a compact ball-shape structure, with coils linked together by a large number of intermolecular bonds. Treatments have to be carried out to destroy these intermolecular bonds and align protein chains to form fibers.

Manufactured protein fibers developed between late nineteenth and mid-twentieth centuries often had poor mechanical properties, and they often were blended with other natural or synthetic polymer fibers. Some manufactured protein fibers, such as milk-based protein fibers, had an unpleasant odor when wet. As a result, due to technical and economic challenges, these manufactured protein fibers failed to become mainstream fibers.

Since late twentieth century, manufactured protein fibers with different structures and properties are being developed with new technologies, such as the use of chemical and biochemical treatments and the spinning of protein/synthetic polymer bicomponent fibers. Figure 5.21 shows a SEM image of a core-sheath soybean protein/polyvinyl alcohol bicomponent fiber.

REFERENCES

[1]   Abdullah, M.A., Rahmah, A.U., and Man, Z., "Physicochemical and Sorption Characteristics of Malaysian Ceiba Pentandra (L.) Gaertn. as a Natural Oil Sorbent", *Journal of Hazardous Materials*, 177, 683–691, 2010.

[2]   Ansell, M.P., and Mwaikambo, L.Y., "The Structure of Cotton and Other Plant Fibres", in *Handbook of Textile Fibre Structure, Volume II: Natural, Regenerated, Inorganic and Specialist Fibres*, editors Eichhorn, S.J., Hearle, J.W.S., Jaffe, M., and Kikutani, T., Woodhead Publishing Limited, 2009.

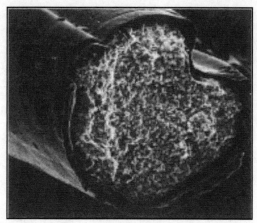

Figure 5.21. SEM image of a core-sheath soybean protein/polyvinyl alcohol fiber. (Zhang, Y., et. al., *Journal of Applied Polymer Science*, 71, 11–19, 1999.)

[3]　Baley, C., Perrot, Y., Busnel, F., Guezenoc, H., and Davies, P., "Transverse Tensile Behaviour of Unidirectional Plies Reinforced with Flax Fibres", *Materials Letters*, 60, 2984–2987, 2006.

[4]　Brooks, M.M., "Regenerated Protein Fibres: a Preliminary Review", in *Handbook of Textile Fibre Structure, Volume II: Natural, Regenerated, Inorganic and Specialist Fibres*, editors Eichhorn, S.J., Hearle, J.W.S., Jaffe, M., and Kikutani, T., Woodhead Publishing Limited, 2009.

[5]　Cook, J.G., *Handbook of Textile Fibres, Volume I—Natural Fibres*, Woodhead Publishing Limited, 2001.

[6]　Ciechanska, D., Wesolowska, E., and Wawro, D., "An Introduction to Cellulosic Fibres", in *Handbook of Textile Fibre Structure, Volume II: Natural, Regenerated, Inorganic and Specialist Fibres*, editors Eichhorn, S.J., Hearle, J.W.S., Jaffe, M., and Kikutani, T., Woodhead Publishing Limited, 2009.

[7]　Dyer J., and Daul, G., "Rayon Fibers", in *Handbook of Fibre Science and Technology, Volume IV. Fibre Chemistry*, editors Lewin, M., and Pearce, E.M., Marcel Dekker, 1985.

[8]　Feughelman, M., "Natural Protein Fibers", *Journal of Applied Polymer Science*, 83, 489–507, 2002.

[9]　Fink, H.P., Philipp, B., "Models of Cellulose Physical Structure form the Viewpoint of the Cellulose I to Cellulose II Transition, *Journal of Applied Polymer Science*, 30, 3779–3790, 1985.

[10] Fink, H.P., Weigel, P., Purz, H.J., and Ganster, J., "Structure Formation of Regenerated Cellulose Materials from nmMO-Solutions", *Progress in Polymer Science*, 26, 1473–1524, 2001.

[11] Ganster, J., Pink, H.P., "The Structure of Man-Made Cellulosic Fibres", in *Handbook of Textile Fibre Structure, Volume II: Natural, Regenerated, Inorganic and Specialist Fibres*, editors Eichhorn, S.J., Hearle, J.W.S., Jaffe, M., and Kikutani, T., Woodhead Publishing Limited, 2009.

[12] Harris, M., *Handbook of Textile Fibers*, Harris Research Laboratories, 1954.

[13] He, J.H., Ren, Z.F., Fan, J., and Xu, L., "Hierarchy of Wool Fibers and its Interpretation Using E-Infinity Theory", *Chaos, Solitons and Fractals*, 41, 1893–1841, 2009.

[14] Hearle, J.W.S., "An Introduction to Protein Fibres", in *Handbook of Textile Fibre Structure, Volume II: Natural, Regenerated, Inorganic and Specialist Fibres*, editors Eichhorn, S.J., Hearle, J.W.S., Jaffe, M., and Kikutani, T., Woodhead Publishing Limited, 2009.

[15] Hearle, J.W.L., "Physical Structure and Properties of Cotton", in *Cotton: Science and Technology*, editors Gordon S., and Hsieh, Y.L., Woodhead Publishing Limited, 2007.

[16] Hearle, J.W.S., "Physical Structure and Fibre Properties", in *Regenerated Cellulose Fibres*, editor Woodings, C., Wooding Publishing Limited, 2001.

[17] Hsieh, Y.L., "Chemical Structure and Properties of Cotton", in *Cotton: Science and Technology*, editors Gordon S., and Hsieh, Y.L., Woodhead Publishing Limited, 2007.

[18] Khalifa, I.B., Ladhari, N., Touay, M., "Application of Sericin to Modify Textile Supports", *Journal of the Textile Institute*, 103, 370–377, 2012.

[19] Kosan, B., Michels, C., and Meister, F., "Dissolution and Forming of Cellulose with Ionic Liquid", *Cellulose*, 15, 59–66, 2008.

[20] Lim, T.T., and Huang, X., "Evaluation of Kapok (*Ceiba Pentandra* (L.) Gaertn.) as a Natural Hollow Hydrophobic—Oleophilic Fibrous Sorbent for Oil Spill Cleanup", *Chemosphere*, 66, 955–963, 2007.

[21] Marshall, R.C., Orwin, D.F.G., and Gillespie, J.M., "Structure and Biochemistry of Mammalian Hard Keratin", *Electron Microscopy Reviews*, 4, 47–83, 1991.

[22] McKittrick, J., Chen, P.Y., Bodde, S.G., Yang, W., Novitskaya, E.E., and Meyers, M.A., "The Structure, Functions, and Mechanical Properties of Keratin", *The Journal of The Minerals, Metals & Materials Society*, 64, 449–468, 2012.

[23] Meyer, K.H., and Misch, L., "Cellulose: Crystal Structure", *Helv Chim Acta*, 20, 232–244, 1937.

[24] Mwaikambo, L.Y., "Review of the History, Properties and Application of Plant Fibres", *African Journal of Science and Technology*, 7, 120–133, 2006.

[25] O'Sullivan, A.C., "Cellulose: the Structure Slowly Unravels", *Cellulose*, 4, 173–207, (1997).

[26] Qi, H., Cai, J., Zhang, L., Nishiyama, Y., and Rattaz, A., "Influence of Finishing Oil on Structure and Properties of Multi-Filament Fibers from Cellulose Dope in NaOH/Urea Aqueous Solution", *Cellulose*, 15, 81–89, 2008.

[27] Shibata, S., Cao, Y., and Fukumoto, I., "Press Forming of Short Natural Fiber-Reinforced Biodegradable Resin: Effects of Fiber Volume and Length on Flexural Properties", *Polymer Testing*, 24, 1005–1011, 2005.

[28] Thomason, J.L., Carruthers, J., Kelly, J., and Johnson, G., "Fibre Cross-section Determination and Variability in Sisal and Flax and its Effects on Fibre Performance Characterisation", *Composites Science and Technology*, 71, 1008–1015, 2011.

[29] Tortora, P.G., *Understanding Textiles*, Fourth Edition, Macmillian Publishing Company, 1992.

[30] Troëdec, M.L., Peyratout, C.S., Smith, A., Chotard, T., "Influence of Various Chemical Treatments on the Interactions between Hempfibres and a Lime Matrix", *Journal of the European Ceramic Society*, 29, 1861–1868, 2009.

[31] Vollrath, Porter, D., Dicko, C., "The Structure of Silk", in *Handbook of Textile Fibre Structure, Volume II: Natural, Regenerated, Inorganic and Specialist Fibres*, editors Eichhorn, S.J., Hearle, J.W.S., Jaffe, M., and Kikutani, T., Woodhead Publishing Limited, 2009.

[32] Wakelyn, P.J., Edwards, J.V., Bertoniere, N.R., Triplett, B.A., Hunter, L., French, A.D., Rousselle, M.A., McAlister, D.D., Thibodeaux, D.P., Goynes, W.R. Jr., and Gamble, G.R., *Cotton Fiber Chemistry and Technology*, Taylor & Francis Group, 2007.

[33] Warner, S.B., *Fiber Science*, Prentice Hall, 1995.

[34] Woodings, C., "Applications Development", in *Regenerated Cellulose Fibres*, editor Woodings, C., Woodhead Publishing, 2001.

[35] Mortmann, "The Structure and Properties of Wool and Hair Fibres", in *Handbook of Textile Fibre Structure, Volume II: Natural, Regenerated, Inorganic and Specialist Fibres*, editors Eichhorn, S.J., Hearle, J.W.S., Jaffe, M., and Kikutani, T., Woodhead Publishing Limited, 2009.

[36] Zhang, K., Si, F.W., Duan, H.L., and Wang, J., "Microstructures and Mechanical Properties of Silks of Silkworm and Honeybee", *Acta Biomaterialia*, 6, 2165–2171, 2010.

[37] Zhang, Y., Ghasemzadeh, S., Kotliar, A.M., Kumar, S., Presnell, S. Williams, L.D., "Fibers from Soybean Protein and Poly(vinyl alcohol)", *Journal of Applied Polymer Science*, 71, 11–19, 1999.

PROBLEMS

(1) Natural cellulose and manufactured cellulose fibers have different crystalline structures. Describe the difference.

(2) Describe the cellular structure of cotton fibers.

(3) What is the helix angle of the microfibrils when they are aligned in parallel in the secondary walls of cotton fibers?

(4) How do the cross-sectional and longitudinal shapes change when fresh cotton fibers are dried?

(5) What are the major differences between the physical structures of cotton and other natural cellulose fibers?

(6) Describe the main physical structure features of manufactured cellulose fibers.

(7) Describe the physical structure of wool.

(8) Most wool fibers have a natural helical crimp. Why?

(9) Describe the physical structure of silk.

(10) What are the major differences between the physical structures of wool and silk?

CHAPTER 6

Structure of Non-Polymer Fibers

A wide range of non-polymer fibers, such as carbon, glass, silicon carbide, boron, asbestos, and metal fibers, now is available commercially. Among them, carbon fibers often are made by heat-treating precursor fibers of polymer materials, such as polyacrylonitrile and rayon. Glass fibers, silicon carbide fibers and metal fibers are made directly from non-polymer raw materials. Compared with polymer fibers, non-polymer fibers often are stronger, stiffer, more heat resistant, and less flammable. However, except for metal fibers, non-polymer fibers also are characterized by their brittleness. These property characteristics are directly related to the atomic arrangement and the defect structure of non-polymer fibers. There are many different types of non-polymer fibers, but this chapter only discusses the structure of two most used non-polymer fibers: carbon and glass fibers.

6.1 CARBON FIBERS

Carbon fibers have diameters ranging from 5 to 10 μm, and they are mainly composed of carbon atoms. Carbon fibers have excellent properties, such as high modulus, high strength, low weight, high chemical resistance, high temperature tolerance and low thermal expansion, and often are combined with other materials to form high-strength, high-modulus, and low-weight composites.

6.1.1 ATOMIC ORDER

The ideal graphite crystal is composed of infinite sheets of carbon atoms arranged in a hexagonal pattern, i.e., graphene sheets. These graphene sheets are stacked in a regular ABAB sequence with atoms in alternate planes aligning with each other (Figure 6.1). An important characteristic of the graphite crystal is the different

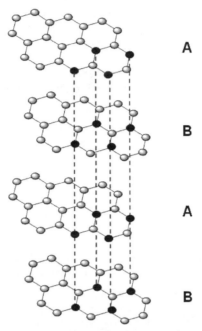

Figure 6.1. Arrangement of carbon atoms in graphite.

bonding types within and between the graphene sheets. Within the graphene sheets, the carbon atoms are held together by strong covalent bonds and the bond length is 0.142 nm. Van der Waals forces hold these graphene sheets together and the distance between adjacent sheets is 0.335 nm. This unique characteristic makes the graphite crystal one of the most anisotropic structures, i.e., exhibiting different properties when measured along different directions. For example, the van der Waals forces can break easily under external stress, and as a result the graphene sheets slide over one another. This sliding makes graphite an excellent lubricant.

Unlike a graphite crystal that is formed by perfect graphene sheets, the basic unit of carbon fibers is the imperfect graphene sheet. Imperfect graphene sheets contain a high number of defects, such as vacancies and impurity atoms, and are strongly distorted in-plane (Figure 6.2). Carbon fibers are based on the stacking of these imperfect graphene sheets. Due to the high-density in-plane defects and distorted sheet shape, the stacking of graphene sheets in carbon fibers is less ordered than that in graphite crystal, leading to a so-called "turbostratic" structure (Figure 6.3). The arrangement of the sheet planes determines the mechanical properties of carbon fibers. To achieve high fiber modulus and strength, the good alignment of the graphene sheets parallel to the fiber axis is desired. Although the alignment of graphene sheets in the "turbostratic" structure of carbon fibers is not perfect, it can be improved by selectively adjusting the processing parameters used during the fiber formation. For example, when the heat-treatment temperature exceeds 1700°C, carbon fibers are converted to graphite fibers, in which the alignment of graphene sheets is similar to that in graphite crystals.

6.1.2 MORPHOLOGY

Carbon fibers typically are straight, without crimp (Figure 6.4). The cross-sectional shape of carbon fibers typically is circular (Figure 6.5). However, carbon fibers with other cross-sectional shapes also exist.

The arrangement of crystallites in the cross-section of carbon fibers is complex and is affected by the precursor type and structure, fiber spinning conditions,

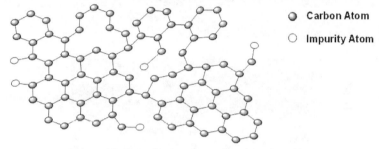

      ○ **Carbon Atom**

      ○ **Impurity Atom**

Figure 6.2. Imperfect graphene sheet in carbon fibers.

Carbon Fiber

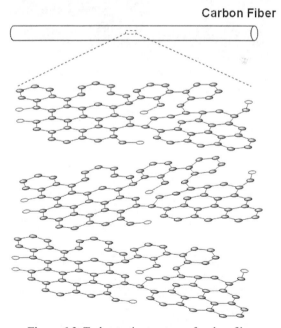

Figure 6.3. Turbostratic structure of carbon fibers.

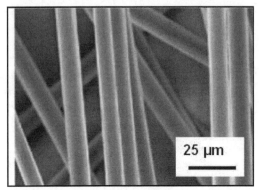

Figure 6.4. Longitudinal SEM image of carbon fibers. (Sharma, S.P., et. al., *Surface and Coatings Technology*, 203, 1329–1335, 2009.)

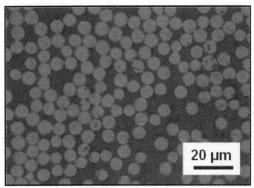

Figure 6.5. Cross-sectional SEM image of carbon fibers. (Petrović, Ž., et. al., *Thin Solid Films*, 513, 193–200, 2006.)

and carbonization temperature. In carbon fibers, graphene sheets stack together to form crystallites and the stacking thickness varies from a few nanometers to tens of nanometers. These crystallite sheets are preferentially oriented along the fiber axis. Figure 6.6 shows the arrangement of crystallite sheets in a carbon fiber. In this particular carbon fiber, the crystallite sheets twist, fold and join each other to form a radial texture at the fiber cross-section. In addition to the radial structure, other types of cross-sectional morphology can be found in carbon fibers. Figure 6.7 shows a few examples of possible cross-sectional morphology of carbon fibers.

6.2 GLASS FIBERS

Glass fibers are based on silica (SiO_2), with the addition of different oxides. Glass fibers also have good mechanical properties and often are used as an insulating material or reinforcement for making composites. Although they are not as strong as carbon fibers, glass fibers are much cheaper and less brittle.

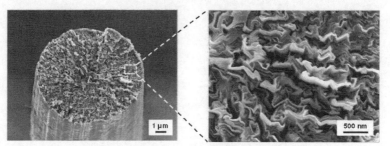

Figure 6.6. Arrangement of crystallite sheets in a carbon fiber. (Naito, K., et. al., *Carbon*, 46, 189–195, 2008.)

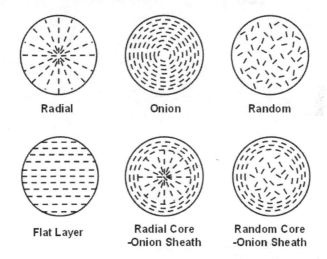

Radial Onion Random

Flat Layer Radial Core -Onion Sheath Random Core -Onion Sheath

Figure 6.7. Possible cross-sectional morphology of carbon fibers.

6.2.1 ATOMIC ORDER

In its pure form, silica exist as a macromolecule, $(SiO_2)_n$, in which SiO_4 groups are configured as a tetrahedron with the silicon atom in the center and four oxygen atoms at the corners (Figure 6.8). When SiO_2 crystallizes, the SiO_4 tetrahedrons form crystals by sharing the oxygen atoms at the corners. Figure 6.9 shows the two-dimensional arrangement of silicon and oxygen atoms in a SiO_2 crystal.

Unlike pure SiO_2 crystals, the atoms in glass fibers are arranged in a less ordered pattern (Figure 6.10). This is related to the fiber formation process. During fiber formation, the raw materials are melted, extruded, and allowed to cool quickly. The viscosity of the fluid is so high that the atoms are unable to move to the low potential energy positions in the crystal unit cells. The disordered pattern of the liquid is "frozen" into the solid fiber. Therefore, glass fibers usually are amorphous and regarded as a supercooled fluid. Glass fibers are transparent because the length scale over which the disorder occurs is smaller than the wavelength of the visible light and is unable to scatter the light.

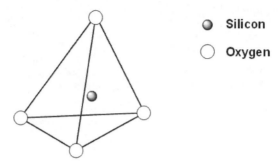

Figure 6.8. Tetrahedral structure of SiO2.

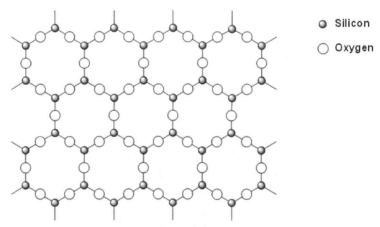

Figure 6.9. Two-dimensional arrangement of silicon and oxygen atoms in a SiO_2 crystal.

In pure silica, each silicon atom is linked to four oxygen atoms by covalent bonding, and hence a high processing temperature is required for fiber formation. Therefore, it is common to introduce impurity atoms (such as Ca, Na, K, etc.) that have lower valence to break up the network by forming ionic bonds with oxygen (Figure 6.11). The introduction of impurities lowers the processing temperature and the cost of the glass fibers. However, the strength and modulus of glass fibers also are reduced.

6.2.2 COMPOSITION

Commercial glass fibers contain significant amounts of impurity atoms that lower the processing temperature and the product cost. Atoms listed in the first column (e.g., Na and K), second column (e.g., Mg, Ca, and Ba) and third column (e.g., B and Al) of the periodic table make up a significant percentage of the composition of glass fibers. But other atoms (e.g., Fe and Ti) also are introduced in many glass

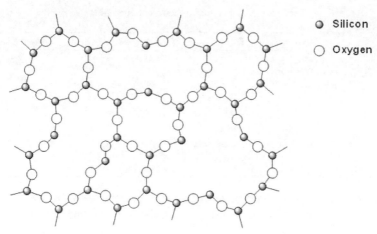

Figure 6.10. Two-dimensional arrangement of silicon and oxygen atoms in glass fibers.

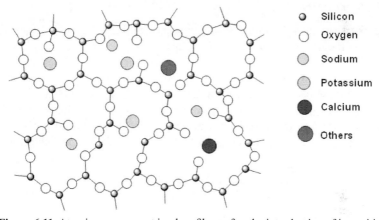

Figure 6.11. Atomic arrangement in glass fibers after the introduction of impurities.

fibers. These atoms exist as cations and disrupt the corner bonding of the tetrahedral SiO_4 units, resulting in significant changes in the properties of glass fibers. Table 6.1 shows the composition of several important glass fibers.

Glass fibers are designated as "A" glasses when they are made of soda-lime-silica glasses that are similar to these used in glass bottles and flat glass. Among the glass fibers shown in Table 6.1, A-glass fibers have the highest SiO_2 content. On the other hand, E-glass fibers (E for electrical) has the lowest SiO_2 content. They draw well and have good mechanical, electrical and weathering properties. S-glass (S for strength) and C-glass (C for corrosion) fibers have the same SiO_2 content, but the contents of other components are different. S-glass fibers have higher strength, modulus, and thermal resistance than other types of glass

Table 6.1. Composition of different glass fibers.

	A Glass	E-glass	S-Glass	C-Glass	Wool Glass
SiO_2	71.8	52.4	64.4	64.4	63.5
$Na_2O + K_2O$	14.2	0.8	0.3	9.6	16.2
CaO	8.8	17.2	—	13.4	9.0
MgO	3.8	4.6	10.3	3.3	5.2
B_2O_3	—	10.6	—	4.7	2.9
BaO	—	.	—	0.9	—
$Al_2O_3 + Fe_2O_3$	1.5	14.4	25.0	4.1	3.0

fibers, but C-glass fibers have better resistance to correction. Wool glass fibers, also called fiberglasses, are used as thermal insulators for buildings.

6.2.3 MORPHOLOGY

Glass fibers are amorphous and have simple morphology. Figures 6.12 and 6.13 show longitudinal and cross-sectional SEM images of glass fibers, respectively. Most glass fibers are straight and have circular cross-section. However, glass fibers with other cross-sectional structures also exist. Figure 6.14 shows a SEM image of hollow glass fibers. These hollow glass fibers have higher rigidity than regular fibers. When used as the reinforcement in composites, hollow glass fibers cannot only provide the desired structural improvement, but also introduce a reservoir suitable for the containment of a healing agent, which makes the composites self-healing.

Figure 6.12. Longitudinal SEM image of glass fibers. (Etcheverry, M., et. al., *Composites Part A: Applied Science and Manufacturing*, 39, 1915–1923, 2008.)

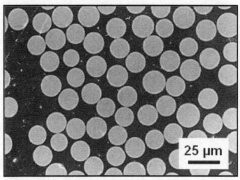

Figure 6.13. Cross-sectional SEM image of glass fibers. (Lassila, L.V.J., et. al., *Biomaterials*, 23, 2221–2229, 2002.)

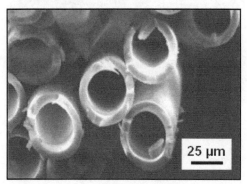

Figure 6.14. SEM image of hollow glass fibers. (Murphy, E.B., et. al., *Progress in Polymer Science*, 35, 223–251, 2010.)

REFERENCES

[1]   Cato, A.D., and Edie, D.D., "Flow Behavior of Mesophase Pitch", *Carbon*, 41, 1411–1417, 2003.

[2]   Chand, S., "Review Carbon Fibers for Composites*", Journal of Materials Science*, 35, 1303–1313 (2000).

[3]   Donnet, J.B., and Qin, R.Y., "Study of Carbon Fiber Surfaces by Scanning Tunnelling Microscopy, Part I. Carbon Fibers from Different Precursors and After Various Heat Treatment Temperatures", *Carbon*, 30, 787–796, 1992.

[4]   Etcheverry, M., Ferreiraa, M.L., Capiati, N.J., Pegoretti, A., and Barbosa, S.E., "Strengthening of Polypropylene-Glass Fiber Interface by Direct Metallocenic Polymerization of Propylene onto the Fibers", *Composites Part A: Applied Science and Manufacturing*, 39, 1915–1923, 2008.

[5]   Frank, E., Hermanutz, F., and Buchmeiser, M.R., "Carbon Fibers: Precursors, Manufacturing, and Properties", *Macromolecular Materials and Engineering*, 297, 493–501, 2012.

[6]   Hong, S.H., Korai, Y., and Mochida, I., "Development of Mesoscopic Textures in Transverse Cross-section of Mesophase Pitch-Based Carbon Fibers", *Carbon*, 37, 917–930, 1999.

[7]   Hull, D., and Clyne, T.W., *An Introduction to Composite Materials*, Second Edition, Cambridge University Press, 1996.

[8]   Johnson, D.J., Tomizuka, I., and Watanabe, O., "The Fine Structure of Pitch-Based Carbon Fibres", *Carbon*, 13, 529–534, 1975.

[9]   Jones, F.R., and Huff, N.T., "The Structure and Properties of Glass Fibres", *Handbook of Textile Fibre Structure. Volume 2: Natural Regenerated, Inorganic and Specialist Fibres*, Editors Eichhorn, S.J., Hearle, J.W.S., Jaffe, M., and Kikutani, T., Woodhead Publishing Limited, 2009.

[10]   Lassila, L.V.J., Nohrström, T., and Vallittu, P.K., "The Influence of Short-Term Water Storage on the Flexural Properties of Unidirectional Glass Fiber-Reinforced Composites", *Biomaterials*, 23, 2221–2229, 2002.

[11]   Matsumoto, T. "Mesophase Pitch and its Carbon Fibers", *Pure and Applied Chemistry*, 57, 1553–1562, 1985.

[12]   Murphy, E.B., and Fred Wudl, F., "The World of Smart Healable Materials", *Progress in Polymer Science*, 35, 223–251, 2010.

[13]   Naito, K., Tanaka, Y., Yang, J.M., and Kagawa, Y., "Tensile Properties of Ultrahigh Strength PAN-Based, Ultrahigh Modulus Pitch-Based and High Ductility Pitch-Based Carbon Fibers", *Carbon*, 46, 189–195, 2008.

[14]   Paris, O., and Peterlik, H., "The Structure of Carbon fibers", *Handbook of Textile Fibre Structure. Volume 2: Natural Regenerated, Inorganic and Specialist Fibres*, Editors Eichhorn, S.J., Hearle, J.W.S., Jaffe, M., and Kikutani, T., Woodhead Publishing Limited, 2009.

[15]   Petrović, Ž., Metikoš-Huković, M., Z. Grubač, Z., and Omanović, S., "The Nucleation of Ni on Carbon Microelectrodes and Its Electrocatalytic Activity in Hydrogen Evolution", *Thin Solid Films*, 513, 193–200, 2006.

[16]   Sharma, S.P., and Lakkad, S.C., "Morphology Study of Carbon Nanospecies Grown on Carbon Fibers by Thermal CVD Technique", *Surface and Coatings Technology*, 203, 1329–1335, 2009.

[17]   Sheshin, E.P., "Properties of Carbon Materials, Especially Fibers, For Field Emitter Applications", *Applied Surface Science*, 215, 191–200, 2002.

[18] Toyoda, M., and Inagaki, M., "Exfoliation of Carbon Fibers", *Journal of Physics and Chemistry of Solids*, 65, 109–117, 2004.

PROBLEMS

(1) Compared with polymer fibers, what are the unique features of non-polymer fibers?

(2) What are the excellent properties of carbon fibers?

(3) Describe the turbostratic structure of carbon fibers.

(4) How are the crystallite sheets arranged in carbon fibers?

(5) What are the main differences between carbon and graphite fibers?

(6) What is the most important component in glass fibers? What are the other possible components?

(7) Describe the atomic order of glass fibers.

(8) What are wool glass fibers? What is the major application for wool glass fibers?

(9) Are common glass fibers amorphous or crystalline? Why?

(10) What are the typical longitudinal and cross-sectional shapes of carbon and glass fibers?

CHAPTER 7

Structure of Nanofibers

Nanoscience is the study of atoms, molecules, and objects with sizes ranging from 1 to 100 nm. However, the term "nanofibers" traditionally has been used for fibers with diameters less than 1000 nm. Nanofibers are an important class of material that is useful in a variety of applications, including filtration, tissue engineering, protective clothing, composites, battery separators, energy storage, etc. Methods used to produce nanofibers include, but are not limited to, electrospinning, centrifugal spinning, melting blowing, bicomponent fiber separation, phase separation, template synthesis, and self-assembly. This chapter focuses on the main structural characteristics of electrospun nanofibers. Chapter 12 will discuss the fiber formation process of electrospinning and the diameter control of electrospun nanofibers. Chapter 13 will discuss the other nanofiber formation methods.

7.1   A BRIEF DESCRIPTION OF ELECTROSPINNING PROCESS

Electrospinning is a simple, non-mechanical technique for fabricating nanofibers. Figure 7.1 shows a nozzle-based electrospinning setup. High voltage is applied between a spinning fluid contained in a syringe and a metallic collector. When the voltage reaches a critical value, electrostatic forces overcome the surface tension of the fluid and eject a liquid jet from the nozzle of the spinneret (metallic needle). The electrically charged jet then undergoes a stretching-and-whipping process, during which the jet diameter decreases from hundreds of micrometers to as small as tens of nanometers. The as-spun nanofibers are accumulated on the surface of the grounded collector. The electrospinning process is relatively slow, and a single syringe shown in Figure 7.1 can only produce 1–100 mg nanofibers per hour. The production rate can be improved significantly by connecting a large number of

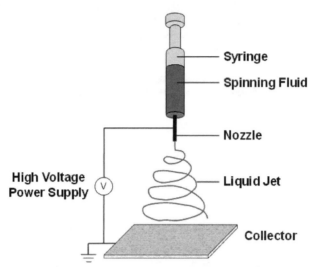

Figure 7.1. Schematic of a basic electrospinning setup.

individually charged syringes in parallel or by directly spinning from a liquid bath using a nozzle-less process.

7.2 MATERIAL TYPE

Historically, electrospinning was used to produce nanofibers from polymer materials. However, electrospun nanofibers of carbon, ceramic, metal and composite materials also have been recently developed.

7.2.1 POLYMERS

Nanofibers can be electrospun from both synthetic and natural polymers. Figures 7.2 and 7.3 show SEM images of electrospun polyacrylonitrile and silk fibroin nanofibers, respectively.

During the electrospinning of polymer nanofibers, a high degree of molecular alignment could be achieved by the large effective draw ratio exerted by the electrostatic force. However, the crystallization process is retarded due to the rapid solidification of the stretched polymer chains during electrospinning. Basically, the stretched polymer chains do not have sufficient time to form crystallites. Therefore, electrospun nanofibers often have lower degree of crystallinity and lower crystallization temperature than the corresponding bulk material, but the polymer chains in the amorphous phase may show a certain degree of orientation. The crystallite structure of electrospun nanofibers can be described using a modified fringed micelle model (Figure 7.4). However, other crystallite structures also can be formed by selectively adjusting the electrospinning parameters.

Figure 7.2. SEM image of polyacrylonitrile nanofibers.

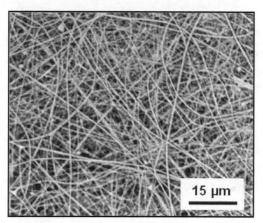

Figure 7.3. SEM image of silk fibroin nanofibers.

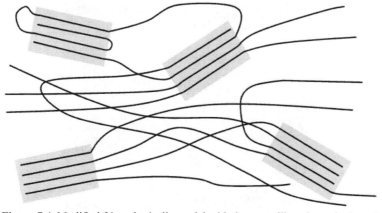

Figure 7.4. Modified fringed micelle model with the crystalline phase shadowed.

7.2.2 CARBONS

Carbon nanofibers often are prepared by the electrospinning of precursor polymers, such as polyacrylonitrile, polyimide, and pitch, etc., followed by the carbonization of the resultant precursor fibers. Figure 7.5 shows a SEM image of carbon nanofibers, which were prepared by the carbonization of electrospun polyacrylonitrile nanofibers at 700°C in argon gas. The crystalline structure of carbon nanofibers is mainly determined by the precursor type and carbonization conditions, such as carbonization temperature and heating rate. Electrospun carbon nanofibers shown in Figure 7.5 have a disordered carbon structure due to the relatively low carbonization temperature. However, with increase in carbonization temperature, carbon nanofibers present more ordered structure. When the carbonization temperature is greater than 1800°C, carbon nanofibers could be converted to graphite nanofibers, which have highly ordered graphite structure.

7.2.3 CERAMICS

Ceramic nanofibers also can be synthesized by the calcination of electrospun precursor nanofibers. Electrospun ceramic nanofibers were first reported by Dai and his coworker in 2002. Since then, more than twenty ceramic systems (e.g., SiO_2, Al_2O_3, and ZrO_2) have been fabricated as nanofibers. Ceramic fibers can be either amorphous or polycrystalline, depending on the material type and processing conditions. Figure 7.6 shows ZrO_2 nanofibers, which were synthesized from zirconium oxychloride ($ZrOCl_2$) precursor. During electrospinning, polyvinyl alcohol (PVA) was added to achieve desirable solution viscosity and improve the electrospinnability. The electrospun $ZrOCl_2$/PVA nanofibers were heat-treated to form ZrO_2 nanofibers, during which $ZrOCl_2$ was converted to $ZrOCl_2$ while PVA was pyrolyzed.

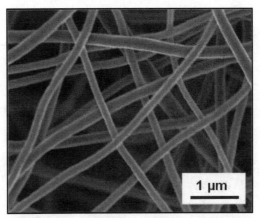

Figure 7.5. SEM image of carbon nanofibers.

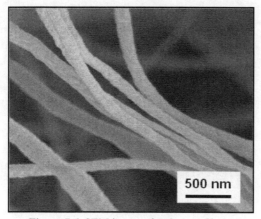

Figure 7.6. SEM image of ZrO$_2$ nanofibers.

7.2.4 METALS

Metal nanofibers also have been produced using electrospinning. Bognitzki et al. fabricated Cu nanofibers by the electrospinning of a copper nitrate-polyvinylbutyral (PVB) solution, followed by heat treatments in air and hydrogen. The heat treatment in air converts copper nitrate to copper oxide and decomposes PVB, while the heat treatment in hydrogen changes copper oxide to metallic copper. In addition to copper nanofibers, iron, cobalt and nickel nanofibers also have been prepared by the similar approach.

7.2.5 COMPOSITES

Composite nanofibers have been made by electrospinning solutions that contain nanoparticles, such as silica, titania, carbon black, silver, and iron oxides. The nanofiber matrices can be polymer, carbon, or ceramic. For carbon and ceramic matrices, post-electrospinning treatments are needed to convert their precursors into carbon and ceramic materials.

Figure 7.7 shows a TEM image of Si/PAN composite nanofibers. These nanofibers were prepared by direct electrospinning of a PAN solution containing Si nanoparticles. One common problem of using this method is the aggregation of nanoparticles inside the fiber matrix. The formation of aggregates can be minimized by adding surfactants to the electrospinning solution, modifying the surface of the nanoparticles, or using a soluble precursor of the nanoparticles. For example, Ag/PAN composite nanofibers have been produced by the electrospinning of AgNO$_3$/PAN nanofibers, following by the reduction of AgNO$_3$ to Ag nanoparticles using plasma treatment. Since the Ag nanoparticles are reduced directly from the soluble AgNO$_3$ salt, they are homogeneously dispersed in the PAN nanofiber matrix (Figure 7.8).

Figure 7.7. SEM image of Si/PAN composite nanofibers. (Ji, L., et al., *Carbon*, 47, 3219–3226, 2009.)

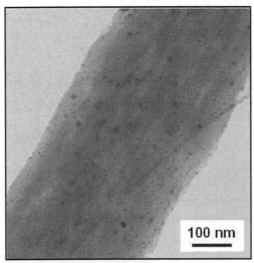

Figure 7.8. TEM image of an Ag/PAN composite nanofiber. (Shi, Q., et. al., *European Polymer Journal*, 47, 1402–1409, 2011.)

Composite nanofibers also have been made by introducing nanoparticles into or onto nanofibers after electrospinning. Figure 7.9 shows a TEM image of Pt-Ru/carbon composite nanofibers, which were fabricated by electrodepositing Pt nanoparticles directly onto the surface of electrospun carbon nanofibers. Electrodeposition of metal particles can be carried out by applying a constant voltage or successive voltammetric cycles. The nanoparticle size can be controlled by selectively adjusting the electrodeposition conditions, such as voltage, time, cycle rate, and cycle number. In addition to electrodeposition, chemical deposition also can be used.

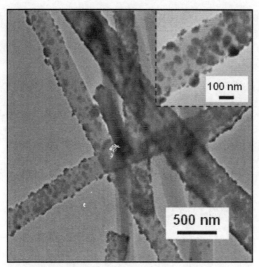

Figure 7.9. TEM image of Pt-Ru/carbon composite nanofibers. (Lin, Z., et. al., *Journal of Materials Research*, 25, 1329–1335, 2010.)

7.3 FIBER DIAMETER

Fiber diameter is the most important structure parameter for electrospun nanofibers. The smallest fiber diameter achieved so far is 1.6 nm by Huang and his coworker for electrospun Nylon 4,6 nanofibers. However, most electrospun nanofibers have diameters ranging from 50 nm to 1 μm. The diameter of electrospun nanofibers is dependent on a number of processing parameters: (*i*) intrinsic properties of the spinning solution such as material type, molecular weight, solution concentration, rheological behavior, conductivity, and surface tension; (*ii*) operational conditions such as voltage, flow rate, nozzle diameter, spinneret configuration, and spinneret-collector distance. Detailed discussion on the diameter control for electrospun nanofibers is presented in Chapter 12.

7.4 FIBER MORPHOLOGY

Electrospun nanofibers usually exhibit a solid interior. However, electrospun nanofibers with other morphologies also exist.

7.4.1 *POROUS NANOFIBERS*

Porous nanofibers have large surface areas and are useful for applications such as filtration, catalysis, fuel cells, supercapacitors, and tissue engineering. The porous structure typically is obtained by adding pore generators during the electrospinning process. Examples of pore generators include, but are not limited to, polymers, nanoparticles, and salts. These generators are added directly into the electrospinning solutions. After electrospinning, they are removed to form small pores. Figure 7.10 shows a SEM image of a porous carbon nanofiber, prepared by using poly(L-lactide) (PLLA) as the pore generator. During the preparation of these nanofibers, PAN and PLLA were first blended and electrospun. The as-spun precursor nanofibers then were heat-treated in argon to decompose PLLA while converting PAN to carbon. The decomposition of PLLA led to the formation of a porous structure. Figures 7.11 and 7.12 show SEM images of porous carbon and MnO$_2$/carbon nanofibers, in which the pores were generated by using SiO$_2$ nanoparticles and Mn acetate salt, respectively.

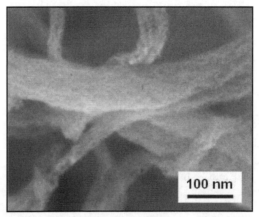

Figure 7.10. SEM image of porous carbon nanofibers, in which the pores were generated by PLLA polymer. (Ji, L., et. al., *Journal of Polymer Science: Part B: Polymer Physics*, 47, 493–03, 2009.)

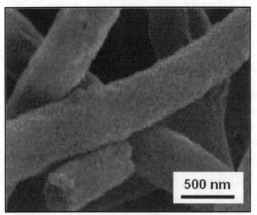

Figure 7.11. SEM image of porous carbon nanofibers, in which the pores were generated by SiO$_2$ nanoparticles. (Ji, L., et. al., *Carbon*, 47, 3346–3354, 2009.)

7.4.2 CORE-SHEATH NANOFIBERS

Core-sheath nanofibers have been produced by co-electrospinning two different spinning solutions using a spinneret comprising two coaxial needles. Figure 7.13 illustrates a schematic of the coaxial spinneret system. During electrospinning, two different solutions are used as inner and outer fluids, respectively. Figure 7.14 shows a TEM image of a polybutadiene rubber (BR)/polyvinylpyrrolidone (PVP) nanofiber prepared by the coaxial spinneret system. In this nanofiber, BR is the core and PVP is the sheath.

7.4.3 HOLLOW NANOFIBERS

Hollow nanofibers also can be prepared using the same coaxial spinneret system, as shown in Figure 7.13. To obtain the hollow structure, the material used for

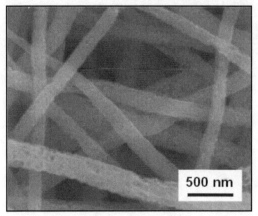

Figure 7.12. SEM image of porous MnO$_2$/carbon nanofibers, in which the pores were generated by Mn acetate salt. (Ji, L., et. al., *Journal of Materials Chemistry*, 19, 5593–5601, 2009.)

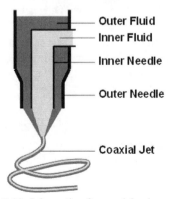

Figure 7.13. Schematic of a coaxial spinneret system.

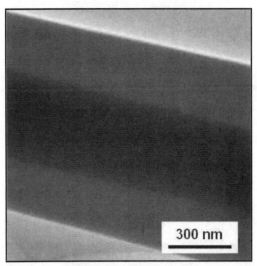

Figure 7.14. TEM image of a core-sheath BR/PVP nanofiber. (Haiyan Wu, et. al., *Materials Letters*, 84, 5–8, 2012.)

the fiber core must be degradable or extractable without damaging the sheath. Figure 7.15 shows a SEM image of hollow TiO_2 nanofibers. During electrospinning, mineral oil was used as the core fluid and a titanium isopropoxide $[Ti(OiPr)_4]$/ PVP solution as the outer fluid. The electrospun nanofibers were then heat-treated to remove mineral oil and PVP while converting $Ti(OiPr)_4$ to TiO_2.

7.4.4 MULTICHANNEL NANOFIBERS

Multichannel nanofibers can be prepared by using a multichannel spinneret (Figure 7.16). Examples of multi-channel TiO_2 nanofibers are shown in Figure 7.17. The cross-sectional structures of the multichannel spinnerets used for preparing these nanofibers also are shown. During electrospinning, paraffin oil was used as the inner fluid and a titanium isopropoxide/PVP solution as the outer fluid. The electrospun nanofibers were then heat-treated to decompose PVP and covert titanium isopropoxide into TiO_2 for forming the sheath. The paraffin oil also was removed during heat treatment for creating the hollow channels.

7.4.5 NANOFIBERS WITH OTHER MORPHOLOGIES

In addition to the different nanofibers discussed previously, nanofibers with other morphologies, such as porous core-sheath, porous hollow, ribbon-like, branched, helical structures, also have been developed.

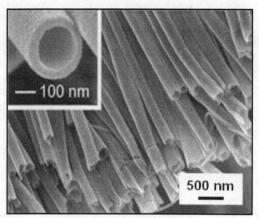

Figure 7.15. SEM image of hollow TiO$_2$ nanofibers. (Li, D., et. al., *Advanced Materials*, 16, 1151–1170, 2004.)

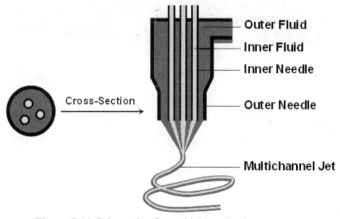

Figure 7.16. Schematic of a multichannel spinneret system.

7.5 FIBER ASSEMBLIES

In addition to the structures of individual nanofibers, the assembly structures play a significant role in determining the properties and applications of electrospun nanofibers. Electrospun nanofibers often are deposited as nonwoven porous mats, and the pore size and porosity of these mats need be controlled. Other assembly structures, such as continuous nanofiber filaments, aligned nanofiber sheets, nanofiber arrays, and nanofiber yarns, also have been produced by using special nanofiber collecting systems that can adjust the fiber jet movement through controlling the distribution of electric field.

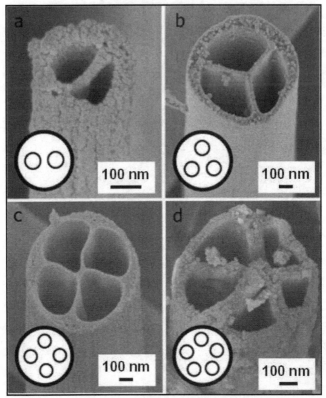

Figure 7.17. SEM images of multichannel TiO_2 nanofibers with different channel numbers. The inset in each figure shows the cross-sectional structure of the spinneret system used for fabricating the nanofiber. (Zhao, Y., et. al., *Journal of American Chemical Society*, 129, 764–765, 2007.)

7.5.1 NANOFIBER NONWOVENS

The most important assembly for electrospun nanofibers is the randomly-oriented, porous nonwoven mat. Electrospun nanofiber nonwovens typically are collected by depositing dry fibers on the surface of a flat collecting plate, and the bending instability associated with the spinning jet helps achieve the randomly oriented nanofiber assembly. Through careful control of processing parameters, electrospun nanofiber nonwovens can be produced over a wide range of porosity values, from nearly nonporous films to very porous and delicate fibrous structures. The pore sizes of electrospun nanofiber nonwovens can vary from hundreds of nanometers to tens of micrometers.

According to the statistical geometry of electrospun nanofiber nonwovens, the pore size is dominantly determined by the fiber diameter, but other fiber variables, such as porosity, areal density, and fiber density, also have influence.

During electrospinning, the pore size can be reduced by decreasing the distance between the spinneret and the collector, increasing the time of nanofiber collection, increasing polymer concentration, or decreasing applied voltage. Figure 7.18 shows that the pore size of PAN nanofiber mats decreases significantly when the spinneret-collector distance decreases from 15 to 3 cm.

In most electrospinning setups, the nanofiber collecting plate is made of a conductive material, such as aluminum foil, which is electrically grounded. When a nonconductive material is used as the collector or placed on the collector surface, charges on the electrospinning jet can quickly accumulate on the nonconductive collecting surface, which hinders the further deposition of nanofibers. In addition, due to the repulsive forces of the accumulated charges, nanofibers that are collected on the nonconductive surface usually have a lower packing density than those collected on a conducting surface. In some cases, the repulsive forces of the accumulated charges on the deposited nanofibers may even cause the formation of large-pore structures, such as dimples.

7.5.2 *Nanofiber Filaments and Aligned Nanofiber Sheets*

Continuous nanofiber filaments can be obtained by collecting fibers on a cylindrical collector with a high rotating speed, i.e., a rotating drum (Figure 7.19A). By increasing the duration of electrospinning, flat sheets or tubes consisting of aligned nanofibers also can be obtained by using this method. The orientation of nanofibers in these assemblies is an important structure parameter, which can be controlled by changing the rotating speed of the drum. Matthews et al. studied the electrospinning of collagen nanofibers and found that, at low speeds (< 500 rpm), a random mix of nanofibers was collected. However, when the rotating speed was increased to 4,500 rpm, the nanofibers showed significant alignment along the axis of rotation.

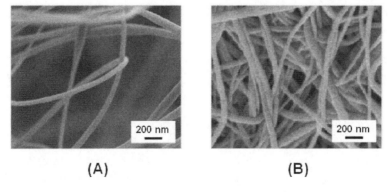

(A) **(B)**

Figure 7.18. SEM images of PAN nanofiber nonwovens with different pore sizes. Spinneret-collector distance: (A) 15 cm, and (B) 3 cm.

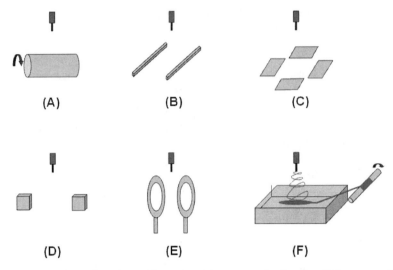

Figure 7.19. Schematics of nanofiber collecting systems for forming different nanofiber assembly structures: (A) rotating drum for continuous nanofiber filament and aligned nanofiber sheet; (B) parallel electrodes for aligned nanofiber array; (C) counter-electrodes for cross-bar nanofiber array; (D) blades for nanofiber yarn; (E) parallel rings for twisted nanofiber yarn; and (F) liquid bath for continuous nanofiber yarn.

One advantage of using a simple rotating drum is that a large area of aligned nanofiber sheets can be easily fabricated. However, the disadvantage is that nanofibers are easy to break at high rotating speeds and highly aligned fiber sheets are difficult to produce. Modifications have been made to lower the rotating speed, avoid the nanofiber breakage, and/or improve the nanofiber alignment. For example, a sharp pin structure can be introduced into the rotating drum to create an electric field that starts from the tip of the needle and converges at the tip of the sharp pin. Using this modified drum, Sundaray et al. fabricated highly aligned polymethyl methacrylate (PMMA) nanofiber sheets at a rotating speed of 2,000 rpm. Figure 7.20 shows a SEM image of a thin sheet of aligned PMMA nanofibers. Another simple approach is to use a rotating wire drum, with which highly aligned nanofiber sheets can be produced at a rotating speed as low as 1 rpm. Highly aligned nanofiber sheets also can be fabricated by placing knife-edge electrodes below the rotating drum.

7.5.3 NANOFIBER ARRAYS

The orientation of nanofibers in assemblies also can be controlled by using a collector consisting of two parallel conducting electrodes separated by an insulating gap (Figure 7.19B). The introduction of the insulating gap to the collector changes the configuration of the electric field, which stretches the fibers to be aligned

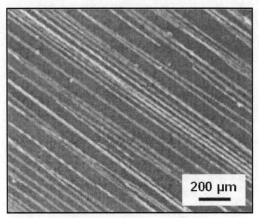

Figure 7.20. SEM image of a thin sheet of aligned PMMA nanofibers. (Sundaray, B., et. al., *Applied Physics Letters*, 84, 1222–1224, 2004.)

perpendicular to the electrodes to form a nanofiber array. The electrostatic repulsions between the charged nanofibers can further enhance the alignment in the array. One major difference of these nanofiber arrays from the aligned nanofiber sheets described in section 7.5.2 is that the size of nanofiber arrays is limited by the width of the insulating gap, which typically is no more than several centimeters. When the gap width is too large, there will be a greater tendency for the nanofibers to be deposited on the electrode rather than across the gap, and the degree of alignment will be significantly decreased.

However, one advantage of this parallel-electrode collector over the rotating drum is the resultant nanofiber arrays can be easily transferred onto other substrates. Single nanofibers also can be collected across the gap and removed for the construction of single-fiber devices. In addition, more complex nanofiber arrays can be obtained by modifying the parallel-electrode collector system. For example, cross-bar arrays of electrospun nanofibers can be obtained by using four counter-electrodes, as shown in Figure 7.19C. A SEM image of cross-bar array of PVP nanofibers is shown in Figure 7.21. Other complex arrangements of nanofiber arrays also can be obtained by adding more counter electrodes and/or rearranging the electrodes.

7.5.4 NANOFIBER YARNS

One simple means to obtain nanofiber yarns is to directly twist electrospun nanofiber mats. Figure 7.22 shows a poly(vinylidene fluoride-co-hexafluoropropylene) (PVDF-HFP) nanofiber yarn prepared by twisting a narrow fibrous strip cut directly from an electrospun nanofiber mat. Higher-quality nanofiber yarns can be obtained by using a collector consisting of two conducting blades placed in line (Figure 7.19D) or using a collector with two rings placed in parallel (Figure 17E).

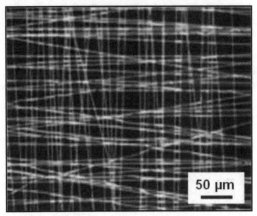

Figure 7.21. SEM image of cross-bar array of aligned PVP nanofibers. (Li, D., et. al., *Advanced Materials*, 16, 361–366, 2004.)

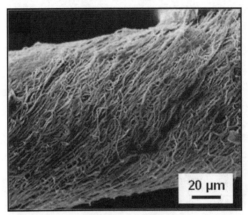

Figure 7.22. SEM image of a PVDF-HFP nanofiber yarn. (Zhou, Y., et. al., *Journal of Materials Research*, 27, 537–544, 2012.)

Nanofiber yarns described above have limited length. Continuous nanofiber yarns can be obtained by depositing nanofibers into a water bath, followed by drawing these nanofibers from the water in the form of a yarn using a rotating drum (Figure 17F).

REFERENCES

[1]   Bognitzki, M., Frese, T., Steinhart, M., Greiner, A., Wendorff, J.H., Schaper, A., and Hellwig, M., "Preparation of Fibers with Nanoscaled Morphologies: Electrospinning of Polymer Blends", *Polymer Engineering and Science*, 41, 982–989, 2001.

[2] Dai, H., Gong, J., Kim, H., and Lee, D., "A Novel Method for Preparing Ultra-Fine Alumina-Borate Oxide Fibres via an Electrospinning Technique", *Nanotechnology*, 13, 674–677, 2002.

[3] Garg, K., Sell, S.A., Bowlin, G.L., "Electrospinning and Its Influence on the Structure of Polymeric Nanofibers", in *Handbook of Textile Fibre Structure. Volume 1: Fundamentals and Manufactured Polymer Fibres*, Editors Eichhoorn, S.J., Hearle, J.W.S., Jaffe, M., and Kikutani, T., Woodhead Publishing Limited, 2009.

[4] Haiyan Wu, H., Hu, Q., Zhang, L., Fong, H., and Tian, M., "Electrospun Composite Nanofibers of Polybutadiene Rubber Containing Uniformly Distributed Ag Nanoparticles", *Materials Letters*, 84, 5–8, 2012.

[5] Huang, C., Chen, S., Lai, C., Reneker, D.H., Qiu, H., Ye, Y., and Hou, H., "Electrospun Polymer Nanofibers with Small Diameters", *Nanotechnology*, 17, 1558–1563, 2006.

[6] Ji, L., Lin, Z., Medford, A.J., and Zhang, X., "Porous Carbon Nanofibers from Electrospun Polyacrylonitrile/SiO$_2$ Composites as an Energy Storage Material", *Carbon*, 47, 3346–3354, 2009.

[7] Ji, L., Medford, A.J., and Zhang, X., "Fabrication of Carbon Fibers with Nanoporous Morphologies from Electrospun Polyacrylonitrile/Poly(L-lactide) Blends", *Journal of Polymer Science: Part B: Polymer Physics*, 47, 493–503, 2009.

[8] Ji, L., Medford, A.L., and Zhang, X., "Porous Carbon Nanofibers Loaded with Manganese Oxide Particles: Formation Mechanism And Electrochemical Performance as Energy-Storage Materials", *Journal of Materials Chemistry*, 19, 5593–5601, 2009.

[9] Ji, L., Saquing, C., Khan, S.A., and Zhang, X., "Preparation and Characterization of Silica Nanoparticulate-Polyacrylonitrile Composite and Porous Nanofibers", *Nanotechnology*, 19, 085605, 2008.

[10] Ji, L., and Zhang, X., "Electrospun Carbon Nanofibers Containing Silicon Particles as an Energy-Storage Medium", *Carbon*, 47, 3219–3226, 2009.

[11] Katta, P., Alessandro, M.R., Ramsier, R.D., and Chase, G.G., "Continuous Electrospinning of Aligned Polymer Nanofibers onto Wire Drum Collector", *Nano Letters*, 4, 2215–2218, 2004.

[12] Li, D., Wang, Y., and Xia, Y., "Electrospinning Nanofibers as Uniaxially Aligned Arrays and Layer-by-Layer Stacked Films", *Advanced Materials*, 16, 361–366, 2004.

[13] Li, D., Wang, Y., and Xia, Y., "Electrospinning of Polymeric and Ceramic Nanofibers as Uniaxially Aligned Arrays", *Nano Letters*, 3, 1167–1171, 2003.

[14] Li, D., and Xia, Y., "Electrospinning of Nanofibers: Reinventing the Wheel", *Advanced Materials*, 16, 1151–1170, 2004.

[15] Lin, Z., Ji, L., Toprakci, O., Krause, W., and Zhang, X., "Electrospun Carbon Nanofiber-Supported Pt–Pd Alloy Composites for Oxygen Reduction", *Journal of Materials Research*, 25, 1329–1335, 2010.

[16] Matthews, J.A., Wnek, G.E., Simpson, D.G., and Bowlin, G.L., "Electrospinning of Collagen Nanofibers", *Biomacromolecules*, 3, 232–238, 2002.

[17] McCann, J.T., Li, D., and Xia, Y., "Electrospinning of Nanofibers with Core-Sheath, Hollow, or Porous Structures", *Journal Materials Chemistry*, 15, 735–738, 2005.

[18] Norris, I.D., Shaker, M.M., Ko, F.K., and MacDiarmid, A.G., "Electrostatic Fabrication of Ultrafine Conducting Fibers: Polyaniline/Polyethylene Oxide Blends", *Synthetic Metals*, 114, 109–114, 2004.

[19] Ramakrishna, S., Fujihara, K., Teo, T.C., and Ma, Z., *An Introduction to Electrospinning and Nanofibers*, World Scientific Publishing, 2005.

[20] Shi, Q., Vitchuli, N., Nowak, J., Caldwell, J.M., Breidt, F., Bourham, M., Zhang, and McCord, M., "Durable Antibacterial Ag/Polyacrylonitrile (Ag/PAN) Hybrid Nanofibers Prepared by Atmospheric Plasma Treatment and Electrospinning", *European Polymer Journal*, 47, 1402–1409, 2011.

[21] Sundaray, B., Subramanian, V., Natarajan, T.S., Xiang, R.Z., Chang, C.C., and Farm, W.S., "Electrospinning of Continuous Aligned Polymer Fibers", *Applied Physics Letters*, 84, 1222–1224, 2004.

[22] Teo, W.E., Kotaki, M., Mo, X.M., and Ramakrishna, S., "Porous Tubular Structures with Controlled Fibre Orientation Using a Modified Electrospinning Method", Nanotechnology, 16, 918–924, 2005.

[23] Teo, W.E., and Ramakrishna, S., "A Review on Electrospinning Design and Nanofibre Assemblies", *Nanotechnology*, 17, R89–R106, 2006.

[24] Teo, W.E., and Ramakrishna, S., "Electrospun Fibre Bundle Made of Aligned Nanofibres over Two Fixed Points", *Nanotechnology*, 16, 1878–1884, 2005.

[25] Toprakci, O., Toprakci, H.A.K., Ji, L., Lin, Z., Xu, G., and Zhang, X., "Carbon Nanotube-Loaded Electrospun LiFePO4/Carbon Composite Nanofibers as Stable and Binder-Free Cathodes for Rechargeable Lithium-Ion Batteries", *ACS Applied Materials & Interfaces*, 4, 1273–1280, 2012.

[26] Wendorff, J.H., Agarwal, S., and Greiner, A., *Electrospinning: Materials, Processing, and Applications*, Wiley-VCH, 2012.

[27] Zhao, Y., Cao, X., and Jiang, L., "Bio-mimic Multichannel Microtubes by a Facile Method", *Journal of American Chemical Society*, 129, 764–765, 2007.

[28] Zhang, S., Lu, Y., Xu, G., Li, Y., and Zhang, X., "LiF/Fe/C Nanofibers as High-Capacity Cathode Material for Li-Ion Batteries", *Journal of Physics D: Applied Physics*, 45, 395301, 2012.

[29] Zhang, X., "Processing-Structure relationships of Electrospun Nanofibers", in *Nanofibers: Fabrication, Performance, and Applications*, Editor Chang, W.N., Nova Science Publishers, 2009.

[30] Zhou, Y., Fang, J., Wang, X., and Lin, T. "Strip Twisted Electrospun Nanofiber Yarns: Structural Effects on Tensile Properties", *Journal of Materials Research*, 27, 537–544, 2012.

PROBLEMS

(1)   What are the main components of a basic electrospinning set-up?

(2)   Describe the electrospinning process.

(3)   How carbon and ceramic nanofibers can be made by electrospinning?

(4)   What are the main approaches for making electrospun composite nanofibers?

(5)   How can hollow and core-sheath nanofibers be made by electrospinning?

(6)   What are the possible assemblies of electrospun nanofibers?

PART II

Fiber Formation

CHAPTER 8

Flow Behavior of Polymers

Synthetic polymer fibers and manufactured natural polymer fibers typically are produced by melt, solution, dispersion, or gel spinning. To convert the polymer components into the desired fiber structure, it is important to understand their flow behavior. Knowledge in polymer flow behavior can lead to: (*i*) the intelligent selection of suitable polymers or polymer compounds that can be made into fibers; (*ii*) the establishment of qualitative, and to some extent quantitative, relationships between processing conditions, fiber structures, and fiber properties; and (*iii*) the minimization or removal of the processing faults and defects that are of rheological origin. This chapter addresses the basic knowledge related to the flow behavior of polymers. The use of such knowledge in the formation of synthetic polymer fibers and manufactured natural polymer fibers will be discussed in Chapters 9 and 10, respectively.

8.1   BASIC DEFINITIONS

Figure 8.1 shows the flow profile of a fluid (e.g., polymer melt or solution) between two large parallel plates. The bottom plate is stationary and the top plate is movable. An external force is applied to the top plate and moves it at a constant velocity. The polymer fluid in contact with each plate has the same velocity as that plate. The velocities of intermediate layers of the fluid increase uniformly from one plate to another, as shown by the arrows. As a result, the fluid layers slide smoothly over one another and the flow is laminar.

In the laminar flow as shown in Figure 8.1, the shear stress (τ) is the applied force (F) divided by the area (A) of each plate:

$$\tau = \frac{F}{A} \qquad (8.1)$$

117

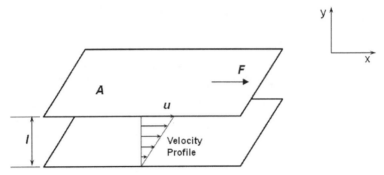

Figure 8.1. Simple shear flow of a polymer fluid.

Shear rate ($\dot{\gamma}$), *i.e.*, the rate of change of shear strain, is given by:

$$\dot{\gamma} = \frac{d\gamma}{dt} \tag{8.2}$$

where γ is the shear strain, *i.e.*, dx/dy.

   Assuming the displacement of the top plate in time dt is dx, the velocity (u) of the top plate is:

$$u = \frac{dx}{dt} \tag{8.3}$$

The velocity gradient in the y direction, i.e., from the bottom plate to the top plate is:

$$velocity\ gradient = \frac{du}{dy} = \frac{u}{l} \tag{8.4}$$

Equation 8.2 then can be rearranged to:

$$\dot{\gamma} = \frac{d}{dt}(\gamma) = \frac{d}{dt}\left(\frac{dx}{dy}\right) = \frac{d}{dy}\left(\frac{dx}{dt}\right) = \frac{du}{dy} = \frac{u}{l} \tag{8.5}$$

Therefore, Equations 8.2 and 8.4 are equivalent expressions and velocity gradient is an alternative definition of shear rate.

   The viscosity (η) of the fluid can then be defined as:

$$\eta \equiv \frac{\text{Shear Stress}}{\text{Shear Rate}} = \frac{F/A}{u/l} = \frac{\tau}{\dot{\gamma}} \tag{8.6}$$

Viscosity is the fluid's resistance to flow and is a measure of the frictional forces between the molecules in the fluid. Hence, viscosity is an important parameter for studying the flow behavior of polymers. According to Equation 8.6, the unit of viscosity is that of force times distance, divided by area times speed. The SI unit is $1 \text{ N·m}/[\text{m}^2 \cdot (\text{m/s})] = 1 \text{ N·s/m}^2 = 1 \text{ Pa·s}$. The cgs unit for viscosity is dyn·s/cm². Another commonly used unit is poise, in honor of the French scientist Jean Louise Marie Poiseuille: $1 \text{ poise} = 1 \text{ dyn·s/cm}^2 = 10^{-1} \text{ N·s/m}^2$.

8.2 NEWTONIAN AND NON-NEWTONIAN FLUIDS

8.2.1 *NEWTONIAN FLUID*

The ideal Newtonian fluid is a fluid in which the shear stress-shear rate curve is linear and passes through the origin. Figure 8.2A shows the shear stress-shear rate curve of a Newtonian fluid. The slope of the curve is the viscosity of the fluid and it keeps constant when the shear rate changes (Figure 8.2B). Newtonian fluids typically are formed by small molecules, where the structure and orientation do not change with the intensity of shearing. Examples of Newtonian fluids include water, gasoline, motor oils, and many organic solvents.

8.2.2 *NON-NEWTONIAN FLUIDS*

Many fluids, including polymer melts and solutions, are non-Newtonian. The three most important non-Newtonian fluids are Bingham, shear-thickening, and shear-thinning fluids. Figure 8.3 compares the shear stress-shear rate curves of these three non-Newtonian fluids with that of an ideal Newtonian fluid.

The Bingham fluid has a linear shear stress-shear strain relationship, but a critical shear stress is required to initiate the flow. The shear stress-shear rate curve of a Bingham fluid does not pass through the origin, and it can be expressed as:

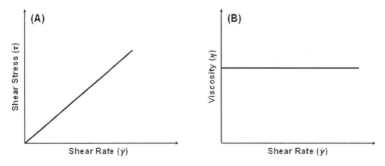

Figure 8.2. (A) Shear stress-shear rate curve, and (B) viscosity-shear rate curve of a Newtonian fluid.

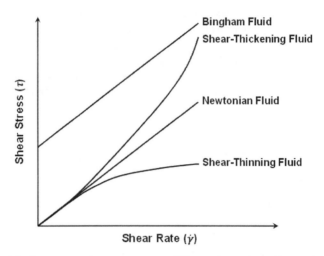

Figure 8.3. Shear stress-shear rate curves of Newtonian and non-Newtonian fluids.

$$\tau = \tau_{critical} + \eta\dot{\gamma} \qquad (8.7)$$

where $\tau_{critical}$ is the critical stress required to initiate the flow. The Bingham fluid typically has an internal structure that collapses above the critical shear stress. Examples of Bingham fluids include suspensions, slurries, and pulps.

The shear-thickening fluid, also called dilatant fluid, shows an increase in its resistance to flow with increasing shear rate. The most common shear-thickening fluids are concentrated suspensions. In a concentrated suspension, as long as there are balanced inter-particle interactions, such as van der Waals forces, the particles remain suspended. However, when the shear rate increases, particles enter a state of flocculation and can be no longer held in suspension. The suspension has the tendency to behave like a solid, and this causes the viscosity to increase. However, when the shear stress is removed, the particles spread apart and once again form a stable suspension. Some polymer pastes also have shear-thickening behavior at certain shear rate ranges. In addition, polymers that crystallize under stress may exhibit shear-thickening behavior.

Most polymer melts and solutions are shear-thinning fluids, which also are called pseudoplastic fluids. The resistance of a shear-thinning fluid decreases with increasing shear rate. The shear-thinning behavior typically is related to the "disentanglement" of polymer chains with increasing shear rate (Figure 8.4). In polymer fluids, the long and one-dimensional polymer chains often are extensively entangled. Under shear, polymer chains start to disentangle and this reduces the fluid's resistance to flow, causing the shear-thinning behavior. In addition to the disentanglement effect, the orientation of polymer chains under shear also plays a role in the shear-thinning behavior.

Theoretically, in shear-thickening and shear-thinning flows, there is not a characteristic "viscosity" since $\eta = \tau/\dot{\gamma}$ is not a constant. Therefore, the term "apparent viscosity" (η_a) is introduced and it is defined as the shear stress divided by shear rate:

$$\eta_a \equiv \frac{\tau}{\dot{\gamma}} \tag{8.8}$$

This apparent viscosity increases with shear rate for shear-thickening fluids, is independent of shear rate for Newtonian fluids, and decreases with shear rate for shear-thinning fluids (Figure 8.5). Therefore, while reporting the apparent viscosities of polymer melts or solutions, it is important to mention the shear rates or shear stresses used during the measurements. In this book, for the purpose of simplicity, "apparent viscosity" will be called as "viscosity" and be given the symbol η.

To mathematically describe the flow behaviors of shear-thickening and shear-thinning fluids, a power law equation can be used:

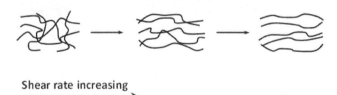

Shear rate increasing

Figure 8.4. "Disentanglement" of polymer chains under stress.

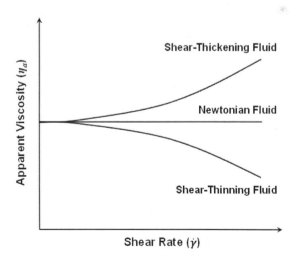

Figure 8.5. Apparent viscosity-shear rate curves of Newtonian, shear-thickening, and shear-thinning fluids.

$$\tau = K\left(\dot{\gamma}\right)^{n} \tag{8.9}$$

where K is the fluid consistency index, and n the power law index. In logarithmic form, Equation 8.9 can be written as:

$$\log \tau = \log K + n \log \dot{\gamma} \tag{8.10}$$

This means that the logarithmic shear stress-shear strain curve produced by Equation 8.10 is a straight line. Figure 8.6 compares the $\log \tau - \log \dot{\gamma}$ curves of Newtonian, shear-thickening, and shear-thinning fluids. The curves of all three fluids are straight lines, but with different slopes. The curve slope is determined by the n value of the fluid. The fluid exhibits: Newtonian behavior when $n = 1$, shear-thickening behavior when n > 1, and shear-thinning behavior when $n < 1$.

Based on the definition of viscosity, the power law equation can be rearranged to obtain:

$$\eta = K\left(\dot{\gamma}\right)^{n-1} \tag{8.11}$$

Equation 8.11 also can be rewritten in the logarithmic form:

$$\log \eta = \log K + \left(n-1\right) \log \dot{\gamma} \tag{8.12}$$

According to Equation 8.12, the $\log \eta - \log \dot{\gamma}$ curves of Newtonian, shear-thickening, and shear-thinning fluids also are straight lines and the slopes are determined by the n-1 values.

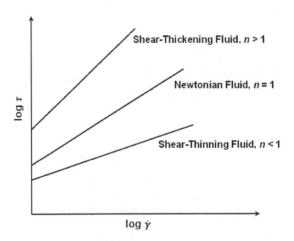

Figure 8.6. $\log \tau - \log \dot{\gamma}$ curves of Newtonian, shear-thickening, and shear-thinning fluids.

8.3 TIME-DEPENDENT FLUIDS

The Newtonian and non-Newtonian fluids discussed in section 8.2 are time independent; that is, the viscosity remains constant as long as the shear rate does not change. However, some fluids exhibit time-dependent flow behavior and their viscosities change with the time of shearing. Two most important time-dependent fluids are thixotropic and rheopectic. At a fixed shear rate, the viscosity of a thixotropic fluid decreases with time, while the viscosity of a rheopectic fluid increases with time (Figure 8.7).

The decrease of viscosity of the thixotropic fluid indicates a progressive breakdown of its structure. One classic example of thixotropic fluid is the ketchup, which splashes after a period of vigorous tapping. Another example is the synovial fluid found in joints between some bones. Thixotropic fluid often is compared with the shear-thinning fluid. Figure 8.8 shows the shear stress-shear rate curves of thixotropic and shear-thinning fluids under continuously increasing and then decreasing shear rate. For the thixotropic fluid, in the time interval between making the measurement at decreasing shear rate and making measurement at increasing shear rate, the viscosity already has decreased since it is time dependent, and this leads to the formation of the characteristic hysteresis curve, as shown in Figure 8.8A. However, for the shear-thinning fluid, although the viscosity changes with shear rate, it does not change with time. As a result, the curves with increasing shear rate and with decreasing shear rate overlap with each other (Figure 8.8B).

The rheopectic fluid also is called an anti-thixotropic fluid. In a rheopectic fluid, the increase in viscosity with time often is caused by the formation of

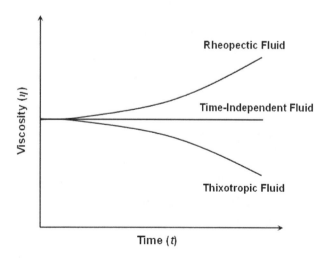

Figure 8.7. Evolution of viscosity with time for time-independent, thixotropic, and rheopectic fluids.

intermolecular forces. Wet concrete, in which water molecules react with the cement and bond the other components together, is a good example of rheopectic fluid. The comparison between rheopectic and shear-thickening fluids is similar to that between thixotropic and shear-thinning fluids. Figure 8.9 compares the shear stress-shear rate curves of thixotropic and shear-thickening fluids. The rheopectic fluid shows the characteristic hysteresis, with the shear rate decreasing curve located above the shear rate increasing curve. However, the shear-thickening fluid is time-independent and the two curves overlap (Figure 8.9B).

Polymer melts and solutions may present thixotropic or rheopectic behavior if they degrade or crosslink during shear, especially at elevated temperatures. Polymers that do not experience reactions during shear traditionally are considered as time-independent fluids. However, recent research shows the disentanglement of polymer chains during shear may cause time-dependent effects. Compared with most traditional thixotropic and rheopectic fluids, the time-dependent effects caused by polymer chain disentanglement are relatively small. Hence, in this book, all polymer melts and solutions are treated as time-independent shear-thinning fluids.

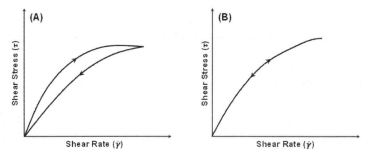

Figure 8.8. Shear stress-shear rate curves for (A) a thixotropic fluid, and (B) a shear-thinning fluid under continuously increasing and then decreasing shear rate.

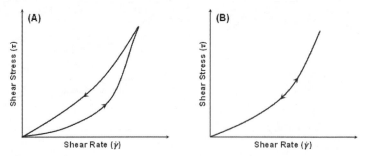

Figure 8.9. Shear stress-shear rate curves for (A) a rheopectic fluid, and (B) a shear-thickening fluid under continuously increasing and then decreasing shear rate.

8.4   FLOW BEHAVIOR OF POLYMERS

8.4.1   *FLOW CURVES OF POLYMERS*

As discussed above, polymer melts and solutions can be treated as shear-thinning fluids. However, this is true only over a certain shear rate range. Figure 8.10 shows the typical logarithmic flow curves of polymer melts and solutions over a very wide range of shearing. Three different regions can be found in the flow curves:

1.   A "lower Newtonian" region exists at low shear rates or stresses, and this leads to the definition of zero-shear viscosity (η_0), i.e., value of η as $\dot{\gamma} \rightarrow 0$.
2.   The shear-thinning region is observed over several decades of intermediate shear rates.
3.   At very high shear rates, an "upper Newtonian" region is attained and the viscosity is defined as η_∞.

The presence of three regions is mainly due to the disentanglement effect of polymer chains. At low shear rates, the polymer chains are extensively entangled and have the greatest resistance to flow. The shear stress at this region is not sufficient to disentangle the polymer chains. As a result, the viscosity is independent on the shear rate or stress and the polymer fluid is at its "lower Newtonian" region. At that region, the polymer fluid has its highest viscosity, i.e., η_0, which can be used as an important characteristic parameter for describing the polymer fluid.

As the shear rate increases to a high enough value, the shear stress starts to disentangle and orient the polymer chains, and higher shear stress or strain leads to greater disentanglement effect. As a result, the polymer fluid enters the shear-thinning region. However, at very high shear rates, the polymer chains are completely disentangled and oriented, and the viscosity becomes constant again, indicating the polymer fluid enters an "upper Newtonian" region.

For the formation of synthetic polymer fibers and manufactured natural polymer fibers, it is important to disentangle and orient polymer chains to achieve good mechanical properties. Therefore, the formation of these polymer fibers is not carried out at the "lower Newtonian" region. On the other hand, the "upper Newtonian" region also is not desired. The intense shearing at the "upper Newtonian" region could lead to extensive breakage of polymer chains, leading to mechanical degradation. Therefore, polymer fibers are processed in the shear-thinning region. In the remaining sections of this chapter, only the shear-thinning region will be discussed.

8.4.2   *CARREAU EQUATION*

Many equations have been proposed to quantitatively represent the flow curves of polymer melts and solutions. Among them, the power law equation discussed in section 8.2.2 is probably the simplest and is adequate for many engineering purposes. However, the power law can reasonably approximate only portions of the actual flow curves over a relatively narrow shear rate range. To represent the flow curves over a wider shear rate range, the *Carreau equation* often is used:

$$\frac{\eta - \eta_\infty}{\eta_0 - \eta_\infty} = \left[1 + \left(\lambda_c \dot{\gamma}\right)^2\right]^{\frac{n-1}{2}}$$

(8.13)

where λ_c is the time constant, and n the power law index. η_0 and η_∞ are the viscosity at zero shear rate and the viscosity at infinite shear rate, respectively, as shown in Figure 8.10. The *Carreau equation* has four parameters (λ_c, n, η_0, and η_∞) and can quantitatively represent the flow curves of polymer over a wide range of shear rate.

In practical application, to represent the polymer flow curves in a relatively narrow shear rate range (e.g., one or two decades of shear rate), the power law equation has sufficient accuracy. To represent the polymer flow curves in a wider shear rate range (e.g., three or four decades), the *Carreau equation* can be used. In addition to these two equations, other models also have been developed. The interested reader is referred to the works by Tanner (2000), Dealy and Larson (2006), and Brazel and Rosen (2012).

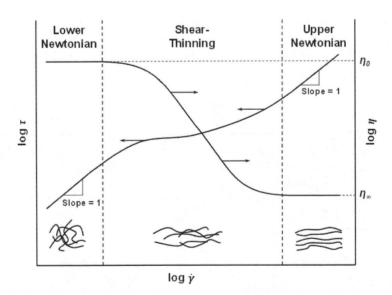

Figure 8.10. Typical $\log \tau - \log \dot{\gamma}$ and $\log \eta - \log \dot{\gamma}$ curves of polymer melts and solutions over a very wide range of shearing rates.

8.5 CAPILLARY FLOW OF POLYMERS

Synthetic polymer fibers and manufactured natural polymer fibers typically are produced by melt, solution, dispersion, or gel spinning. In these processes, polymer fluids are extruded through dies to form one-dimensional fiber structures (Figure 8.11). The dies typically have small diameters so thin fibers can be obtained. As a result, in order to form fibers with desired structure and properties, it is critically important to understand the capillary flow of polymers, i.e., the flow behavior in a small-diameter pipe.

To quantitatively describe the flow of polymer fluids through a small-diameter pipe, the following assumptions are necessary:

1. No-slip at the wall, i.e., the velocity of the polymer fluid at the wall of the pipe is zero.
2. The flow pattern is constant along the pipe.
3. The polymer fluid is time-independent.
4. The polymer fluid is incompressible.
5. The polymer flow is isothermal; and
6. The force of gravity is negligible.

8.5.1 SHEAR STRESS AT WALL

The shear stress at the wall of the pipe can be obtained by considering the balance of forces. Figure 8.12 shows the balance of forces on an element of polymer fluid

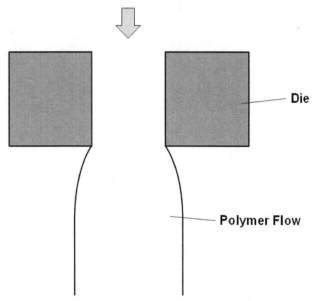

Figure 8.11. Polymer flow through a die.

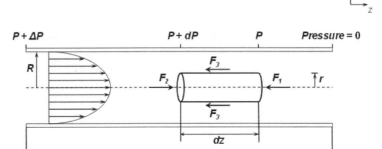

Figure 8.12. Balance of forces on a fluid element in a pipe with length L and radius R.

in a pipe with length L and radius R. The length and radius of the fluid element are dz and r, respectively. The total pressure drop along the pipe is ΔP and the pressure drop along the fluid element is dP.

If the polymer flow is steady, the sum of all the forces acting on the fluid element is zero:

$$\sum F = F_1 + F_2 + F_3 = 0 \tag{8.14}$$

where F_1 and F_2 are hydrostatic forces, and F_3 is the drag on the surface of the element. F_1, F_2 and F_3 can be expressed by:

$$F_1 = P\pi r^2$$

$$F_2 = -[P + dP]\pi r^2$$

$$F_3 = \text{(surface area)} \times \text{(drag/unit surface)}$$

$$= \text{surface area} \times \text{shear stress}$$

$$= 2\pi r dz \tau$$

As a result, Equation 8.14 can be rewritten as:

$$\sum F = P\pi r^2 - [P + dP]\pi r^2 + 2\pi r dz \tau = 0 \tag{8.15}$$

The shear stress on the fluid element then can be obtained:

$$\tau = \frac{r}{2}\left(\frac{dP}{dz}\right) \tag{8.16}$$

Since the flow pattern is constant along the pipe length, dP/dz is constant and Equation 8.16 can be rewritten as:

$$\tau = \frac{r\Delta P}{2L} \qquad (8.17)$$

From Equation 8.17, it can be concluded the shear stress τ has a linear relationship with the element radius r, and it increases from zero at the pipe center linearly with r to a maximum (τ_w) at the wall. The shear stress at the wall is then given by:

$$\boxed{\tau_w = \frac{R\Delta P}{2L}} \qquad (8.18)$$

Therefore, when a polymer fluid flows through a pipe with known dimensions (i.e., L and R), the shear stress at the pipe wall can be easily obtained from the pressure drop between the ends of the pipe. In addition, the shear stress at an arbitrary point in the pipe can be obtained by:

$$\tau = \frac{r}{R}\tau_w \qquad (8.19)$$

8.5.2 SHEAR RATE AT WALL

The shear rate at the wall of the pipe is related to the volumetric flow rate Q, which can be measured experimentally. The volumetric flow rate also can be obtained by integrating the velocity profile over the cross-sectional area of the pipe. Figure 8.13 shows the velocity profile of a polymer fluid in a pipe with radius R. The velocity of the fluid at distance r from the pipe center is u_z. The velocity at the wall (i.e., $r = R$) is zero since there is no slip at the wall. Shear rate is the same as the velocity gradient, and hence the shear rate at any point in the pipe is defined as $-du_r/dr$.

As shown in Figure 8.13, the volumetric flow rate can be calculated from the volume under the curve:

$$Q = \int_0^R 2\pi r u_z\, dr = 2\pi \int_0^R r u_z\, dr \qquad (8.20)$$

where $2\pi r u_z\, dr$ is the volume of a fluid shell with thickness dr, height u_z, and a radius of r.

Equation 8.20 can be integrated by parts by letting $g = u_z$ and $dh = rdr$ in the equation of by parts:

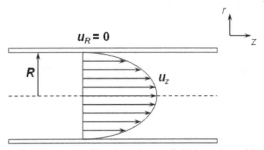

Figure 8.13. Velocity profile of a polymer fluid in a pipe with radius R.

$$\int g\, dh = hg - \int h\, dg \qquad (8.21)$$

Hence, $dg = du_z$ and $h = r^2/2$. Equation 8.20 can then be rewritten as:

$$Q = 2\pi \int_0^R u_z r\, dr = 2\pi \left\{ \left[\frac{r^2}{2} u_z \right]_0^R - \int_0^R \left(r^2/2 \right) du_z \right\} \qquad (8.22)$$

Since $u_z = 0$ when $r = R$, the first term in Equation 8.22 is zero. As a result,

$$Q = -\pi \int_0^R r^2\, du_z = -\pi \int_0^R r^2 \frac{du_z}{dr}\, dr \qquad (8.23)$$

As discussed in the section 8.5.1, the shear stress is also related to r, which is the distance from the pipe center. From Equation 8.19, the following equation can be obtained:

$$r = \frac{R}{\tau_w} \tau \qquad (8.24)$$

Substituting Equation 8.24 and $\dot{\gamma} = -du_r/dr$ into Equation 8.23 leads to:

$$Q = \frac{\pi R^3}{\tau_w^3} \int_0^{\tau_w} \dot{\gamma} \tau^2\, d\tau \qquad (8.25)$$

which can be rearranged to:

$$\frac{\tau_w^3 Q}{\pi R^3} = \int_0^{\tau_w} \dot{\gamma} \tau^2\, d\tau \qquad (8.26)$$

By differentiating both sides with respect to τ_w, the following equation can be obtained:

$$\frac{1}{\pi R^3}\left(\tau_w^3\frac{dQ}{d\tau_w}+3\tau_w^2 Q\right)=\dot{\gamma}_w\tau_w^2 \tag{8.27}$$

Substituting $\tau_w = R\Delta P/2L$ into Equation 8.27 gives the *Rabinowitsch equation*:

$$\boxed{\dot{\gamma}_w=\frac{1}{\pi R^3}\left[3Q+\Delta P\frac{dQ}{d\Delta P}\right]} \tag{8.28}$$

The *Rabinowitsch equation* allows the calculation of the shear rate at the pipe wall from three measurable quantities: R, Q, and ΔP. Since the flow properties of a fluid are independent of the pipe structure, the τ_w-$\dot{\gamma}_w$ curve of the fluid is the same as the τ-$\dot{\gamma}$ curve. Therefore, by using Equation 8.18 and the *Rabinowitsch equation*, the flow curve, *i.e.*, τ-$\dot{\gamma}$ or $\log\tau$-$\log\dot{\gamma}$, can be obtained. However, the use of the *Rabinowitsch equation* sometimes is tedious, and hence it often is simplified by using the following mathematical rearrangements.

Equation 8.27 can first be rearranged to:

$$\dot{\gamma}_w=\frac{3}{4}\left(\frac{4Q}{\pi R^3}\right)+\frac{\tau_w}{4}\frac{d\left(4Q/\pi R^3\right)}{d\tau_w} \tag{8.29}$$

Since $\dfrac{d\left(\log x\right)}{dx}=\dfrac{1}{x}$, $y\dfrac{dx}{dy}$ becomes $x\dfrac{d\log x}{d\log y}$. As a result, Equation 8.29 can be rearranged to:

$$\dot{\gamma}_w=\frac{3}{4}\left(\frac{4Q}{\pi R^3}\right)+\frac{1}{4}\left(\frac{4Q}{\pi R^3}\right)\frac{d\log\left(4Q/\pi R^3\right)}{d\log\tau_w} \tag{8.30}$$

To simplify Equation 8.30, the derivative can be defined as $1/n'$, *i.e.*,

$$n'=\frac{d\log\tau_w}{d\log\left(4Q/\pi R^3\right)}=\frac{d\log\left(R\Delta P/2L\right)}{d\log\left(4Q/\pi R^3\right)} \tag{8.31}$$

Equation 8.30 can then be rewritten as:

$$\dot{\gamma}_w=\left(\frac{3n'+1}{4n'}\right)\frac{4Q}{\pi R^3} \tag{8.32}$$

This simple equation is known as the *Metzner form* of the *Rabinowitsch equation*. Now, the flow curve (τ-$\dot\gamma$ or log τ-log $\dot\gamma$) of the fluid can be obtained by using Equations 8.18 and 8.32.

From Equation 8.31, the following relationship also can be obtained:

$$\log\left(\frac{R\Delta P}{2L}\right) = n'\log\left(\frac{4R}{\pi R^3}\right) + \log K' \tag{8.33}$$

According to Equation 8.33, the shear stress at the wall can be calculated by:

$$\tau_w = \frac{R\Delta P}{2L} = K'\left(\frac{4Q}{\pi R^3}\right)^{n'} \tag{8.34}$$

If the polymer fluid follows the power law relationship, i.e., $\tau_w = K(\dot\gamma_w)^n$, Equation 8.32 can be used to obtain:

$$\tau_w = K\left(\frac{3n'+1}{4n'}\right)^n\left(\frac{4Q}{\pi R^3}\right)^n \tag{8.35}$$

Comparing Equations 8.34 and 8.35, it is seen that K' and n' can be obtained from the fluid consistency index K and the power law index n:

$$K' = K\left(\frac{3n+1}{4n}\right)^n \tag{8.36}$$

and

$$n' = n \tag{8.37}$$

The *Metzner form* of the *Rabinowitsch equation* (Equation 8.32) can then be re-written to:

$$\boxed{\dot\gamma_w = \left(\frac{3n+1}{4n}\right)\frac{4Q}{\pi R^3}} \tag{8.38}$$

For Newtonian flow ($n = 1$), the term $4Q/\pi R^3$ is in fact the true shear rate at all. However, for non-Newtonian flow, the term $4Q/\pi R^3$ is known as the apparent shear rate at wall ($\dot\gamma_{w,a}$), i.e.,

$$\dot\gamma_{w,a} = \frac{4Q}{\pi R^3} \tag{8.39}$$

In many applications, the flow curves (τ-$\dot\gamma$ or log τ-log $\dot\gamma$) of the fluids are obtained by using Equations 8.18 and 8.39, and Equation 8.38 is used as a correction for non-Newtonian flows.

8.5.3 CALCULATION OF VISCOSITY

The viscosity of the polymer fluid can be calculated from Equations 8.32 and 8.34:

$$\eta = \frac{\tau_w}{\dot\gamma_w} = K' \left(\frac{3n'+1}{4n'}\right)^{-1} \left(\frac{4Q}{\pi R^3}\right)^{n'-1} \tag{8.40}$$

For polymer fluids that follow the power law relationship, Equation 8.40 can be rearranged to:

$$\eta = K\left(\frac{3n+1}{4n}\right)^{n-1}\left(\frac{4Q}{\pi R^3}\right)^{n-1} = K\left(\frac{3n+1}{4n}\right)^{n-1}\left(\dot\gamma_{w,a}\right)^{n-1} = K\left(\dot\gamma_w\right)^{n-1} \tag{8.41}$$

8.5.4 CORRECTIONS OF FLOW CURVES

As discussed above, the flow curves of polymer fluids can be obtained by Equations 8.18 and 8.38 (or 8.39), and the viscosities of the fluids can be calculated by Equation 8.41. While deriving these equations, one of the assumptions is that the flow pattern is constant along the pipe. However, in a real capillary flow, the polymer fluid exhibits different flow patterns in the entrance and exit regions of the pipe. For example, the pressure drops at the die entrance and exit regions are different from $\Delta P/L$. Therefore, corrections, e.g., Bagley correction, are needed to address the entrance and exit effects. Another assumption is that there is no slip at the wall. However, in a real flow, polymer fluid may slip at the wall and this reduces the shear rate near the wall. The Mooney analysis can be used to address the effect of the wall slip. In addition, the velocity profile shown in Figure 8.13 is a parabolic flow. However, the true flow in the die orifice is not necessarily a simple parabolic flow, and hence Weissenberg-Rabinowitsch correction often is used to correct the shear rate at the wall for the non-parabolic velocity profile.

Detailed mathematical treatments for these corrections are not discussed here, but they can be found in the references listed at the end of this chapter.

8.6   EXTERNAL FACTORS AFFECTING THE VISCOSITY OF POLYMERS

The flow of a polymer occurs when the polymer chains slide against each other. The viscosity of a polymer fluid is its resistance to flow and is a measure of the frictional forces between the molecules in the fluid. The viscosity of polymer fluids is affected by a number of external factors, such as temperature, shear rate, and pressure.

8.6.1   EFFECT OF TEMPERATURE

It is well-known that an increase in temperature can reduce the polymer viscosity. The viscosity-temperature relationship of polymers often is described by the *Arrhenius equation*:

$$\eta = Ae^{\Delta E/RT} \tag{8.42}$$

where A is a structure constant, ΔE the activation energy, R the gas constant, and T the absolute temperature of the polymer. The increase in temperature leads to increased intermolecular distance and reduced intermolecular interaction, which—in turn—results in improved polymer chain mobility. As a result, the viscosity of the polymer fluid decreases with increase in temperature.

The *Arrhenius equation* can be rearranged to:

$$\ln \eta = \ln A + \frac{\Delta E}{R} \frac{1}{T} \tag{8.43}$$

This indicates that the $\ln \eta$-$1/T$ plot is a straight line and the slope is $\Delta E/R$ (Figure 8.14). Since the value of the gas constant is 8.314 J·mol^{-1} K^{-1}, the activation energy can be calculated directly from the slope of the $\ln \eta$-$1/T$ plot. When a polymer has a higher activation energy, its viscosity is more sensitive to the change in temperature.

The activation energy of polymers is closely related to their chemical structures. Table 8.1 shows the activation energies of some polymer melts. In general, flexible polymer chains with weak intermolecular interactions (e.g., polyethylene and polypropylene) have low activation energies, while polymers with rigid chains or strong intermolecular interactions (e.g., acetate and polyacrylonitrile) have high activation energies. Figure 8.15 shows the effect of polymer chemical structure on the viscosity-temperature relationship. It is seen that the viscosity of polymers with rigid chains or strong intermolecular interactions is sensitive to the change in temperature. However, the viscosity of flexible polymer chains with weak intermolecular interactions is less sensitive to temperature. This provides important guidance for the control of polymer spinning processes. To spin

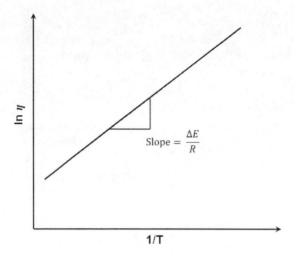

Figure 8.14. A typical ln η-1/T plot.

fibers from polymers with rigid chains or strong intermolecular interactions (e.g., acetate and polyacrylonitrile), it is effective to reduce their viscosities by increasing the processing temperature. On the other hand, to spin fibers from polymers with flexible chains and weak intermolecular interactions (e.g., polyethylene and

Table 8.1. Activation energies of polymer melts.

Polymer	Activation Energy (kcal/mole)
Polyethylene, linear	6.3–8.2
Polypropylene	9.0–10.1
Nylon 6	17.2–18.6
Nylon 6,6	16.2
Polyester	13.1–20.1
Polycarbonate	21.9
Polystyrene	25.5
Polyacrylonitrile	36.5–41.0
Acetate	34.2

Sources: Porter, R.S., et. al., *Journal of Polymer Science, Part C. Polymer Symposia*, 15, 365–371, 1967.; Saini, D.R., et al., *Journal of Macromolecular Science, Part B. Physics*, 22, 437–449, 1983.

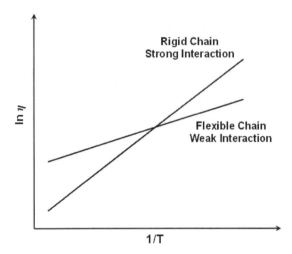

Figure 8.15. Effect of chemical structure on the viscosity-temperature relationship of polymers.

polypropylene), increasing temperature may not be sufficient to reduce their viscosities and other approaches are needed.

For fiber spinning processes, another commonly used equation for the viscosity-temperature relationship is:

$$\eta = ae^{-bT} \tag{8.44}$$

where both a and b are constants. The constant b indicates the temperature sensitivity of the polymer and is typically in the range of 0.01–$0.1°C^{-1}$.

The validity of Equations 8.43 and 44 is related to the glass transition temperature (T_g) of polymers. For many polymers, these two equations only hold at $T > T_g + 100°C$. For temperatures ranging from T_g to $T_g + 100°C$, the Williams-Landel-Ferry (WLF) equation can be used:

$$\log\frac{\eta}{\eta_{T_g}} = \frac{-17.4\left(T-T_g\right)}{51.6+T-T_g} \tag{8.45}$$

where η_{T_g} is the viscosity at T_g.

8.6.2   EFFECT OF SHEAR RATE

As discussed in previous sections, most polymer fluids exhibit shear-thinning behavior, i.e., the viscosity decreases with increase in shear rate. The shear-thinning behavior of polymer fluids is related to the "disentanglement" phenomenon. With increase in shear rate, more polymer chains are being disentangled and oriented, leading to lower resistance to the flow, i.e., lower viscosity. The viscosity-shear rate relationship can be described by using the power law equation or the *Carreau equation*.

The disentanglement process is affected by the chemical structure of polymers. Figure 8.16 shows the effect of polymer chemical structure on the viscosity-shear rate relationship. For polymers with flexible chains and weak intermolecular in-teractions (e.g., polyethylene and polypropylene), their conformations can be changed easily and increasing shear rate is effective for disentangling the polymer chains. As a result, their viscosities decrease rapidly with an increase in shear rate. However, for polymers with rigid chains or strong intermolecular interactions (e.g., acetate and polyacrylonitrile), it is more difficult to change their conforma-tions by shear and their viscosities are less sensitive to the shear rate.

Based on the discussion in sections 8.6.1 and 8.6.2, the following guidelines can be used if the polymer viscosity needs to be reduced during fiber formation:

1. For polymers with flexible chains and weak intermolecular interactions, it is more effective to increase the shear rate.
2. For polymers with rigid chains or strong intermolecular interactions, it is more effective to increase the temperature.

In real applications, many other factors can affect the actual viscosity of a polymer. As a result, these guidelines may not work for some polymers. In addi-tion, there are limitations while increasing the temperature or shear rate. For ex-ample, the processing temperature cannot be too close to the polymer degradation

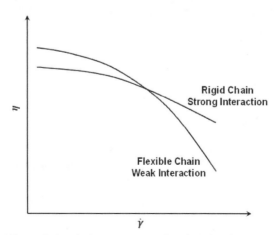

Figure 8.16. Effect of chemical structure on the viscosity-shear rate relationship of polymers.

temperature since polymer chains tend to break at elevated temperatures. The shear rate also is limited by the capacity of the equipment used for the fiber formation. Moreover, extremely high shear rate could cause instable flow and make the fiber spinning process impossible.

8.6.3   EFFECT OF PRESSURE

During fiber formation, polymer fluids are extruded through die orifices under pressure. Figure 8.17 shows the effect of pressure on the viscosity of polymers. In general, the increase in pressure leads to reduced intermolecular distance and increased intermolecular interaction. As a result, the viscosity increases. The effect of increasing pressure is similar to that of decreasing temperature. For example, for many polymer melts, applying a pressure of 10 MPa is equivalent to decreasing the temperature by around 5°C.

The relationship between viscosity and pressure (P) can be described by:

$$\eta = \alpha e^{\beta P} \qquad (8.46)$$

where α and β are constants. The constant β typically is in the order 2×10^{-8} Pa^{-1}. This indicates a pressure increase of 10 MPa could cause the viscosity to increase by 22%.

Equations 8.44 and 46 can be combined to give the following equation that includes both the temperature and pressure dependences of the viscosity:

$$\eta = De^{-bT + \beta P} \qquad (8.47)$$

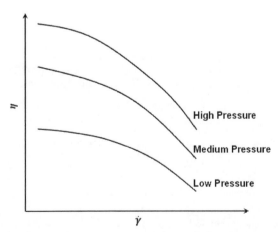

Figure 8.17. Effect of pressure on the viscosity of polymers.

where D is a constant. Equation 8.47 can be used in conjunction with the power law equation or the *Carreau equation* to describe the viscosity as a function of T, $\dot{\gamma}$, and P.

8.7 STRUCTURAL FACTORS AFFECTING THE VISCOSITY OF POLYMERS

Polymers with different structures show different flow behaviors. For fiber formation, the most important structural factors are chain rigidity, intermolecular interaction, molecular weight, and molecular weight distribution. Other factors, such as crosslinking degree, side chain length and flexibility, also affect the viscosity of polymers, but they are less important since fiber spinning processes require polymers that are linear and are not crosslinked.

8.7.1 EFFECT OF CHAIN RIGIDITY AND INTERMOLECULAR INTERACTION

As discussed in the previous section, the polymer chain rigidity and intermolecular interaction affect the viscosity-temperature and viscosity-shear rate relationships. In general, polymers with rigid chains have higher resistance to flow and their viscosities often are greater than those of flexible chains. Similarly, polymers with strong intermolecular interactions have higher viscosities than those with weak interactions. In addition, the viscosities of polymers with rigid chains or strong intermolecular interactions are sensitive to the change in temperature, but are less sensitive to shear rate.

8.7.2 EFFECT OF MOLECULAR WEIGHT

With increase in molecular weight, the viscosities of polymers increase since longer polymer chains have greater resistance to the flow. The actual viscosity-molecular weight relationship of polymers is complex. For most polymers, the viscosity at zero shear rate (η_0) has the following relationship with the weight average molecular weight ($\bar{M}_w$):

$$\eta_0 = K_L \bar{M}_w^{1.0}, \text{ at } \bar{M}_w < \bar{M}_c \tag{8.48}$$

$$\eta_0 = K_H \bar{M}_w^{3.4}, \text{ at } \bar{M}_w < \bar{M}_c \tag{8.49}$$

where K_L and K_H are constants. $\bar{M}_c$ is the critical molecular weight, at which the chain entanglements begin to dominate the rate of slippage of the polymer chains. When the weight average molecular weight is less than $\bar{M}_c$, the average polymer chain length is smaller than the average distance between entanglements, and as a result, the viscosity is determined mainly by the average size of the polymer chains and is proportional to the molecular weight. However, when the weight average molecular weight is greater than $\bar{M}_c$, there is a significant amount of entanglements and the resistance to flow increases quickly. As a result, the viscosity is proportional to $\bar{M}_w^{3.4}$. Figure 8.18 shows the effect of weight average molecular weight on the zero-shear viscosity of polymers.

For most polymers, the $\bar{M}_c$ value ranges from 1,000 to 30,000 g/mol. The weight average molecular weights of most polymer fibers are greater than their corresponding $\bar{M}_c$ values so they can be spun into the fiber form and have sufficient mechanical properties. However, compared with most other polymer products, polymer fibers typically have lower molecular weights. According to Equation 8.49, lower molecular weight leads to significantly smaller viscosity, which allows the polymer fluids to pass through the small die orifices to form fibers.

Equations 8.48 and 49 show the effect of molecular weight on the zero-shear viscosity. The formation of polymer fibers is carried out at high shear rates. Figure 8.19 shows the viscosity-molecular weight relationships at different shear rates. It is seen that at $\bar{M}_w < \bar{M}_c$, the shear rate does not affect the viscosity-molecular weight relationship since there is no significant entanglements in the system. However, at $\bar{M}_w > \bar{M}_c$, the slope of the η- $\bar{M}_w$ curve decreases with increase in shear rate since more entanglements are disentangled at high shear rates. At very high shear rates, the viscosity could be proportional to the molecular weight.

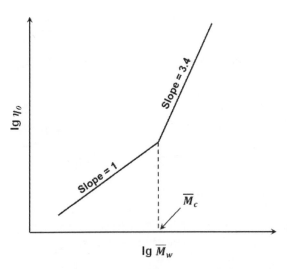

Figure 8.18. Effect of weight average molecular weight on the zero-shear viscosity of polymers.

8.7.3 EFFECT OF MOLECULAR WEIGHT DISTRIBUTION

At a fixed molecular weight, the viscosity of polymers changes with change in molecular weight distribution. Figure 8.20 shows the effect of molecular weight distribution on the η-$\dot{\gamma}$ curve of polymers. Typically, when the molecular weight distribution is narrower, the polymer fluid is more Newtonian and the power law index n is closer to unit. When the molecular weight distribution is broader, the polymer fluid becomes more non-Newtonian and n decreases. This is because polymers with broad molecule weight distributions have a larger number of extremely long chains. These long chains can form entanglements easily, leading to

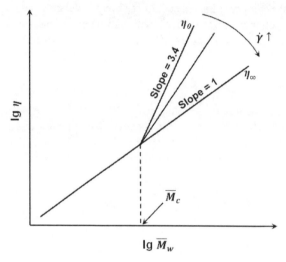

Figure 8.19. Effect of shear rate on the viscosity-molecular weight relationship of polymers.

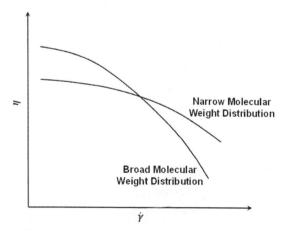

Figure 8.20. Effect of molecular weight distribution on the viscosity of polymers.

higher viscosities at low shear rates. However, at high shear rates, the entanglements formed by the long chains can be disentangled and the viscosity decreases rapidly with an increase in shear rate.

8.8   ELASTIC EFFECTS

As discussed above, polymer chains tend to be disentangled and oriented under shear. One important result of the disentanglement and molecular orientation under shear is the decrease of viscosity with increasing shear rate. However, the flow of polymers is not pure viscous flow, and it has elastic component since the change of chain conformations is not completely irreversible. Upon the release of the shear, the polymer chains tend to recoil and be pulled back by the restraining force. Such elastic response has significant effect on the fiber formation processes.

8.8.1   DIE SWELLING

One important elastic effect is the die swell behavior, i.e., the extrudate diameter is greater than the die diameter. This is because that while passing through the die, the polymer chains are being disentangled and oriented, producing normal stress. Due to the limited die length, disentanglement and orientation of polymer chains are not complete in the die. When exiting the die, the normal stress disappears and the polymer chains coil. As result, the extrudate expands perpendicular to the flow direction (Figure 8.21). The die swell ratio (B) is defined as:

$$B = \frac{D_{max}}{D_0} \tag{8.50}$$

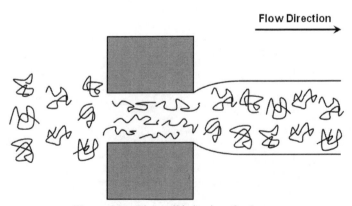

Figure 8.21. Die swell behavior of polymers.

where D_0 is the die diameter, and D_{max} the maximum diameter of the extrudate (e.g., as-spun fiber before drawing). Under certain conditions, the die swell ratio could reach 400% or even higher. The die swell ratio is closely related to the molecular weight of polymers. Typically, with an increase in molecular weight, the amount of die swell increases.

The die swell ratio is affected by the design of the die. For example, when the die diameter is fixed, the die swell ratio decreases with an increase in die length (Figure 8.22). The die swell ratio also is affected by temperature and shear rate. In general, the die swell ratio decreases with increase in temperature. However, the die swell-shear rate relationship is more complex. Figure 8.23 shows a typical die swell-shear rate curve of polymers. The die swell ratio increases with shear up to a limit, beyond which the die swell decreases. It is important to notice that the maximum die swell often occurs at a shear rate, which is just slightly lower than the onset of melt fracture.

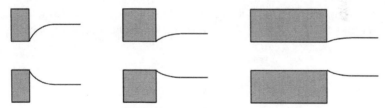

Figure 8.22. Effect of die length on the die swell.

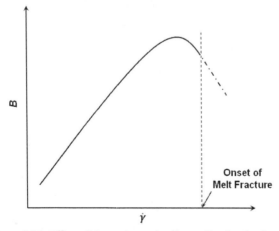

Figure 8.23. Effect of shear rate on the die swell ratio of polymers.

8.8.2 MELT FRACTURE

As shown in Figure 8.23, when the shear rate exceeds a critical value, melt fracture occurs and polymers no longer extrude smoothly. Melt fracture starts with barely visible surface defects, but at higher shear rates the as-spun fibers can have different morphologies. In some cases, as-spun fibers present "sharkskin", in others the fibers look like screwed threads. The as-spun fibers also can have rod-like cross-sections, twisted into the form of spirals. These are just a few examples, and many other types of morphologies can be observed when melt fracture occurs. At very high shear rates, the melt fracture could lead to the loss of cohesion.

It is commonly agreed the melt fracture behavior is related to the elasticity of polymer fluids. The formation of different morphologies may be due to some secondary effects. For the formation of polymer fibers, melt fracture is not desired, and hence the fiber spinning processes need to be carried out below the critical shear rate ($\dot{\gamma}_c$), i.e., the onset of melt fracture. Therefore, it is important to determine the critical shear rate for polymers. In general, with increase in molecular weight, the critical shear rate decreases (Figure 8.24). This means the melt fracture occurs more easily for longer polymer chains since they are more elastic. In practical applications, the critical shear rate can be increased by increasing the processing temperature (Figure 8.25).

8.9 ELONGATIONAL VISCOSITY

So far, the discussion in this chapter focuses on shear flow. However, the elongational flow of polymers also is important for fiber formation. In a pure shear flow, the velocity gradient is normal to the flow direction. On the other hand, the

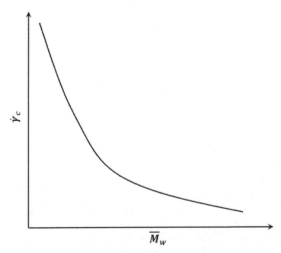

Figure 8.24. Effect of molecular weight on the critical shear rate of polymers.

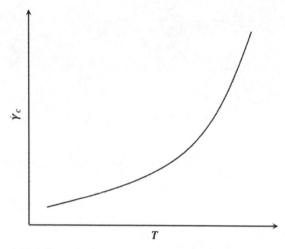

Figure 8.25. Effect of temperature on the critical shear rate of polymers.

velocity gradient in an elongational flow is in parallel with the flow direction. When polymer fluid flows through the die, the velocity gradient is normal to the flow direction and hence the flow is a shear flow. However, when the polymer fluid is converging into the small-diameter die, velocity gradient also is developed in parallel with the flow direction, and hence the flow in the entry region is partially an elongational flow. When the polymer fluid exits the die orifice, the velocity gradient becomes in parallel with the flow direction again due to the tension force, and the shear flow changes to elongational flow until the polymer is solidified. Therefore, it is important to study the elongational flow of polymers.

The elongational viscosity (η_e) is the resistance of the fluid to elongational flow. The elongational viscosity can be defined as:

$$\eta_e = \sigma \, / \, \frac{du}{dz} \tag{8.51}$$

where σ is the tensile stress, and du/dz is velocity gradient in the flow direction. Trouton studied the relationship between the elongational viscosity and shear viscosity (η), and found the elongation to shear viscosity ratio is equal to 3:

$$\frac{\eta_e}{\eta} = 3 \tag{8.52}$$

This relationship, known as the Trouton ratio, is valid at low stresses or rates. Figure 8.26 compares the elongational viscosity-stretch rate ($\dot{\varepsilon}$) relationship to the shear viscosity-shear rate relationship over a wide range of strain rates. At low rates, the elongational viscosity is three times of the shear viscosity. Shear

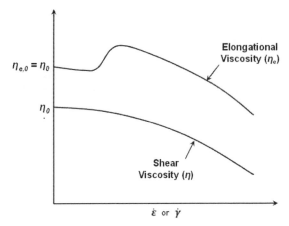

Figure 8.26. Elongational viscosity-stretch rate and shear viscosity-shear rate relationships of polymers.

viscosity decreases with increase in shear rate, i.e., shear-thinning behavior. However, the elongational viscosity-stretch rate curve has a strain hardening region, in which the elongational viscosity increases with stretch rate. After the strain hardening region, the elongational viscosity decreases again with increase in stretch rate.

When the elongational viscosity starts to decrease after the strain hardening region, the elongational viscosity-stretch rate relationship can be described by:

$$\eta_e = \frac{\eta_{e,0}}{1+\left(a\eta_{e,0}\dot{\varepsilon}\right)^b} \qquad (8.53)$$

where $\eta_{e,0}$ is the zero stretch rate viscosity, and a and b are empirical constants.

The elongational viscosity also is a function of temperature. At $T > T_g + 100°C$, the elongational viscosity-temperature relationship follows the Arrhenius equation. When the temperature is between T_g and $T_g + 100°C$, the temperature dependence of elongational viscosity can be described by the WLF equation.

When the polymer fluid exits the die orifice during fiber formation, the crystalline structure starts to be developed. The elongational viscosity increases rapidly as the crystallization process starts. When the degree of crystallinity still is low, the effect of crystallinity on the elongational viscosity is given by:

$$\eta_e = Hexp\left(c\theta^d\right) \qquad (8.54)$$

where θ is the relative crystallinity, and H, c and d are empirical constants.

When the degree of crystallinity becomes higher, the small crystals act as "physical crosslinks". Ziabicki suggests when the number of such physical crosslinks exceeds a critical value, the following equation can be used to describe the temperature and crystallinity dependences of the elongational viscosity:

$$\eta_e = f(T) / \left[1 - \frac{\theta}{\theta_{cr}} \right]^\alpha \tag{8.55}$$

where $f(T)$ is a function of temperature, θ_{cr} the crystallinity when the number of physical crosslinks exceed the critical value, and α a constant. Experimental data show the θ_{cr} value could be very low, 2–3%. Therefore, even a relatively low degree of crystallinity can drastically change the elongational viscosity and then significantly affects the fiber formation process.

REFERENCES

[1] Baird, D.G., and Collias, D.I., *Polymer Processing: Principles and Design*, John Wiley & Sons, 1998.

[2] Barnes, H.A., Hutton, J.F., and Walters, K., *An Introduction to Rheology*, Elsevier, 1989.

[3] Brazel, C.S., and Rosen, S.L., *Fundamental Principles of Polymeric Materials*, Third edition, John Wiley & Sons, 2012.

[4] Brydson, J.A., *Flow Properties of Polymer Melts*, Van Nostrand Reinhold Company, 1981.

[5] Dealy, J.M., and Larson, R.G, *Structure and Rheology of Molten Polymers*, Hanser Gardner Publications, 2006.

[6] Han, C.D., *Rheology and Processing of Polymeric Materials: Volume 1: Polymer Rheology*, Oxford University Press, 2007.

[7] Han, C.D., *Rheology and Processing of Polymeric Materials: Volume II: Polymer Processing*, Oxford University Press, 2007.

[8] Kontopoulou, M., *Applied Polymer Rheology: Polymeric Fluids with Industrial Applications*, John Wiley & Sons, 2012.

[9] Park, H.M., Hong, S.M., and Lim, J.Y., "Estimation of Rheological Parameters Using Velocity Measurements", *Chemical Engineering Science*, 62, 6806–6815, 2007.

[10] Park, H.M., Shin, K.S. and Choi, Y.J., "Rheometry Using Velocity Measurements", *Rheologica Acta*, 48, 433–445, 2009.

[11] Porter, R.S., and Johnson, J.F., "Temperature Dependence of Polymer Viscosity. The Influence of Shear Rate and Stress", *Journal of Polymer Science, Part C. Polymer Symposia*, 15, 365–371, 1967.

[12] Painter, P.C., and Coleman, M.M., *Fundamentals of Polymer Science: An Introductory Text*, Second Edition, CRC Press, 1997.

[13] Saini, D.R., and Shenoy, A.V., "A New Method for the Determination of Flow Activation Energy of Polymer Melts", *Journal of Macromolecular Science, Part B. Physics*, 22, 437–449, 1983.

[14] Shaw, M.T., *Introduction to Polymer Rheology*, John Wiley & Sons, 2012.

[15] Tanner, R.I., *Engineering Rheology*, Second Edition, Oxford University Press, 2000.

[16] Zhang, X., Pan, Y., Cheng, Jianfeng, and Yi, X., "The Influence of Low-Melting-Point Alloy on the Rheological Properties of a Polystyrene Melt", *J. Mater. Sci.*, 35, 4573–4581, 2000.

[17] Ziabicki, A., "The Mechanisms of 'Neck-Like' Deformation in High-Speed Melt Spinning. 1. Rheological and Dynamic Factors", *Journal of Non-Newtonian Fluid Mechanics*, 30, 141–155, 1988.

[18] Ziabicki, A., "The Mechanisms of Neck-Like Deformation in High-Speed Melt Spinning .2. Effects of Polymer Crystallization", *Journal of Non-Newtonian Fluid Mechanics*, 30, 157–168, 1988.

PROBLEMS

(1) What are Newtonian, Bingham, shear-thinning, and shear-thickening flows?

(2) Why do polymers often exhibit shear-thinning behavior?

(3) What are rheopectic and thixotropic fluids?

(4) A typical shear stress-shear rate curve for a polymer can be divided into lower Newtonian, shear-thinning, and upper Newtonian regions if the shear rate range is very wide. Explain how the polymer chains behave under shear in these three regions.

(5) What are the shear stress and shear rate at wall when a polymer flows through a small-diameter pipe.

(6) Discuss and explain how you would expect the viscosity of a polypropylene melt to vary with:

   (i)   Molecular weight
   (ii) Chain rigidity

(iii) Intermolecular interaction
(iv) Temperature
(v) Strain rate

(7) Two major approaches can be used to reduce the polymer viscosity: (*i*) increasing the temperature, and (*ii*) increasing the shear rate. To reduce the viscosity of a polymer composed of flexible chains, which approach is more effective? How about a polymer with strong intermolecular interaction?

(8) The viscosity of a polymer can be reduced by two simple approaches: (*i*) increasing the temperature, and (*ii*) increasing the shear rate. What are the limitations for these two approaches?

(9) What is die swell? Why does the die swell behavior occur when a polymer is extruded?

(10) What is the cause of melt fracture?

(11) What is the relationship between elongational viscosity and shear viscosity?

CHAPTER 9

Formation of Synthetic Polymer Fibers

Despite the variety of synthetic polymers, only a few of them can be made into useful fibers. Fiber-forming polymers typically are linear and are capable of being oriented. If side groups are present, they must be simple and/or polar. The molecular weights of fiber-forming polymers must be high enough for achieving good mechanical and thermal stability, and at the same time, low enough for dissolving or melting for extruding into fibers. These linear, moderate-molecular weight polymers can be made into fibers by melt spinning, solution spinning, gel spinning, liquid crystal spinning, dispersion spinning, etc. This chapter focuses on the fundamental aspects of the melt spinning process. Other spinning processes will be briefly discussed.

9.1 MELT SPINNING

Melt spinning typically is used to make fibers from polyolefins, nylons, and polyesters. One major advantage of melt spinning is that it does not require a purification step since no solvent is used. Another advantage is that melt spinning has very high production speed, which ranges from several hundred meters per minute to several thousand meters per minute.

9.1.1 FIBER FORMATION PROCESS

The melt spinning process involves melting and extrusion of the fiber-forming polymer through a spinneret, i.e., a multihole capillary die, followed by cooling and solidification to form filaments. Figure 9.1 shows a schematic of the melt spinning process. The fiber-forming polymer used typically is in the form of dried granules or pellets. The dry polymer is fed into an extruder through a hopper.

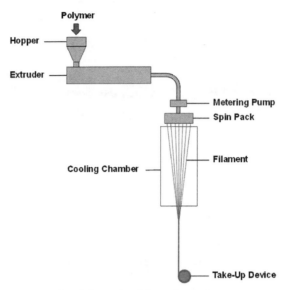

Figure 9.1. Schematic of the melt spinning process.

The extruder melts and conveys the polymer into a metering pump. The metering pump delivers the polymer melt at an accurately controlled rate into the spin pack, where the polymer is filtered and pushed through the holes of the spinneret. The extruded filaments pass through a cooling chamber to be solidified. The rates of cooling and solidification in the cooling chamber typically are controlled by cross air blow. Heated cells and liquid baths also may be used in some cases to reduce or increase the cooling and solidification rates. During the solidification process, a take-up device typically is used to create a tensional force to draw down the filaments to smaller diameters. The resultant filaments often are passed directly to the drawing process to improve the physical structure and mechanical properties.

Many processing parameters affect the structure of melt-spun fibers. The most important processing parameters are:

1. Spinneret orifice shape, dimension, and number.
2. Extrusion temperature.
3. Mass flow rate through each spinneret hole.
4. Take-up velocity.
5. Length of the spinline, and
6. Cooling condition.

During melt spinning, these parameters must be carefully controlled so the desired structure and properties can be achieved for melt-spun fibers. To understand how to control these processing parameters, an engineering analysis of the melt spinning process is required. The basic engineering analysis involves the flow of polymer melts, the balances of forces and energies, and the development of molecular orientation and crystalline structure. The flow behavior of polymers has been discussed in Chapter 8. The following sections address the force balance, energy balance, and molecular orientation and crystallization in the spinline.

9.1.2 FORCE BALANCE

Figure 9.2 shows forces acting on a single filament in a spinline. The balance of forces on the filament can be described as:

$$F_{rheo,z} = F_{rheo,0} + F_{surf} + F_{inert} + F_{drag} - F_{grav} \tag{9.1}$$

where $F_{rheo,z}$ is the rheological force at a distance z from the spinneret, $F_{rheo,0}$ the rheological force at $z = 0$ (*i.e.*, spinneret exit), F_{surf} the surface tension at the interface between the filament and the cooling medium, F_{inert} the inertial force produced by the acceleration of the filament, F_{drag} the drag force caused by the fiber moving through the cooling medium, and F_{grav} the gravitational force.

For melt spinning, the surface tension of polymer melt typically is small compared to other forces, and it can be assumed that:

$$F_{surf} = 0 \tag{9.2}$$

The inertial force can be expressed by:

$$F_{inert} = w\left(u_z - u_0\right) \tag{9.3}$$

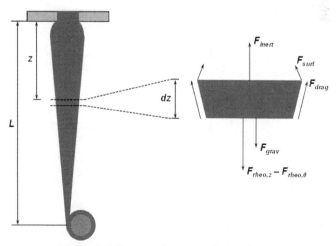

Figure 9.2. Forces acting on a spinning filament.

where w is the mass throughput rate per spinneret hole, u_z the velocity of the filament at a given point, and u_0 the velocity of the filament at the exit of the spinneret.

The drag force can be written as:

$$F_{drag} = \int_0^z \pi d_z \tau_z dz \qquad (9.4)$$

where d_z is the diameter of the filament at a given point, τ_z the shear stress at the fiber surface caused by the friction with the cooling medium. If the cooling medium is air, the shear stress at the fiber surface is given by:

$$\tau_z = \frac{1}{2} \rho_a u_{rel}^2 C_{drag} \qquad (9.5)$$

where ρ_a is the density of air, u_{rel} the relative axial velocity of the filament and the cooling air, and C_{drag} the drag coefficient. If the cooling air does not move parallel to the filament, the relative axial velocity u_{rel} is the same as the filament velocity u_z. Equation 9.4 then can be rewritten as:

$$F_{drag} = \frac{1}{2} \int_0^z \rho_a C_{drag} u_z^2 \pi d_z dz \qquad (9.6)$$

There are many different methods for calculating the drag coefficient. One of the most commonly used methods is to relate the drag coefficient to the Reynolds number (R_e) by:

$$C_{drag} = K R_e^{-n} \qquad (9.7)$$

where the exponent n typically ranges from 0.6 to 0.8, and K ranges from 0.23 to >1. The Reynolds number R_e can be expressed by:

$$R_e = \frac{\rho Q}{\pi D_0 \eta} \qquad (9.8)$$

where ρ is the density of the polymer, Q the volumetric throughput rate per spinneret hole, D_0 the diameter of the spinneret hole, and η the viscosity of the polymer melt. When cooling mediums other than air are used, Equation 9.6 still may be valid, but appropriate medium densities and drag coefficient values must be used.

The gravitational force is given by:

$$F_{grav} = \int_0^z \pi \left(\frac{d_z}{2}\right)^2 \rho g \, dz \qquad (9.9)$$

where ρ is the density of the filament, and g the acceleration of gravity. According to the material balance, the mass throughput rate can be written as:

$$w = \rho A_z u_z = \rho \pi \left(\frac{d_z}{2}\right)^2 u_z \qquad (9.10)$$

where A_z is the cross-sectional area of the filament at a given point. The gravitational force can then be rewritten as:

$$F_{grav} = \int_0^z \frac{w}{u_z} g \, dz \qquad (9.11)$$

Based on Equations 9.2, 9.3, 9.6, and 9.11, the force balance can be rewritten as:

$$F_{rheo,z} = F_{rheo,0} + w(u_z - u_0) + \frac{1}{2} \int_0^z \rho_a C_{drag} u_z^2 \pi d_z \, dz - \int_0^z \frac{w}{u_z} g \, dz \qquad (9.12)$$

Compared with $F_{rheo,0}$, it is more convenient to measure the rheological force $F_{rheo,L}$ at the take-up device, *i.e.*, $z = L$, where L is the distance between the take-up device and the spinneret. Therefore, the rheological force at a given point can be given by:

$$F_{rheo,z} = F_{rheo,L} - w(u_L - u_z) - \frac{1}{2} \int_z^L \rho_a C_{drag} u_z^2 \pi d_z \, dz + \int_z^L \frac{w}{u_z} g \, dz \qquad (9.13)$$

where u_L is the velocity of the filament at the take-up device, *i.e.*, the take-up velocity. At the take-up device, the $F_{rheo,L}$ is equal to the measurable take-up tension force:

$$F_{rheo,L} = F_{take-up} \qquad (9.14)$$

By using Equation 9.13, the rheological force at a given point in the spinning filament can be calculated from measurable quantities. The gradient of axial tension along the spinning filament can be obtained from:

$$\frac{dF_{rheo,z}}{dz} = w\frac{du_z}{dz} + \frac{1}{2}\rho_a C_{drag} u_z^2 \pi d_z - \frac{w}{u_z}g \qquad (9.15)$$

In melt spinning, the tensile stress developed in the filament is a very important parameter and it largely determines the final structure and properties of the melt-spun filaments. The tensile stress (σ_z) at a given point is related to the rheological stress by:

$$\sigma_z = \frac{F_{rheo,z}}{\pi\left(\dfrac{d_z}{2}\right)^2} \qquad (9.16)$$

Therefore, the tensile stress along the filament also can be obtained from measurable quantities.

Based on the force balance analysis described above, the contributions of different forces to the rheological force and tensile stress can be obtained. Figure 9.3 shows the rheological force, inertial force, drag force and gravitational force along a thin spinning filament. The actual curve shapes vary from polymer to polymer and are affected by various processing parameters. Curve shapes that are completely different from those shown in Figure 9.3 are possible. For the example

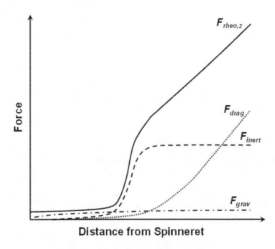

Figure 9.3. Evolutions of rheological, inertial, drag and gravitational forces along the spinline.

shown in Figure 9.3, the gravitational force is the dominant force in the vicinity of the spinneret. However, the gravitational force is small compared to other forces when the distance from spinneret is significant. Except for the vicinity of the spinneret, the inertial and drag forces are the major components for the rheological force. The inertial force develops earlier than the drag force, and it levels off as the filament is solidified and the diameter becomes relatively constant. Since the structure of the polymer filament is mainly developed before the filament is completely solidified, the inertial force is the dominant force that determines the physical structure of the filament. The drag force develops later, and it continues to increase even after the filament is solidified. As a result, it eventually could become greater than the inertial force if the length of the spinline is long enough.

The velocity, velocity gradient and filament diameter also can be obtained from the force balance analysis. Figure 9.4 shows the filament velocity as a function of distance from the spinneret. In the vicinity of the spinneret, the velocity of filament may reduce slightly due to the die swell phenomenon. After that, the velocity of the filament keeps on increasing until the filament is solidified, after which the velocity levels off. At higher spinning speed, the velocity developed along the spinline also is higher.

The velocity gradient (du_z/dz) along the spinline is shown in Figure 9.5. The entire spinline can be divided into three regions:

1. Die swell region ($0 \leq z < l_s$): negative velocity gradient ($du_z/dz < 0$).
2. Elongation region ($l_s \leq z < l_\infty$): positive velocity gradient ($du_z/dz > 0$).
3. Rigid motion region ($l_\infty \leq z < L$): zero velocity gradient ($du_z/dz = 0$).

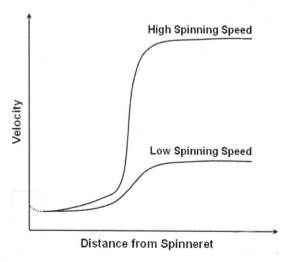

Figure 9.4. Evolution of filament velocity along the spinline.

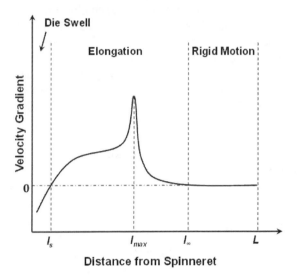

Figure 9.5. Evolution of velocity gradient along the spinline.

The length (l_s) of the die swell region is short, ranging from a fraction of a millimeter to several millimeters. In the die swell region, the molecular orientation developed in the spinneret channel is relaxed and polymer chains coil, leading to a negative velocity gradient. The elongation region plays the most important role in determining the diameter and physical structure of the melt-spun filament. The velocity gradient is positive and molecular orientation occurs because of the elongational flow. The length ($l_\infty - l_s$) of the elongation region ranges from 0.3 to 1.5 meters, depending on the cooling condition, filament thickness, take-up velocity, etc. The solidification and crystallization are completed in the rigid region. The velocity gradient is zero in the rigid region. However, the crystallization process in the rigid region is promoted by the molecular orientation, and hence the rigid region still affects the structure and properties of the resultant fiber.

The evolution of filament diameter is shown in Figure 9.6. In the vicinity of the spinneret, the filament diameter experiences a small increase due to the die swell phenomenon. At high spinning speed, the filament diameter reduces rapidly after the die swell region and then it levels off after the filament is solidified. At low spinning speed, the die swell in the vicinity of the spinneret does not have apparent change; however, the reduction rate of filament diameter in the elongation region becomes lower.

9.1.3 ENERGY BALANCE

The temperature of the spinning filament is a function of distance from the spinneret and is determined by the energy balance along the spinline. Heat transfer from the filament involves three mechanisms: conduction, radiation, and convection. The conduction of heat occurs: (1) from the hotter section of the filament to the cooler section of the filament, and (2) from the filament to cooler objects in contact with the filament, such as the take-up device. Compared to other mechanisms, the conduction of heat in the melt spinning process is negligible.

The heat transferred by radiation is strongly dependent on the temperature of the spinning filament. The apparent heat transfer coefficient for radiation can be expressed by:

$$\alpha^*_{rad} = K \frac{T^4 - T_a^{\,4}}{T - T_a} \qquad (9.17)$$

where K is a constant, T the absolute temperature of the radiating body, and T_a the absolute temperature of air (or other cooling medium). For the spinning of inorganic fibers, such as glass fibers, the temperature of the spinning filament is high (600–1100°C) and the radiation is significant. However, polymers typically are extruded at temperatures below 300°C, and the temperature of the spinning filament decreases quickly after exiting the spinneret. Hence, during the melt spinning of polymer fibers, the effect of radiation is appreciable only in the vicinity of the spinneret. Experimental work shows that even in the vicinity of the spinneret, the radiation heat transfer does not exceed 10–15% of convection heat transfer. Therefore, the convection of heat is the main mechanism for the heat transfer along the spinline. In most theoretical analyses, radiation is either neglected or is incorporated into the convective contribution by selecting an appropriate heat transfer coefficient.

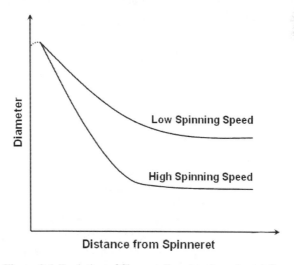

Figure 9.6. Evolution of filament diameter along the spinline.

Many theories have been developed to predict the heat transfer coefficients of spinning filaments. One of the commonly used relationships is given by Kase and Matsuo:

$$\alpha^* = 0.42 \frac{k_a}{d} \left(\frac{\rho_a u_f d}{\eta_a} \right)^{\frac{1}{3}} \left[1 + \left(8 \frac{u_c}{u_f} \right)^2 \right]^{\frac{1}{6}}$$

(9.18)

where k_a is the thermal conductivity of air, d the diameter of the spinning filament, ρ_a the density of air, η_a the viscosity of air, u_f the velocity of the filament, and u_c the transverse velocity of air (*i.e.*, the component of air velocity perpendicular to the filament).

In addition to heat transfer, the crystallization of the polymer also contributes to the change of temperature along the spinning filament. When a polymer crystallizes, it releases a certain amount of heat to form a low-energy, ordered structure. The latent heat of crystallization slows the temperature reduction along the spinline. The effect of crystallization on the filament temperature may not be apparent when polyester (especially, polyethylene terephthalate, PET) is melt-spun at low or moderate spinning speeds. This is because polyester has slow crystallization kinetics and it may not crystallize in the spinline. However, for the melt spinning of polyolefins and nylons, the crystallization effect has to be taken into consideration since these polymers crystallize rapidly along the spinline. In addition, for the high-speed melt spinning of polyester fibers, the crystallization effect cannot be neglected since the crystallization process is promoted by the high spinning speed.

Neglecting the radial temperature variations within the filament, the energy balance of the spinning filament can be written as:

$$\frac{dT}{dz} = -\frac{\pi d \alpha^* \left(T - T_a \right)}{w C_p} + \frac{\Delta H_c}{C_p} \frac{d\theta}{dz}$$

(9.19)

where w is the mass throughput rate per spinneret hole, C_p the heat capacity of the polymer, ΔH_c the heat of crystallization, and θ the degree of crystallinity. On the right side of Equation 9.19, the first term is the contribution of heat transfer, and the second term is the contribution of crystallization. Based on the energy balance, the temperature distribution along the filament can be obtained.

Figure 9.7 shows the filament temperature as a function of distance from the spinneret. When polyester fibers are melt-spun, the crystallization effect can be neglected, the filament temperature decreases with increasing distance from the spinneret due to the heat transfer. When polyolefin and nylon fibers are melt-spun, a slight shoulder appears on the temperature-distance curve due to the crystallization effect. Figure 9.8 compares the temperature and crystallinity of a polyolefin

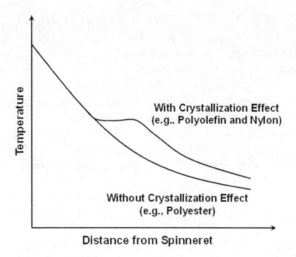

Figure 9.7. Evolution of filament temperature along the spinline.

or nylon filament along the spinline. The shoulder at the temperature-distance curve occurs at the same point when the crystallization starts. In some cases, the crystallization effect is so significant a slight increase in filament temperature can be observed.

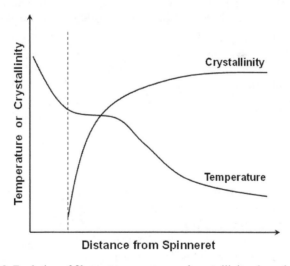

Figure 9.8. Evolution of filament temperature and crystallinity along the spinline.

9.1.4 MOLECULAR ORIENTATION

Molecular orientation is critically important for achieving good mechanical behavior for polymer fibers. The high degree of molecular orientation is produced mainly in the drawing step, which will be discussed in section 9.7. However, some orientation also is developed during the melt spinning process. As discussed in Chapter 8, the capillary flow of the polymer in the spinneret channels facilitates the orientation of polymer chains along the flow direction. However, compared with the molecular orientation developed along the spinline after the polymer exits from the spinneret, the degree of molecular orientation produced in the spinneret channels is insignificant due to the following two reasons:

1. The time for the polymer to pass through the spinneret channel is rather short and is not sufficient for the molecular orientation to be fully developed.
2. The polymer jet exiting from the spinneret is subject to relaxation, which is indicated by the die swell phenomenon. As a result, the molecular orientation developed in the spinneret is largely relaxed.

After the polymer is extruded from the spinneret, the elongational flow of the spinning filament leads to molecular orientation in both amorphous and crystalline phases. For the melt spinning of polyester fibers, the polymer crystallizes slowly and the molecular orientation developed along the spinline is contributed mainly by the amorphous phase. However, for polyolefin and nylon fibers, the rapid crystallization process determines that the molecular orientation involves both the amorphous and crystalline phases.

For uniaxial molecular orientation, an orientation factor can be used to describe the orientation of polymer chains relative to the filament axis. In general, the orientation factor (f) of a spinning filament is expressed by:

$$f = \frac{\overline{\alpha_z - \alpha_r}}{\alpha_1 - \alpha_2} = \frac{\overline{3\cos^2 \phi} - 1}{2} \tag{9.20}$$

where $\overline{\alpha_z - \alpha_r}$ is the mean difference between the components of the polarizability in the filament axial and radial directions, $\alpha_1 - \alpha_2$ the difference between the polarizability parallel to and perpendicular to the polymer chain segment, and ϕ the angle between the polymer chain axis and the filament axis. According to Equation 9.20, $f = 1$ and $\phi = 0$ when all polymer chains are oriented parallel to the filament axis, and $f = 0$ and $\phi = 54°44'$ when all polymer chains are randomly dispersed without molecular orientation.

One of the most convenient methods to study the molecular orientation in a filament is the use of birefringence. The birefringence (Δn) of a filament is basically the refractive index difference between the axial and radial directions:

$$\Delta n = n_z - n_r \tag{9.21}$$

where n_z and n_r are the reflective indices on the filament axial and radial directions, respectively. For fibers made from the same type of polymer, a higher birefringence value indicates a higher degree of molecular orientation.

By using the birefringence, the orientation factor of the spinning filament can be rewritten as:

$$f = \frac{\Delta n}{\Delta n_{intri}} \tag{9.22}$$

where Δn_{intri} is the intrinsic birefringence of the polymer, i.e., the maximum possible birefringence when all polymer chains are perfectly oriented along the filament axis. Since the orientation factor is proportional to the birefringence, many literature reports use the measurable birefringence to directly describe the molecular orientation of polymer fibers.

In the spinline, the birefringence of a completely amorphous filament is proportional to the applied tensile stress (σ_z):

$$\Delta n = C_{opt} \sigma_z \tag{9.23}$$

where C_{opt} is the stress optical coefficient. The applied tensile stress at the take-up device is measurable, and the applied tensile stress at a given point along the spinline can be calculated based on the force balance discussed in section 9.1.2. Therefore, the birefringence of a spinning filament can be obtained by Equation 9.23 as long as the stress optical coefficient is known. According to the rubber elasticity theory, the stress optical coefficient can be given by:

$$C_{opt} = k \frac{\left(n^2 + 2\right)^2}{nT} \left(\alpha_1 - \alpha_2\right) \tag{9.24}$$

where k is a constant, T the absolute temperature of the spinning filament, n is the average reflective index of the polymer, and $\alpha_1 - \alpha_2$ the difference between the polarizability parallel to and perpendicular to the polymer chain segment. Although the stress optical coefficient is inversely proportional to the absolute temperature, many literature reports treat it as a constant while analyzing the birefringence of spinning filaments.

When the molecular orientation of the crystallize phase is taken into consideration, the birefringence of the spinning filament can be expressed by:

$$\Delta n = \left(1 - \theta\right) f_a \Delta n_{intri,a} + \theta f_c \Delta n_{intri,c} + \Delta n_{form} \tag{9.25}$$

where θ is the degree of crystallinity, f_a and f_c the orientation factors of the amorphous and crystalline phases, $\Delta n_{intri,a}$ and $\Delta n_{intri,c}$ the intrinsic birefringences of the amorphous and crystalline phases, and Δ_{form} a form birefringence due to the interaction of the two phases with the light.

Figure 9.9 shows the evolution of birefringence or orientation factor along the spinline at different spinning speeds. The spinning speed affects the development of molecular orientation. With increase in spinning speed, the molecular orientation develops at an earlier time and the maximum orientation that can be developed in the spinline also is higher.

9.1.5 CRYSTALLIZATION

Similar to molecular orientation, the development of crystalline structure plays an important role in melt spinning. In general, the crystallization of polymers occurs between the glass transition temperature (T_g) and melting temperature (T_m). Literature reports show the crystallization could occur above the melting temperature, especially under high molecular orientation. However, the amount of such crystallization is small and has no apparent effect on the final structure and properties of most melt-spun fibers, and hence this chapter will only address the crystallization below T_m.

The crystallization of a polymer involves nucleation and growth processes. In an isothermal crystallization process, the crystallization occurs immediately when the temperature is lower than T_m. However, if the filament temperature is only slightly lower than T_m, the driving force for the nucleation process is low and the polymer crystallizes slowly. On the other hand, if the temperature is too low and is

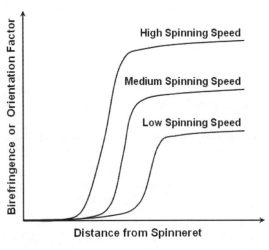

Figure 9.9. Evolution of filament birefringence or orientation factor along the spinline.

Table 9.1. T_m, T_g, T_{max}, and K_{max} of some polymers.

Polymer	T_m (°C)	T_g (°C)	T_{max} (°C)	K_{max} (sec^{-1})
Polypropylene	180	–20	65	0.55
Polyester, polyethylene terephthalate	267	67	190	1.6×10^{-2}
Nylon 6	228	45	146	0.14
Nylon 6,6	264	45	150	1.64

Sources: Ziabicki, A., *Fundamentals of Fiber Formation: the Science of Fibre Spinning and Drawing*, John Wiley & Sons, 1976.

close to the glass transition temperature, the growth of crystals is slow due to the lack of molecular mobility. As a result, the crystallization rate reaches its maximum at an intermediate temperature (T_{max}). Table 9.1 shows the values of T_m, T_g, T_{max}, and maximum crystallization rate (K_{max}) at T_{max} of polymers that commonly are used in melt spinning.

In melt spinning, the crystallization process in the spinning filament involves very high cooling rates (up to 10^3–10^{4}°C/s) and hence it is absolutely non-isothermal. Increasing the cooling rate reduces the time for the polymer to crystallize at a given temperature. Therefore, the polymer crystallization process mainly occurs at temperatures much lower than the melting temperature. If the cooling rate is sufficiently high, the polymer may not crystallize even at the temperature of maximum crystallization rate.

Figure 9.10 shows the so-called "continuous cooling transformation diagram", i.e., the relationship between cooling condition and crystallization kinetics, of a polymer under quiescent condition. In the diagram, the cooling curves are plotted

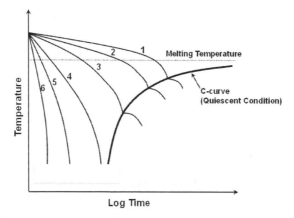

Figure 9.10. Continuous cooling transformation diagram under quiescent condition. A higher number on the cooling curve indicates a higher cooling rate.

for a polymer on temperature versus log time. The cool curves are numbers 1–6, with a higher number indicating a higher cooling rate. The "C curve" on the right bottom corner shows the start of crystallization under quiescent condition. As shown in Figure 9.10, with increase in cooling rate, the crystallization starts at a lower temperature, i.e., greater supercooling is required. If the cooling rates are very high and miss the "nose" of the c-curve, the crystallization will not happen and the resultant product will be completely amorphous (see curves 4, 5 and 6).

In melt spinning, the rate of crystallization is increased due to the development of molecular orientation under stress. As a result, the c-curve of the spinning filament is moved to shorter times. Figure 9.11 shows the continuous cooling transformation diagram of a spinning filament, which is under the tension created by the take-up device. For comparison, the c-curve of the polymer under quiescent condition also is shown in the figure using a dash line. It is seen the c-curve of the filament is shifted to the left, and as a result, the crystallization occurs at higher temperatures. For the cooling curves 4 and 5, the crystallization process does not occur under quiescent condition, but it can be initiated when the polymer is oriented in the spinning filament. The crystallization process in the spinning filament is called stress-induced crystallization or orientated crystallization since it is developed under tensile stress and is highly influenced by molecular orientation.

In the classical treatment, the crystallization kinetics, i.e., the crystallinity (θ)-time (t) relationship, of the isothermal crystallization process is described by the *Avrami equation*:

$$\theta = 1 - exp\left(-kt^{n}\right) \qquad (9.26)$$

where k is the crystallization rate constant, and n the Avrami index. Both k and n can be obtained from isothermal crystallization experiments. For the non-isothermal

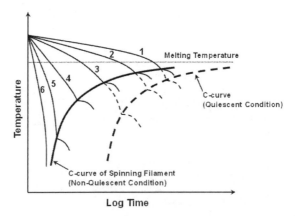

Figure 9.11. Continuous cooling transformation diagram of a spinning filament. A higher number on the cooling curve indicates a higher cooling rate.

crystallization process in melt spinning, the *Avrami equation* is modified by incorporating an "isokinetic approximation":

$$\theta = 1 - exp\left\{-\left[\int_{0}^{t} K\left(T\left(t'\right)\right) dt'\right]^{n}\right\}$$

(9.27)

where n is the same Avrami index derived from isothermal crystallization experiments, $T(t')$ the temperature at time t', and $K(T)$ the non-isothermal crystallization rate at temperature T. For practical treatments, Equation 9.27 often is rewritten to the following differential form:

$$\frac{d\theta}{dt} = nK(T)(1-\theta)\left[\ln\left(\frac{1}{1-\theta}\right)\right]^{\frac{n-1}{n}}$$

(9.28)

Here, the non-isothermal crystallization rate, $K(T)$, is related to the isothermal crystallization rate, $k(T)$, by:

$$K(T) = \left[k(T)\right]^{\frac{1}{n}}$$

(9.29)

Equation 9.28 can be used to describe the kinetics of non-isothermal crystallization process under quiescent condition. However, the crystallization process in the spinning filament is non-quiescent, and the molecular orientation developed under the tensile stress affects the crystallization rate. Therefore, the traditional non-isothermal crystallization rate, $K(T)$, must be replaced with the non-isothermal, stress-induced crystallization rate, $K(T,f)$, where f is the orientation factor. $K(T,f)$ also is called the total crystallization rate. With the total crystallization rate, Equation 9.28 can be rewritten to give:

$$\frac{d\theta}{dt} = nK(T,f)(1-\theta)\left[\ln\left(\frac{1}{1-\theta}\right)\right]^{\frac{n-1}{n}}$$

(9.30)

The relationship between the total crystallization rate and the orientation factor is given by:

$$K(T,f) = K(T,0)exp\left[A(T)f^{2}\right]$$

(9.31)

where $A(T)$ is an empirical parameter and is always positive. For example, the $A(T)$ value for polyester is 210 at 95°C and 940 at 115°C. Therefore, the stress-induced crystallization rate increases monotonically with increase in molecular orientation. Ziabicki suggested the value of $K(T,0)$ at quiescent condition can be approximated by:

$$K(T,0) = K_{max} exp\left[-4\ln\frac{2(T-T_{max})^2}{D^2}\right] \qquad (9.32)$$

where K_{max} is the rate constant at the temperature (T_{max}) of the maximum crystallization rate, and D the half-width of the K-T curve. Substituting Equation 9.32 into Equation 9.31 gives:

$$K(T,f) = K_{max} exp\left[-4\ln\frac{2(T-T_{max})^2}{D^2} + A(T)f^2\right] \qquad (9.33)$$

In addition to Equation 9.33, the total crystallization rate $K(T,f)$ also can be obtained by the combination of rubber elasticity theory and quiescent crystallization theory. For example, Katayama et al. and Patel et al. suggested the total crystallization rate also can obtained by:

$$K(T,f) = K_0 exp\left[-\frac{U^*}{R(T-T_\infty)}\right]exp\left[-\frac{C_0}{T\Delta T + C_1 T^2 f^2}\right] \qquad (9.34)$$

where K_0 and C_0 are constants obtained from quiescent crystallization kinetics data, C_1 a constant determined by back calculation from experimental data obtained from the melt spinline, U^* the activation energy for segmental jumping, R the gas constant, $T_\infty = T_g - 30$, and $\Delta T = T_m - T$.

With the knowledge of the total crystallization rate $K(T,f)$, the kinetics of the non-isothermal, stress-induced crystallization process in melt spinning can be described by using Equation 9.30. Figure 9.12 shows the development of crystallinity along the spinning filament. The crystallinity of the spinning filament increases with increase in spinning speed. Higher spinning speed leads to greater molecular orientation, which in turn promotes the crystallization process. However, the increased spinning speed also leads to higher cooling rate, resulting in lower crystallization temperature. In this case, the crystallization could decrease with increase in spinning speed.

9.1.6 CROSS-SECTIONAL EFFECTS

The analyses discussed in previous sections focus on the structural development along the filament axis with the assumption the cross-sectional structure is uniform. However, several factors could lead to a non-uniform cross-sectional

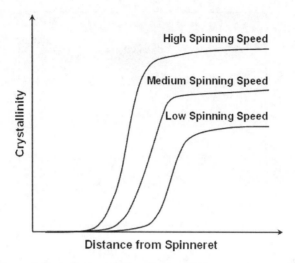

Figure 9.12. Evolution of filament crystallinity along the spinline.

structure for melt-spun filaments. One of the most important factors is the radial temperature gradient. The heat transfer in melt spinning starts from the surface of the spinning filament, and hence the center of the filament typically is hotter than the surface. Theoretical modeling results show the radial temperature gradient of the spinning filament could range from 10^3 to 10^{5}°C/cm. Such large temperature gradients cause variations of viscosity and stress in the fiber cross-section, which in turn lead to non-uniform distributions of molecular orientation and crystallinity. Figure 9.13 shows the variation of molecular orientation across the radial direction of a spinning filament. The skin of the filament has higher molecular orientation than the core. The radial distribution of the crystallinity is similar to that of the molecular orientation. In addition, the size and structure of the crystals also may vary along the radial direction in the cross-section.

Another important factor for causing the non-uniform cross-sectional structure is the cooling method. One commonly used cooling method is the cross air blow process (Figure 9.14). The effect of cross air blow on the molecular orientation distribution across the fiber cross-section is shown in Figure 9.15. Compared with the leeward direction, the cooling rate on the windward direction is greater, and hence the molecular orientation often is higher. Similarly, the distribution of crystallinity in the cross-section also is affected by the non-uniform cooling caused by cross air blow.

The cooling process also can be affected by the cross-sectional shape of the spinning filament. When a non-circular filament is being spun, the cooling process is non-uniform in the cross-section and different parts of the cross-section can exhibit different degrees of molecular orientation and crystallinity.

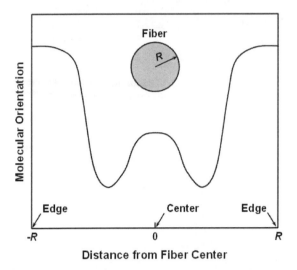

Figure 9.13. Radial distribution of molecular orientation in a filament cross-section.

9.1.7   MULTIFILAMENT EFFECTS

In practical melt spinning, multi filaments are extruded simultaneously from the spinneret. During that process, the conditions applied to each filament may vary. For example, the hot filaments can heat the cooling air as it passes through the multifilament bundle, and as a result the filaments on the leeward side of the bundle experience slower cooling rates than those on the windward side. The high-speed filaments also may impart an axial velocity to the incoming air and

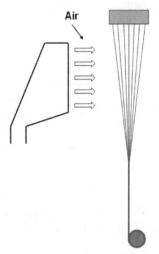

Figure 9.14. Schematic of cross air blow process.

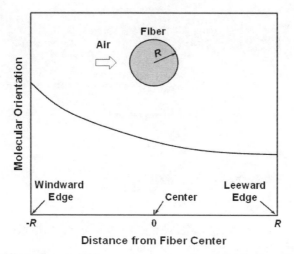

Figure 9.15. Effect of cross air blow on the cross-sectional distribution of molecular orientation in a filament.

reduce the transverse velocity in the cross-blow direction, which in turn lead to variations in drag forces created by the cooling air. As a result, the structure and properties vary from one filament to another in the multifilament bundle.

Although multifilament effects are important, there are few literature reports on this topic mainly because of the complexities associated with accurately describing the heat transfer and dynamics during multifilament spinning. The interested reader is referred to the original works by Yasuda et al. (1978), Ishihara et al. (1989), and Dutta (1987).

9.2   SOLUTION SPINNING

Solution spinning can be used to produce fibers from polymers that do not form thermally stable melts, but can be dissolved in solvents. Two important solution spinning methods are dry spinning and wet spinning. Dry spinning typically is used for polymers that are soluble in volatile solvents. Wet spinning often is used for polymers that are dissolved in non-volatile or thermally unstable solvents.

9.2.1   *Dry Spinning*

Figure 9.16 shows a schematic of the dry spinning process. The spinning solution is delivered into the multi-hole spinneret by a metering pump at an accurately controlled rate. The spinneret often is placed in an enclosed drying tower for solvent recovery. Upon exiting the spinneret, the polymer solution comes into contact with a stream of hot inert gas (typically, air), and the solvent evaporates. The hot gas carries most, if not all, of the solvent evaporated from the polymer

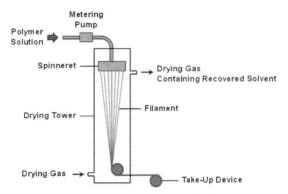

Figure 9.16. Schematic of the dry spinning process.

solution and leaves the drying tower. During this process, the polymer concentration in the filaments increases and the filaments solidify. Dry spinning (100–800 meters per minute) is faster than wet spinning, but slower than melt spinning.

Examples of dry-spun fibers are polyacrylonitrile, polyvinyl chloride, cellulose acetate fibers, among others. Solvents used in dry spinning typically have low boiling point and low vaporization heat. Solvents also should be thermally stable, easily recoverable, nontoxic, and non-explosive. Examples of solvents used in dry spinning include but are not limited to alcohols, acetone, ether, and tetrahydrofuran. For effective solvent evaporation and recovery, the drying gas often is heated and the inlet gas temperature varies from 100 to 250°C, depending on the nature of polymer and solvent. To reduce the amount of solvent used, concentrated polymer solutions are preferred, if possible. Typically, polymer concentrations range from 15 to 40% in practical dry spinning.

The engineering analysis of dry spinning is complex. Compared with melt spinning, dry spinning involves an additional process — mass transfer. The mechanisms of mass transfer in dry spinning include: 1) flash vaporization that takes place at the spinneret exit as a result of decompression of the heated polymer solution, 2) diffusion of solvent within the spinline, and 3) convection of solvent from the spinline surface to the dry gas medium. The mass transfer affects the force balance and energy balance. In the force balance, both the inertial force and drag force are different from those in melt spinning. In the energy balance, the latent heat of solvent vaporization and the convective heat transfer have to be included. For detailed discussion, the interested reader is referred to the works published by Ziabicki (1976), Ohzawa and Nagano (1970), and Gou and McHugh (2004).

9.2.2 WET SPINNING

Figure 9.17 shows the most basic wet spinning process. The spinneret is placed in the spinning bath, which contains a liquid that is miscible with the solvent in the

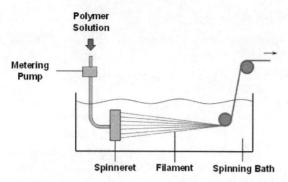

Figure 9.17. Schematic of a basic wet spinning process.

polymer solution, but cannot dissolve the polymer. During spinning, the polymer solution is extruded from the spinneret into the spinning bath and the polymer is precipitated to form solid filaments. The solvent in the polymer solution is removed in the spinning bath by the counter-diffusion mechanism.

There are many different designs of the wet spinning systems. The spinning bath can be situated horizontally or vertically. In vertical spinning bath, the filaments can move upward or downward. In addition to the spinning bath shown in Figure 9.17, more coagulating baths may be needed to remove the solvent, and sometimes further manufacturing steps (e.g., drawing, washing, drying, heat-setting) are incorporated into the wet spinning process.

Wet spinning often is used to process polyacrylonitrile, polyvinyl chloride, polyvinyl alcohol, and cellulose fibers. Polymer concentrations used in wet spinning vary from 5 to 30%, which typically are lower than those in dry spinning. Compared with melt spinning and dry spinning, the wet spinning process has much lower spinning speeds, ranging from 50 to 300 meters per minutes. This is mainly because the filaments undergo much greater drag forces in the liquid baths.

The engineering analysis of the wet spinning process also is complex. During wet spinning, the skin of the filament is solidified first, and as a result, the mass transfer mainly involves the counter-diffusion of solvent and nonsolvent between the solidified skin and the solution core, and between the filament skin and the liquid bath. The solidification process and the diffusion rates are affected by the energy balance. For the force balance, some researchers believe the drag force is the main factor for determining the dynamics of wet spinning; however, others argue the rheological force also plays an important role. Another challenge in the engineering analysis is many physical constants that are needed to describe the wet spinning process are difficult to determine under the complex conditions in the liquid bath. The interested reader is referred to works by Han and Segal (1970), and Ziabicki (1976).

9.3   GEL SPINNING

Gel spinning, also known as dry-wet spinning, can be used to produce high-performance polymer fibers. Different forms of gel spinning are available. Figure 9.18 shows the schematic of a basic gel spinning process. The polymer solution is pumped into the spinneret, which is placed above the spinning bath to create an air gap of short distance. The extruded filaments first pass through the air gap, which is similar to the dry spinning process, and then into the spinning bath, like in the wet spinning. The process allows the formation of gel filaments by thermoreversible gelation. These gel filaments have sufficient mechanical stability and are transferred into an oven to be drawn to high-performance fibers.

For melt and solution spinning processes, the drawing step also is necessary to achieve high molecular orientation and good mechanical properties, and the effects of drawing will be discussed in section 9.7. However, the drawing for gel spinning is unique and is highlighted here. In general, the as-spun gel filaments still contain a large amount of solvent and form swollen networks joined by small crystalline regions (Figure 9.19). The drawing of such gel filaments typically is carried out at an elevated temperature in an oven. Although drawing is possible after complete removal of the solvent prior to the drawing step, the presence of solvent during drawing can help facilitate the movement of polymer chains and lead to extremely high molecular orientation in gel-spun fibers after drawing (Figure 9.20).

Gel spinning enables the production of high-performance fibers from polymers with flexible polymer chains, such as ultra-high molecular weight polyethylene (UHMW-PE). To form gel filaments, the concentration of polymer solution is typically low, e.g., 1–2% for UHMW-PE. The maximum attainable draw ratio (λ_{max}) is related to the initial polymer concentration (c) by:

$$\lambda_{max} \propto c^{-0.5} \tag{9.35}$$

Therefore, lower polymer concentration leads to higher draw ratio, which is beneficial for achieving ultra-high molecular orientation.

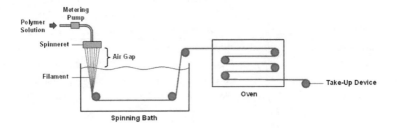

Figure 9.18. Schematic of a basic gel spinning process.

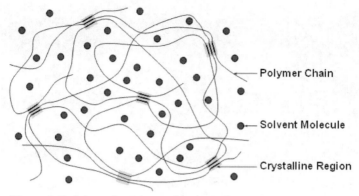

Figure 9.19. Schematic of the swollen network structure in a gel filament.

9.4 LIQUID CRYSTAL SPINNING

High-performance fibers also can be obtained by the spinning of liquid crystalline polymers. Liquid crystals are highly structured liquids, with orientational (nematic and cholesteric) or positional (smectic) order of molecules (Figure 9.21). Liquid crystallinity in polymers may be realized either by dissolving a polymer in a solvent (i.e., lyotropic liquid crystalline polymers) or by heating a polymer above its glass or melting transition point (i.e., thermotropic liquid crystalline polymers). Rod-shaped liquid crystalline polymer chains can make high-performance fibers because it is easy to orient these polymer chains in the fiber longitudinal direction, without chain folding.

Figure 9.22 shows the unusual concentration dependence of the solution viscosity of lyotropic liquid crystalline polymers. With increase in polymer concentration, the viscosity first increases. However, the viscosity decreases rapidly after the concentration reaches a critical value. This is because at low concentrations, the liquid crystalline phase has not been formed and the polymer solution is isotropic, without ordered distribution of polymer chains. The viscosity of the isotropic solution increases with increasing polymer concentration. When the

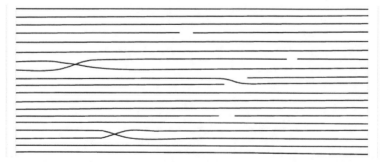

Figure 9.20. Schematic of the high molecular orientation in a gel-spun fiber.

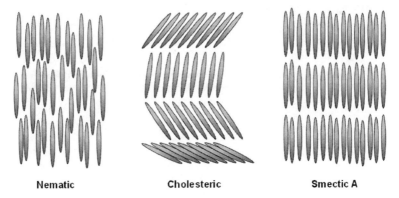

| Nematic | Cholesteric | Smectic A |

Figure 9.21. Nematic, cholesteric and smectic phases of liquid crystals.

concentration reaches the critical value, the liquid crystalline phase is formed and the orientational order of polymer chains reduces the resistance to flow, thereby leading to lower viscosity. For thermotropic liquid crystalline polymers, the viscosity of the polymer melt also decreases rapidly at the temperature when the liquid crystalline phase appears.

Lyotropic liquid crystalline polymers can be spun into fibers by using a wet or gel spinning process, while thermotropic liquid crystalline polymers can be made into fibers by melt spinning. Although both lyotropic and thermotropic liquid crystalline polymers can be made into fibers, most successful liquid crystal fibers are based on lyotropic polymers. One such example is polyphenylene terephthalamide (PPTA, Kevlar®), which was first produced by DuPont in 1972.

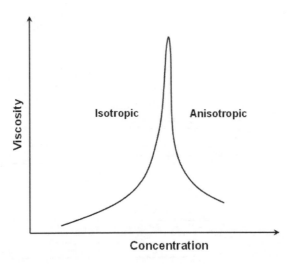

Figure 9.22. Viscosity-concentration relationship of lyotropic liquid crystal polymers.

Kevlar® fibers can be produced by a method that is similar to the gel spinning process (Figure 9.23). However, unlike the gel spinning of UHMW-PE fibers, in which low-concentration solutions are used, Kevlar® fibers are spun from high-concentration solutions, e.g., 20% PPTA in 80% sulfuric acid. In addition, the high molecular orientation of Kevlar® fibers is achieved directly from the liquid crystalline phase.

9.5 DISPERSION SPINNING

Dispersion spinning is used to produce fibers from polymers that are not soluble and can melt only at very high temperatures. For example, polytetrafluoroethylene ($T_m = 327°C$) cannot be spun into fibers by regular melt or solution spinning. To form fibers, fine polytetrafluoroethylene particles can be dispersed in an aqueous solution of destructible, fiber-forming polymer (e.g., polyvinyl alcohol) to make a homogenous dispersion. The dispersion then can be spun into fibers using dry or wet spinning. After the spinning process, a thermal-treatment step is applied to decompose the fiber-forming polymer and sinter or fuse polytetrafluoroethylene particles into fibers.

9.6 REACTION SPINNING

Reaction spinning of monomers or prepolymers can be used to form fibers from re-active starting materials. One good example for reaction spinning is the formation

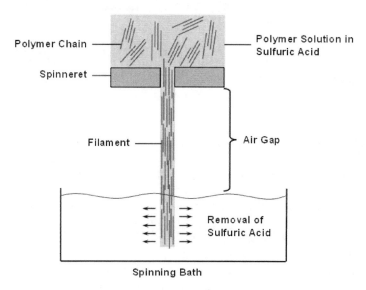

Figure 9.23. Spinning of Kevlar® fibers.

of spandex fibers. Some spandex fibers are produced by using two types of pre-polymers: one is a flexible macroglycol, while the other is a stiff diisocyanate. The macroglycol is a long chain polymer that has hydroxyl groups (-OH) on both ends. This macroglycol part of the spandex fiber is flexible and is responsible for its stretching characteristic. The diisocyanate is a shorter chain polymer, with isocyanate groups (-NCO) on both ends. The diisocyanate part of spandex is rigid and provides strength. During the fiber formation process, these two prepolymers are mixed in a solution with some additives and are forced through the spinneret. After exiting the spinneret, the filaments are heated in the presence of nitrogen and solvent and the two prepolymers react to form solidified spandex fibers.

9.7   DRAWING—AN IMPORTANT "POST-SPINNING" PROCESS

The spinning methods discussed in previous sections can convert polymer melts or solutions into fibers. In many cases, the mechanical properties of as-spun fibers are not sufficient for practical applications. The drawing process is, therefore, introduced to improve the properties of fibers by providing a large, irreversible elongation to as-spun fibers in the solid state to 20–8000% of their original lengths. This elongation enables the extension and parallelization of polymer chains and crystallites along the fiber axial direction, and the molecular orientation developed in drawing often is accompanied by changes in phase structure, such as crystallization or partial destruction of crystallites, and in other structural characteristics.

9.7.1   MODES OF DRAWING

In laboratory research, the drawing of fibers can be conducted by using tensile testing apparatus with a furnace surrounding the fibers. The drawing typically is carried at constant extension or strain rates. However, in most commercial fiber production processes, drawing is carried out continuously either directly after the spinning or else in a separate step with undrawn filaments previously collected on drums, bobbins, etc. During such drawing, the undrawn filaments are supplied at a constant velocity via a rotating feed roll, and taken up on another roll (or rolls) at higher velocities, thereby resulting in the elongation of the filaments in proportion to the draw ratio, i.e., the ratio of the take-up and feed velocities. Depending on the polymer type, the drawing can be carried out in air at room temperature (e.g., nylon), in a hot air chamber (e.g., polyvinyl alcohol), on contact with a hot plate or drums (e.g., polyester), or in liquid baths that contain plasticizers and/or other agents (e.g., acrylic).

The limitation of the laboratory tensile experiments at constant extension or strain rates is the maximum strain rate of tensile testing instruments is one order of magnitude lower than that of the continuous force drawing process used in commercial production. As a result, the differences in the magnitude and kinetics of the structural development in laboratory tensile experiments and commercial drawing process are significant. However, results from laboratory tensile experiments have provided important fundamental understanding on the structural development of filaments during drawing, and they have helped interpret the structure changes of filaments under the more complex drawing in commercial production.

9.7.2 DRAWING OF INITIALLY AMORPHOUS FILAMENTS

Some polymers (e.g., polyester) have slow crystallization kinetics, and they may not have sufficient time to crystallize during spinning. As a result, as-spun filaments made from such polymers are amorphous before drawing. However, during drawing, the development of molecular orientation reduces the energy barrier between the amorphous and crystalline states, permitting crystallization at temperatures where none would occur in the undrawn filaments.

Figure 9.24 shows the development of molecular orientation and crystallinity of initially amorphous fibers. At low draw ratios, the polymer does not crystallize,

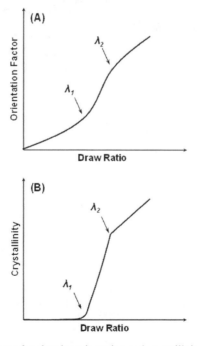

Figure 9.24. Development of molecular orientation and crystallinity of initially amorphous filaments.

but molecular orientation is being developed. At a critical draw ratio (λ_1), the strain-induced crystallization occurs, and both crystallinity and molecular orientation develop rapidly. There is a second critical draw ratio (λ_2), after which the development of molecular orientation and crystallinity slows down. The critical draw ratio λ_1 is determined by the onset of the crystallization process. The critical ratio λ_2 indicates the degree of crystallinity has reached a point, where some of tie molecules between crystallites are fully extended (Figure 9.25). The slowing of orientation and crystallization at draw ratios greater than λ_2 is the result of the formation of taut inter-crystalline tie molecules, which hinder the uncoiling and disentangling of neighboring tie-chains that are not fully extended. The formation of taut tie molecules between crystallites can be demonstrated by rapidly increasing stress required to maintain the constant strain rate at draw ratios greater than λ_2 in laboratory tensile experiments (Figure 9.26).

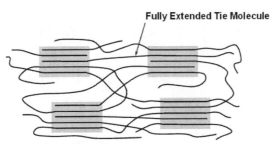

Figure 9.25. Schematic of the formation of fully extended tie molecules between crystallites at high draw ratios.

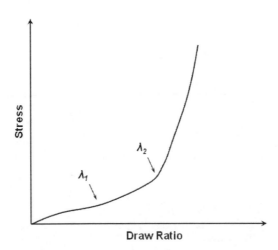

Figure 9.26. Stress-draw ratio curve of initially amorphous filaments in laboratory tensile experiments.

9.7.3 DRAWING OF CRYSTALLIZED FILAMENTS

Many as-spun filaments already are crystallized prior to drawing. For example, undrawn polyethylene and polypropylene fibers often exhibit high level of crystallinity, ranging from 50 to 80%. The degree of crystallinity in undrawn nylon filaments is lower, but it still can reach 35%. However, the crystallites in these filaments are either un-oriented or only have a low orientation degree, and as a result, the mechanical properties of crystallized filaments prior to drawing still are unsatisfactory. By applying the drawing process, the molecular orientation and crystallinity of crystallized filaments can be further improved, leading to higher mechanical properties.

Figure 9.27 shows the development of amorphous and crystalline phases in crystallized filaments. The drawing process increases the molecular orientation for both amorphous and crystalize phases. In general, at low draw ratios, the amorphous phase in the filaments is deformed first and the molecular orientation of the amorphous phase increases. The deformation of the crystalline phase becomes significant when the tie molecules between the adjacent crystallites are highly extended. The deformation of the crystalline phase starts with the increase of the crystallite thickness, followed by the tilting of the crystalline phase. With increase in draw ratio, large crystallites may break up under stress to form smaller fibril-like crystallites. These newly-formed fibrils still are attached to each other by tie molecules, and they slide against each other to align along the drawing direction.

The increased molecular orientation also induces higher degree of crystallinity, especially when the drawing is conducted above the glass transition temperature. Figure 9.28 shows the contents of amorphous and crystalline phases in crystallized

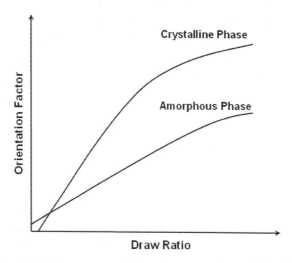

Figure 9.27. Development of molecular orientation in both amorphous and crystalline phases of crystallized filaments.

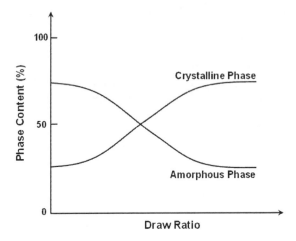

Figure 9.28. Change of phase contents during drawing of crystallized filaments.

filaments. With increase in draw ratio, more amorphous phase is converted into crystalline phase. Studies also show that, in certain crystalline polymers, drawing could cause the transformation of one crystal morphology to another.

9.8 HEAT TREATMENT AFTER DRAWING

The drawing process introduces some instabilities to the fiber structure and properties. For example, the formation of high molecular orientation and the destruction of original crystallites lead to a thermodynamically unstable system, which, given enough time, tends toward some equilibrium by changing structural characteristics, including fiber dimensions, crystallinity, molecular orientation, etc. At room temperature, the changes usually are slow unless stimulated by swelling agents. At elevated temperatures, the changes could occur quickly.

One effective approach to stabilize the fiber structure and properties is to apply a heat treatment process after drawing. This post-drawing process often is called "heat setting". The purpose of the heat treatment is to:

1.   stabilize the fiber dimensions,
2.   equilibrate the crystalline structure,
3.   improve the mechanical properties, and/or
4.   modify the chemical structure, e.g., thermal crosslinking of polyvinyl alcohol fibers.

Depending on the polymer structure and fiber type, the heat treatment process can be carried out by using dry air, water vapor, solid heating elements, or heated liquid baths. Swelling agents (e.g., water) can be used to promote solvent-induced molecular motions, which accelerate the structural stabilization. The heat treatment temperature should be higher than the use temperature of the fibers to ensure their stability under application conditions. Depending on the desired mechanical properties, the heat treatment can be conducted in a free state or under tension. In general, the heat treatment in a free state is more effective in minimizing the residual shrinkage, but the treatment under tension is effective in reducing the strain-at-break.

REFERENCES

[1] Baird, D.G., and Collias, D.I., *Polymer Processing: Principles and Design*, John Wiley & Sons, 1998.

[2] Barham, P.J., and Keller, A., "Review: High-Strength Polyethylene Fibres from Solution and Gel Spinning", *Journal of Materials Science*, 20, 2281–2302, 1985.

[3] Cheng, S.Z.D., Li, F., Li, C.Y., McCreight, K.W., Yoon, Y., and Harris, F.W., "Fibers from Liquid Crystalline Polymers", in *Structure Formation in Polymeric Fibers*, Editor Salem, D.R., Hanser Gardner Publications Inc, 2000.

[4] Cuculo, J.A., Hotter, J.F., and Zhou, Q., "Advances in the Control of Spinline Dynamics for Enhanced Properties", in *Structure Formation in Polymeric Fibers*, Editor Salem, D.R., Hanser Gardner Publications Inc., 2000.

[5] Dutta, A., "Role of Quench Air Profiles in Multifilament Melt Spinning of PET Fibers", *Textile Research Journal*, 57, 13–19, 1987.

[6] George, H.H., "Spinline Crystallization of Polyethylene Terephthalate", in *High-Speed Fiber Spinning: Science and Engineering Aspects*, Editors Ziabicki A., and Kawai, H., Krieger Publishing Company, 1991.

[7] Gou, Z, and McHugh, A.J., "Dry Spinning of Polymer Fibers in Ternary Systems—Part I: Model Development Predictions", *International Polymer Processing*, 19, 244–253, 2004.

[8] Gou, Z, and McHugh, A.J., "Dry Spinning of Polymer Fibers in Ternary Systems—Part II: Data Correlation and Predictions", *International Polymer Processing*, 19, 254–261, 2004.

[9] Gou, Z., McHugh, A.J., "Two-Dimensional Modeling of Dry Spinning of Polymer Fibers", *Journal of Non-Newtonian Fluid Mechanics*, 118, 121–136, 2004.

[10] Han, C.D., *Rheology and Processing of Polymeric Materials: Volume II: Polymer Processing*, Oxford University Press, 2007.

[11]   Han, C.D., and Segai, L., "A Study of Fiber Extrusion in Wet Spinning. I. Experimental Determination of Elongational Viscosity", *Journal of Applied Polymer Science*, 14, 2973–2998, 1970.

[12]   Han, C.D., and Segai, L., "A Study of Fiber Extrusion in Wet Spinning. II. Effects of Spinning Conditions on Fiber Formation", *Journal of Applied Polymer Science*, 14, 2999–3019, 1970.

[13]   Ishihara, H., Hayashi, S., and Ikeuchi, H., "Computer-Simulation of Multi Filament Air Jet Melt Spinning", *International Polymer Processing*, 4, 91–95, 1989.

[14]   Kase, S., "Mathematical Simulation of Melt Spinning Dynamics: Steady-State Conditions and Transient Behavior", in *High-Speed Fiber Spinning: Science and Engineering Aspects*, Editors Ziabicki A., and Kawai, H., Krieger Publishing Company, 1991.

[15]   Kase, S., and Matsuo, T., "Studies on Melt Spinning. I. Fundamental Equations on the Dynamics of Melt Spinning", *Journal of Polymer Science: Part A*, 3, 2541–2554, 1965.

[16]   Kase, S., and Matsuo, T., "Studies on Melt Spinning. II. Steady-State and Transient Solutions of Fundamental Equations Compared with Experimental Results", *Journal of Applied Polymer Science*, 11, 251–287, 1967.

[17]   Katayama, K., and Yoon, M.G., "Polymer Crystallization in Melt Spinning: Mathematical Simulation", in *High-Speed Fiber Spinning: Science and Engineering Aspects*, Editors Ziabicki A., and Kawai, H., Krieger Publishing Company, 1991.

[18]   Kubo, S., "Air Boundary Layer on A Filament in High-Speed Spinning", in *High-Speed Fiber Spinning: Science and Engineering Aspects*, Editors Ziabicki A., and Kawai, H., Krieger Publishing Company, 1991.

[19]   Lemstra, P.J., Bastiaansen, C.W.M., and Rastogi, S., "Basic Aspects of Solution(Gel)-Spinning and Ultra-Drawing of Ultra-High Molecular Weight Polyethylene", in *Structure Formation in Polymeric Fibers*, Editor Salem, D.R., Hanser Gardner Publications Inc, 2000.

[20]   Matsui, M., "Fiber Formation Process in High-Speed Spinning of Polyethylene Terephthalate", in *High-Speed Fiber Spinning: Science and Engineering Aspects*, Editors Ziabicki A., and Kawai, H., Krieger Publishing Company, 1991.

[21]   Nakamura, K., Watanabe, H., Katayama, K., and Amano, T., "Some Aspects of Nonisothermal Crystallization of Polymers. I. Relationship between Crystallization Temperature, Crystallinity, and Cooling Conditions", *Journal of Applied Polymer Science*, 16, 1077–1091, 1972.

[22] Ohzawa, Y., and Nagano, Y., "Studies on Dry Spinning. II. Numerical Solutions for Some Polymer–Solvent Systems Based on the Assumption That Drying is Controlled by Boundary-Layer Mass Transfer", *Journal of Applied Polymer Science*, 14, 11179–1899 (1970).

[23] Patel, R.M., and Spruiell, J.E., "Crystallization Kinetics during Polymer Processing - Analysis of Available Approaches for Process Modeling", *Polymer Engineering and Science*, 31, 730–738, 1991.

[24] Salem, D.R., "Structure Formation during Drawing of Flexible Chain Polymers", in *Structure Formation in Polymeric Fibers*, Editor Salem, D.R., Hanser Gardner Publications Inc, 2000.

[25] Smook, J., and Pennings, A.J., "Preparation of Ultra-High Strength Polyethylene Fibres by Gel-Spinning/Hot Drawing at High Spinning Rates", *Polymer Bulletin*, 9, 75–85, 1983.

[26] Spruiell, J.E., "Structure Formation during Melt Spinning", in *Structure Formation in Polymeric Fibers*, Editor Salem, D.R., Hanser Gardner Publications Inc, 2000.

[27] Yasuda, H., Ishihara, H., and Yanagawa, H., "Computer Simulation of Melt Spinning and Its Application to the Actual Process", *Sen-I-Gakkaishi*, 34, 20–27, 1978.

[28] Ziabicki, A., *Fundamentals of Fiber Formation: the Science of Fibre Spinning and Drawing*, John Wiley & Sons, 1976.

[29] Ziabicki, A., "The Mechanisms of 'Neck-Like' Deformation in High-Speed Melt Spinning. 1. Rheological and Dynamic Factors", *Journal of Non-Newtonian Fluid Mechanics*, 30, 141–155, 1988.

[30] Ziabicki, A., "The Mechanisms of Neck-Like Deformation in High-Speed Melt Spinning .2. Effects of Polymer Crystallization", *Journal of Non-Newtonian Fluid Mechanics*, 30, 157–168, 1988.

[31] Ziabicki, A., and Jarecki, L., "The Theory of Molecular Orientation and Oriented Crystallization in High Speed Spinning", in *High-Speed Fiber Spinning: Science and Engineering Aspects*, Editors Ziabicki A., and Kawai, H., Krieger Publishing Company, 1991.

PROBLEMS

1. What are the main processing parameters that affect the structure of melt-spun fibers?

2. What are the forces that a spinning filament experiences during melt spinning? Which one is the dominating force?
3. Describe the evolution of filament velocity along the spinline during melt spinning.
4. What are the three heat transfer mechanisms? Which one is the dominating mechanism for melt spinning?
5. Describe the evolution of filament temperature along the spinline during melt spinning.
6. What is birefringence and what is its relationship with molecular orientation?
7. Describe the evolution of molecular orientation along the spinline during melt spinning.
8. Describe the evolution of crystallinity along the spinline during melt spinning.
9. Compare the structural evaluation of nylon, polyolefin and polyester filaments during melt spinning.
10. How does the physical structure vary along the radial direction of the cross-section of a melt-spun fiber?
11. Describe dry spinning and wet spinning.
12. Compare the pros and cons of melt spinning, dry spinning, and wet spinning.
13. What is gel spinning? Describe the unique features of gel spinning.
14. What is liquid crystal spinning? Describe the unique features of liquid crystal spinning.
15. Describe the development of molecular orientation and crystallinity while drawing an initially amorphous filament.
16. Describe the development of molecular orientation in both amorphous and crystalline phases while drawing a crystallized filament.
17. What are the possible effects of the "heat setting" process?
18. Several methods can be used to obtain high-performance synthetic fibers. Give three examples.

CHAPTER 10

Formation of Natural Polymer Fibers

The fiber formation processes of natural cellulose and protein fibers are controlled by the genetic codes and are complex. Humans can only have limited influence on the fiber formation processes by selectively adjusting the environmental conditions, such as climate, soil, water source, farming method, etc. On the other hand, manufactured cellulose and protein fibers are formed by using methods similar to those for making synthetic fibers. The processing conditions of these fibers can be adjusted to manipulate the fiber structure and properties.

10.1 NATURAL CELLULOSE FIBERS

Cotton is the most important natural cellulose fiber in the world. For the last twenty years, about 40% of the fiber consumed worldwide is cotton. This section focuses on the formation of cotton fibers.

10.1.1 TYPES OF COTTON

Cotton fibers are seed hairs from plants belonging to the order Malvales, family Malvaceae, tribe Gossypieae, and genus *Gossypium*. There are thirty-three recognized species, but only four are grown on a commercial scale in the world. These four species of cotton are: *hirsutum*, *barbadense*, *aboreum*, and *herbaceum*.

Gossypium hirsutum was developed in the United States from cotton that is native to Central America, Caribbean and Mexico. Currently, about 90% of cotton produced worldwide is *G. hirsutum*. The length of *G. hirsutum* lint fibers ranges from 25 to 36 mm and is suitable for apparel, home furnishing, and industry applications.

Gossypium barbadense is of South American origin and has the longest lengths, ranging from 33 to 36 mm. Egypt and Sudan are the largest producers of *G. barbadense* fibers, but the United States and South America also produce some. *G. barbadense* fibers provide 8% of current world cotton production and are mainly used for high-quality apparel, luxury fabrics, and specialty yarns.

Gossypium arboretum and *Gossypium herbaceum* are Old World cottons that are native to India and Pakistan, and Southern Africa and the Arabian Peninsula, respectively. Both cottons are short (9.5–19 mm) and coarse. They mainly are produced in South Asia and Southeast Asia.

Some cotton species (e.g., *G. hirsutum*) produce two types of fibers: lint fibers and linters (or fuzz fibers). The lint fibers are long (e.g., 25 mm or longer) and thin and can be removed from the seed surfaces easily. On the other hand, linters are short (15 mm or shorter) and coarse, and they are tightly adhered to the seed. Due to the differences in fiber lengths and diameters, lint fibers are suitable for making textile fabrics, but fuzz fibers are not suitable for textile processing. However, fuzz fibers still can be used for batting and padding in bedding, automobile applications, paper making, chemical feed stock for making plastics and rayons, etc.

Traditionally, varietal development of cottons was confined to the breeding methods that depend on crossing parents within species. However, modern biotechnology has enabled the production of biotech or transgenic cottons. The initial biotech cottons were developed for insect resistance and herbicide tolerance. Currently, biotech cottons have been or are being developed to have properties, such as good stress tolerance, high yield potential, improved agronomic performance, etc.

Although there are many different types of cottons, the formation process of cotton fibers is basically the same, as discussed below.

10.1.2 Formation of Cotton

Cotton fibers are the dried cell walls of formerly living cells, which are believed to be the largest single cells in nature. These living cells are the seed coat hairs that outgrow from individual epidermal cells on the outer integument of the ovules in the cotton fruit. Typically, the cotton flower only blooms for one day and becomes senescent afterward. On the day of full bloom, or anthesis, the petals of cotton flower are creamy white (Figure 10.1A), but they quickly change to yellow, then pink, and eventually, dark red. After two or three days, the flower petals wither and fall off from the developing green pod, i.e., the so-called "cotton boll" (Figure 10.1B). Inside the boll, moist cotton fibers are formed and push out from the ovule surfaces of the newly formed seeds. As the fibers continue to grow, the cotton boll turns to brown. Eventually, the boll opens and the fluffy cotton fibers burst forth (Figure 10.1C).

The formation and growth of cotton fibers can be divided into four overlapping but distinct stages, as described below:

> **Stage 1—Initiation:** In general, each cotton boll contains 20–30 ovules, spread in three to five segmented compartments (locules). The ovules are attached to the plant by a connection called the funiculus. On, or slightly before the day of anthesis, the initiation of lint fibers begins from the epidermal cells on the ovule surfaces. Typically, lint fiber development starts at the more rounded end of the seed and proceeds around the seed surface to the micropyle. Approximately, lint fiber cells outgrow from one out of every four epidermal cells. At the initiation stage, the lint fiber cells exhibit a bulbous appearance and are visible above the formerly smooth ovule epidermal surface (Figure 10.2). For some cotton species (e.g., *G. hirsutum*), a second type of fiber cells (linters) begin growing after about six or seven days. The distribution of the lint fibers and linters over the seed surface is neither uniform nor random. In general, the base of the seed produces more lint fibers, but the cells near the tip of the seed mostly produce linters. For other cotton species (e.g., *G. barbadense*), linters are not formed.

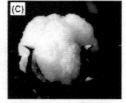

Figure 10.1. Photographs of (A) cotton flower, (B) cotton boll, and (C) open cotton boll. (Provided by Jeffery C. Silvertooth, The University of Arizona.)

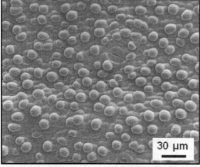

Figure 10.2. SEM image of cotton seed surface with the initiation of lint fiber cells on the day of anthesis. (Hsieh, Y.L., in *Cotton: Science and Technology*, Editors Gordon, S., et al., Woodhead Publishing Limited, 2007.)

Stage 2—Elongation: The elongation of fiber cells begins on the day of anthesis by spherical expansion above the ovular surface and this process continues for 15 to 20 days (Figure 10.3). Initially, the cell elongation orients against the micropyle end of the ovule, but it becomes spiral after two or three days. The primary cell walls continue to elongate, reaching the final fiber lengths in 21–35 days post anthesis. The formation rate of cellulose chains in primary cell walls is around 2 ng/min in this stage. The cellulose microfibrils formed in the primary wall are randomly oriented. The primary cell walls are very thin (0.2 to 0.4 μm) and are covered by a waxy layer or cuticle which provides water resistance to the fiber cells as they grow. The maximum potential length of fiber cells is controlled genetically by different cotton genotypes, but environmental conditions during cell elongation can change the ability of fiber cells to reach their full potential length.

State 3—Secondary Wall Thickening and Maturation: The formation of secondary walls starts around 15 to 20 days post anthesis, and continues for 30 to 45 days until the cell walls are 2–6 μm thick. By the time of fiber mature, more than 90% of the dry weight of the fiber is cellulose, and a lumen also is formed at the center of the fiber. The cellulose formation rate for secondary walls is around 130 nm/min, which is significantly higher than that of primary walls. In addition, the molecular weight of secondary wall cellulose is higher than that of primary wall cellulose. In secondary walls, cellulose microfibrils are subsequently deposited in a helical conformation. Periodically, the orientation gyre of the helical microfibrils changes and creates weak points where fiber breakage is likely under tension. The orientation of microfibrils in secondary walls is an important factor in determining the fiber strength, and it is regulated by the structural orientation in the cytoplasm collectively called the cytoskeleton. At the time of fiber mature, the newly formed cylindrical cotton fibers are fully hydrated and exhibit high intrinsic mobility and porosity in their structure.

State 4—Desiccation: At the last stage, the cotton boll opens and the fibers are desiccated. The desiccation of cotton fibers involves the removal of

Figure 10.3. SEM images of cotton seed surface at the beginning of elongation of fiber cells in one and two days post anthesis. (Hsieh, Y.L., in *Cotton: Science and Technology*, editors Gordon, S., et al., Woodhead Publishing Limited, 2007.)

fluids from the lumens and the loss of intermolecular water from the cellulose. The removal of fluids causes the cylindrical fibers to collapse, thereby leading to the kidney-bean cross-sectional shape and flat, twisted longitudinal structure of dried cotton fibers. The loss of intermolecular water reduces the intermolecular distance between cellulose chains and promotes the formation of intermolecular hydrogen bonds. The collapse of cylindrical fibers and the formation of hydrogen bonds result in irreversible morphology changes, such as increased structural heterogeneity, decreased porosity, and reduced sorption capacity. In addition, the structural changes also lead to an increase in the molecular strains and this ultimately reduces the chain mobility. As a result, these irreversible changes determine the final mechanical properties and surface chemistry of cotton fibers.

The desiccation process completes the formation of cotton fibers, which then can be harvested. Cotton fibers then are separated from the seeds by using a process, called ginning. The ginning process, which can be considered as a part of the harvesting, normally includes conditioning, seed-fiber separation, cleaning, and packaging. After ginning, the cotton fibers then can be turned into different final products by using different processing methods.

10.2 MANUFACTURED CELLULOSE FIBERS

Manufactured cellulose fibers are the first man-made fibers ever produced starting with Rayon fibers and the viscose process invented in late 1800s. Currently, manufactured cellulose fibers are produced by either derivative methods or direct methods. In derivative methods, cellulose polymer chains are chemically modified to form cellulose derivatives, which then are dissolved and spun into fibers. In the direct methods, special solvent systems are used without the chemical modification of the cellulose chains.

10.2.1 DERIVATIVE METHODS

Due to the considerable hydrogen bonding, high molecular weight, and complex crystalline and amorphous structures, cellulose does not melt nor does it dissolve in common organic solvents. Therefore, the production of manufactured cellulose fibers often starts by derivatizing the cellulose polymer chains by chemical approaches.

Among various derivative methods, the viscose process, invented by Cross, Bevan and Beadle in 1892, still is dominating in commercial cellulose fiber production with an annual production of more than 2 million tons. Figure 10.4 shows the flow chart of the viscose process. The viscose process begins with the alkalization step, where the cellulose pulp is treated with an 18–20 % solution of NaOH

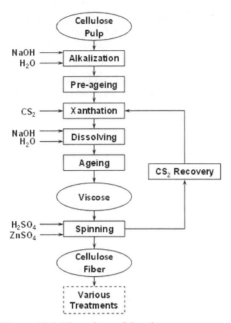

Figure 10.4. Flow chart of the viscose process.

at room temperature to form alkali cellulose. The following is the main reaction in the alkalization step:

$$\text{Cell—OH} + \text{NaOH} \longrightarrow \text{Cell—O}^- \text{Na}^+ + \text{H}_2\text{O} \tag{10.1}$$

The resultant alkali cellulose is pressed to remove most of the excess NaOH solution and is shredded to increase the surface area and make the material easier to process. The shredded alkali cellulose is pre-aged with the presence of oxygen in the ambient air to reduce and control the cellulose molecular weight. After reaching the desired molecular weight, carbon disulfide (CS_2) is added to the shredded alkali cellulose in a specially designed vessel called a Barette at 20–30°C for 1–3 hours to carry out the xanthation step, which leads to the formation of sodium cellulose xanthate. The following is the main reaction in the xanthation step:

$$\text{Cell—O}^- \text{Na}^+ + \text{CS}_2 \longrightarrow \text{Cell—O—}\overset{\overset{\text{S}}{\|}}{\text{C}}\text{—SNa} \tag{10.2}$$

The xanthation process is complex because in addition to Reaction 10.2, many side reactions occur simultaneously upon the addition of CS_2. The following are some important side reactions:

$$CS_2 + H_2O \longrightarrow HS\overset{\displaystyle S}{\overset{\|}{C}}OH \longrightarrow H_2S + COS \qquad (10.3)$$

$$COS + H_2O \longrightarrow HO\overset{\displaystyle S}{\overset{\|}{C}}OH \longrightarrow H_2S + CO_2 \qquad (10.4)$$

$$CO_2 + 2NaOH \longrightarrow Na_2CO_3 + H_2O \qquad (10.5)$$

$$H_2S + CS_2 \longrightarrow HS\overset{\displaystyle S}{\overset{\|}{C}}SH \xrightarrow{\ + 2NaOH\ } NaS\overset{\displaystyle S}{\overset{\|}{C}}SNa + 2H_2O \qquad (10.6)$$

$$NaS\overset{\displaystyle S}{\overset{\|}{C}}SNa + H_2SO_4 \longrightarrow Na_2SO_4 + CS_2 + H_2S \qquad (10.7)$$

After the xanthation step, the sodium cellulose xanthate crumb is dissolved into a 5–8 % NaOH solution below 10°C to form a yellow cellulose xanthate solution, i.e., the so-called viscose. The viscose is ripened (aged) over a period of several hours to several days to achieve a uniform distribution of xanthate groups in cellulose. After the ripening, the viscose is extruded through a spinneret into a spinning bath (coagulation bath), containing H_2SO_4, Na_2SO_4, and $ZnSO_4$. In the coagulation bath, the extrudate is first coagulated and subsequently regenerated into cellulose fibers. CS_2 is recovered and reused. The following is the main reaction during regeneration:

$$Cell\text{—}O\text{—}\overset{\displaystyle S}{\overset{\|}{C}}\text{—}SNa + H_2SO_4 \longrightarrow Cell\text{—}OH + CS_2 + NaHSO_4 \quad (10.8)$$

The structure and properties of viscose fibers can be controlled by selectively modifying the viscos process conditions. Fibers can be made with a symmetrical cross-section or a variety of cross-sectional shapes. By controlling the spinning conditions, the fibers can be spun in a form of skin-core structure. By using additives either in the viscose solution and/or in the coagulation bath, high-wet modulus fibers can be produced.

In addition to the viscose process, other derivative methods exist. For example, the cuprammonium process (or Bembergy process) uses a so-called cuprammonium solution, which is a mixture of copper hydroxide and aqueous ammonia solution, to dissolve cellulose. The cellulose chain interacts with the cuprammonium ions $(Cu(NH_3)_4^{2+})$ to form a complex (Figure 10.5). The interaction between the cellulose chain and the cuprammonium ions is not a primary bond, and hence some researchers consider the cuprammonium process as a direct method. Cuprammonium decomposes when exposed to light, and hence precaution must be taken to limit the exposure of the cuprammonium cellulose solution to light.

Typically, the cuprammonium cellulose solution is spun into a coagulation/re-generating bath using a funnel as a processing aid to protect the delicate as-spun filaments. The alkaline coagulant liquid travels down the funnel and simultane-ously coagulate and stretch the extrudate. The resultant fibers are washed with 5% H_2SO_4 solution to remove any remnant copper or other chemical deposits.

Another important derivate method is the carbamate process, which uses urea instead of CS_2 or cuprammonium as the solvent. The product of the reaction be-tween cellulose pulp and urea is cellulose carbamate, which easily can be dis-solved in aqueous NaOH solution and spun into a coagulation bath to be regener-ated into cellulose fibers.

One common feature of the viscose, cuprammonium, and carbamate processes is the chemically modified cellulose is regenerated into cellulose after the extru-sion. Fibers made from these processes often are called rayon fibers. However, useful fibers can be produced by derivative methods without the regeneration of cellulose. Two important examples are cellulose acetate and cellulose triacetate fibers. Cellulose acetate can be obtained by acetylation of cellulose with acetic acid and acetic anhydride with sulfuric acid as a catalyst. Cellulose triacetate, which is partly saponified to get the desired degree of substitution, is produced by a similar process. Both cellulose acetate and cellulose triacetate keep their de-rivative structure in final fibers. The major difference between these two fibers is that in cellulose acetate fibers, less than 92% but at least 74% of the –OH groups are acetylated, but in triacetate fibers, at least 92% of the hydroxyl groups are acetylated.

10.2.2 DIRECT METHODS

Although cellulose is not soluble in common organic solvents, a series of special solvents have been found to be able to dissolve cellulose. However, only some of them can be used to spin cellulose fibers via direct methods. So far, all these viable direct solvents consist of two components, e.g., N-methylmorpholine-N-oxide/water (NMMO/H_2O), lithium chloride/dimethylacetamide, trifluoroacetic acid/di-chloroethane, calcium thiocyanate/water, ammonia/ammonium thiocyanate, zinc chloride/water, and sodium hydroxide/water.

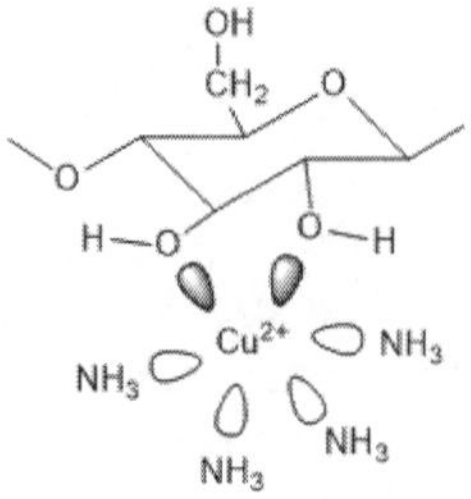

Figure 10.5. Interaction between cellulose and cuprammonium.

The most important direct method is the NMMO or Lyocell process, in which the NMMO/H_2O mixture is used at elevated temperatures as the solvent. In the NMMP process, cellulose pulp is first added to the NMMP mixture, which then is stirred and heated to obtain a homogeneous cellulose solution. N-propyl gallate also is added as an anti-oxidant to stabilize the molecular weight of the cellulose. The cellulose solution is extruded through the spinneret into water to obtain cellulose filaments. NMMP is recovered from the bath and reused. Cellulose fibers made by the NMMO process typically have high crystallinity, high molecular orientation, and high tenacity. However, the NMMP process has not replaced the viscose process in the industry partially because of the fibrillation problem of fibers made by this direct method.

10.3 NATURAL PROTEIN FIBERS

Natural protein fibers include animal hair fibers and extruded protein fibers. This section discusses the formation of two most important natural protein fibers: wool (by sheep) and silk (by silkworm).

10.3.1 FORMATION OF WOOL

Wool fibers are sheep hairs that grow from cavities (follicles) extended from the surface of the sheep skin through the epidermis into the dermis (Figure 10.6). One of the most important functions of the hair follicle is to produce a hair shaft, i.e., the fiber. Follicle formation occurs only once in a sheep's lifetime. At birth, the entire follicle population is initiated and normally does not change thereafter.

Although the total number of follicles does not change during the lifetime of an individual sheep, the hair follicle actually is a regenerating system, manifested by the so-called follicle cycle. A complete follicle cycle consists of four phases: growth (anagen), regression (catagen), rest (telogen), and shedding (exogen). After the shedding phase, the next anagen starts. Hair follicle cycling is a developing process, which occurs over the entire lifetime of a sheep. However, due to the forcefully selection of long fiber length, wool-producing sheep does not actively cycle through all the four phases, but experiences an extremely long anagen period so that high-quality wool fibers can be obtained for practical applications.

Figure 10.6 shows a schematic of a follicle with the major morphological components of the developing fiber. A pear-shaped dermal papilla is located at the bottom of the hair follicle. The dermal papilla plays an important role in inducing the formation of the hair follicle and it also retains this instructive ability throughout the life of the hair follicle. During anagen, the outer cells of the dermal papilla deliver a signal to the surrounding epithelial cells and stimulates them to divide rapidly, thereby leading to the formation of the hair matrix, also known as the follicle bulb. The follicle bulb cells continue to divide for the life of the follicle

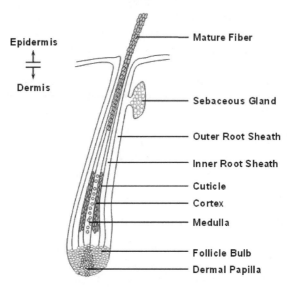

Figure 10.6. Schematic of a follicle showing the major morphological components of the developing fiber.

and provide daughter cells that differentiate to form inner root sheath cells and fiber cells. The inner root sheath consists of three concentric layers: Henle's layer, Huxley's layer, and the inner root sheath cuticle. The Henle's layer is adjacent to the outer root sheath, which separates the entire structure from the dermis. The inner root sheath cuticle provides the support to the maturing fiber until it reaches the level of sebaceous gland, where the inner root sheath cells die and shed from the surface of the epidermis.

Surrounded by the inner root sheath, the fiber cells multiply and the constant stream of cell production pushes the fiber cells upward toward the skin surface. As the fiber cells move up the hair follicle, they begin to differentiate into particular cell types: cuticle and cortex. In addition to cuticle and cortex cells, the follicle also produces a central strand of cells that are loosely organized, forming the medulla in the center of the hair fiber. Eventually, the tip of the fiber penetrates the superficial layers of the epidermis and the mature fiber emerges from the skin surface. In the mature fiber, cells are keratinized and hardened.

Although the keratinized cells in a mature fiber already are dead, the fiber length continues to increase due to the formation of new fiber cells in the follicle. Mature fibers can be sheared after reaching certain length. In most parts of the world, mature fibers can be sheared once a year, in spring or summer. Sheared fibers then can be sorted and graded for use.

10.3.2 FORMATION OF SILK

Silk is a protein fiber spun by silkworm, which is the caterpillar or larva of the domesticated silkmoth, *Bombyx mori*. In addition to silkworm, many other insects or non-insects (e.g., spider) can spin silk fibers. However, the silk of *Bombyx mori* is the mainstay of commercial silk production and consumption. This section will only discuss the formation of silk fiber by silkworm.

Each silkworm has two tubular spinning glands. Each silkworm can use these two glands to extrude two single silk fibers, which are joined together to form one single thread by muscular reaction. Figure 10.7 shows the schematic of two spinning glands, which join together at one end. The main components of the spinning glands are: secretory portion, reservoir, duct, and spinneret. Each gland has its own secretory portion and reservoir, but two glands share one duct and spinneret. The secretory portion is by far the longest and is believed to be responsible for the secretion of the silk protein, fibroin. The reservoir is about one-fourth of the length of the secretory portion, but it has a significantly larger diameter and is associated with the storage of the spinning solution. It also is believed the second silk protein, sericin, is synthesized in the reservoir. The short and narrow duct opens to the outside through the spinneret, which is located on the silkworm's lip.

During the formation of silk, fibroin is synthesized by epithelial cells in the secretory portion of the gland and then stored in a 20–30% aqueous solution in the reservoir. At the same time, the reservoir also synthesizes sericin as a separate layer around the fibroin. The two proteins in the aqueous solution proceed together without mixing into the duct, where the shear rate increases from 2 to 400 s^{-1}. The significant increase in shear rate is made possible by the formation of a liquid crystalline intermediate phase of the silk proteins in the spinning solution. At the spinneret, the two fibroin cores are extruded together, surrounded by a layer of sericin, forming one thread. Upon exiting the spinneret, the silk proteins are

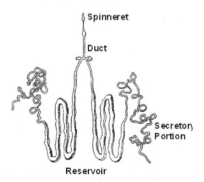

Figure 10.7. Schematic of two silk spinning glands that join just before the duct. (Willcox, P.J., et. al., *Macromolecules*, 29, 5106–5110, 1996.)

converted from a liquid crystalline intermediate phase into semicrystalline fibers, with a high degree of molecular orientation.

The silkworm spins the silk in a figure-8 pattern around itself to form a complete cocoon. The cocoon then can be immersed in hot water to loosen the fibers, which are pulled from the water for use.

10.4 MANUFACTURED PROTEIN FIBERS

Proteins are more complex than cellulose and it is more difficult to produce manufactured protein fibers. So far, there are totally three generations of manufactured protein fibers. The first generation was developed in the late nineteenth and early twentieth centuries, the second in the mid-twentieth century, and the third in the late twentieth and early twenty-first centuries. The production methods for the first and second generations of manufactured protein fibers were similar; however, the methods used for the third generation changed significantly. Therefore, this section discusses the first and second generation protein fibers together, but the third generation separately.

10.4.1 *First and Secondary Generations*

The first generation of manufactured protein fibers was developed in the late nineteenth and early twentieth centuries. These manufactured protein fibers were intended as substitutes for silk, but most of them were never commercially produced. The second generation of manufactured protein fibers was developed and produced in the mid-twentieth century. Many of these manufactured fibers initially were developed as substitutes for wool or silk.

A wide range of animal and vegetable protein sources, such as milk casein, egg white, chicken feathers, fish albumen, collagen, gelatin, hair, hooves, horn, soy beans, corn zein, peanuts, sunflower seeds, hemp seeds, castor oil seeds, were explored as the protein sources for manufactured protein fibers. Many production methods also were developed for converting these proteins into fibers, and most of them at least involved four steps: separation of protein, solubilization of protein, fiber spinning, and insolubilization of protein.

> **Step 1—Protein Separation:** In general, proteins are not in a readily accessible form. For example, many protein sources, such as milk, peanuts and seeds, contain a large amount of oils and fats. Therefore, proteins first were separated from the source material into a suitable form for fiber formation. In some cases, the proteins also were dried and grounded into granules.

> **Step 2—Solubilization:** An appropriate solubilization process is critically important for obtaining a useful spinning solution. For some proteins, such as gelatin, they were dissolved directly in either hot water or glacial acetic

acid after being obtained from slaughterhouse waste. However, if the protein was dried and grounded into granules, a stronger solvent was used. The obtained spinning solutions often were aged to obtain the desired viscosity. During that process, the oxidation and bacterial activity were carefully controlled.

Step 3—Spinning: The spinning solution was extruded through a spinneret into a coagulation bath to form filaments. The coagulation bath typically contained salts and acids, such as sodium sulfate, aluminum sulfate, magnesium sulfate, and sulfuric acid. With the presence of salts and acids, the filament surface coagulated first and this minimized the tendency of filaments to clump together.

Step 4—Insolubilization: The as-spun protein filaments were often soluble. Hence, an insolubilization step was introduced to form networks between protein chains. The degree of cross-linking was important. When the cross-linking degree was too low, the filaments would not have sufficient wet strength to be made into useful products. When the cross-linking degree was too high, the filaments would be brittle. The insolubilization of protein often was carried out in a liquid bath so the filaments could be drawn at the same time to improve the molecular orientation.

Many manufactured protein fibers were commercialized in mid-twentieth century. However, due to technical and economic problems, manufactured protein fibers were not able to compete with either natural fibers or the newly development synthetic fibers at that time. All manufactured protein fibers developed in mid-twentieth century eventually were abandoned by manufacturers.

10.4.2 THIRD GENERATION

In the late twentieth and early twenty-first centuries, manufactured protein fibers attracted attention again due to the demand for fibers with a reduced ecological footprint. Many manufactured protein fibers are being developed with a primary emphasis on imitating the structure and properties of silk.

For this third generation of manufactured protein fibers, milk and soy beans are the two most important protein sources. Chicken feathers also are being widely used in the development. In addition to the common methods used in the first and second generations, many technical innovations have been applied to the production of these manufactured protein fibers. Examples include the use of biochemistry to modify the protein structure, the incorporation of synthetic polymers to improve the fiber strength and modulus, the formation of protein-based copolymers by chemical grafting, etc.

REFERENCES

[1] Adelson, D.L., Cam, G.R., DeSilva, U., and Franklin, I.R., "Gene Expression in Sheep Skin and wool (Hair)", *Genomics*, 83, 95–105, 2004.

[2] Anthony, W.S., "The Harvesting and Ginning of Cotton", in *Cotton: Science and Technology*, editors Gordon S., and Hsieh, Y.L., Woodhead Publishing Limitted, 2007.

[3] Asakura, Yao, J., Yang, M., Zhu, Z., and Hirose, H., "Structure of the Spinning Apparatus of a Wild Silkworm Samia Cynthia Ricini and Molecular Dynamics Calculation on the Structural Change of the Silk Fibroin", *Polymer*, 48, 2064–2070, 2007.

[4] Brooks, M.M., "Regenerated Protein Fibres: A Preliminary Review", in *Handbook of Textile Fibre Structure, Volume II: Natural, Regenerated, Inorganic and Specialist Fibres*, editors Eichhorn, S.J., Hearle, J.W.S., Jaffe, M., and Kikutani, T., Woodhead Publishing Limited, 2009.

[5] Bond, J.J., Wynn, P.C., Brown, G.N., and Moore, G.P.M., "Growth of Wool Follicles in Culture", *In Vitro Cellular & Developmental Biology*, 30A, 90–98, 1994.

[6] Cappello, J., and McGrath, K.P., "Spinning of protein Polymer Fibers", in *Silk Polymers*, editors Kaplan, D., Adams, W.W., Farmer, B., and Viney, C., ACS Symposium Series, *American Chemical Society*, 1993.

[7] Ciechanska, D., Wesolowska, E., and Wawro, D., "An Introduction to Cellulosic Fibres", in *Handbook of Textile Fibre Structure, Volume II: Natural, Regenerated, Inorganic and Specialist Fibres*, editors Eichhorn, S.J., Hearle, J.W.S., Jaffe, M., and Kikutani, T., Woodhead Publishing Limited, 2009.

[8] Cuculo, J.A., Aminuddin, N., and Frey, M.W., "Solvent Spun Cellulose Fibers", in *Structure Formation in Polymeric Fibers*, editor Salem, D.R., Hanser Gardner Publications, 2000.

[9] Ganster, J., and Fink, H.P., "The Structure of Man-Made Cellulosic Fibres", in *Handbook of Textile Fibre Structure, Volume II: Natural, Regenerated, Inorganic and Specialist Fibres*, editors Eichhorn, S.J., Hearle, J.W.S., Jaffe, M., and Kikutani, T., Woodhead Publishing Limited, 2009.

[10] Ho, C.P., Shen, S.M., Tang, P.S., and Yu, S.H., "Physiology of the Silkworm. II. Mechanism of Silk Formation as revealed by X-Ray Analysis of the Contents of the Silk Gland in Bombyx Mori", *Physiological Zoology*, 17, 78–82, 1944.

[11] Hsieh, Y.L., "Chemical Structure and Properties of Cotton", in *Cotton: Science and Technology*, editors Gordon S., and Hsieh, Y.L., Woodhead Publishing Limitted, 2007.

[12] Kerkam, K., Yiney, C., Kaplan, D., and Lombardi, S., "Liquid Crystallinity of Natural Silk Secretions", *Nature*, 349, 596–598, 1991.

[13] Kudlicka, K., Brown, R.M., Li, L., Lee, J.H., Shin, H., and Kuga, S., "β-Glucan Synthesis in the Cotton Fiber", *Plant Physiology*, 107, 111–123, 1995.

[14] Lawrence, C., "The Opening, Blending, Cleaning and Carding of Cotton", in *Cotton: Science and Technology*, editors Gordon, S., and Hsieh, Y.L., Woodhead Publishing Limitted, 2007.

[15] Li, G., and Yu, T., "Investigation of the Liquid-Crystal State in Silk Fibroin", *Makromolekulare Chemie. Rapid communications*, 10, 387–389, 1989.

[16] Li, G., Zhou, P., Shao, Z., Xie, X., Chen, X., Wang, H., Chunyu, L., and Yu, T., "The Natural Silk Spinning Process – A Nucleation-Dependent Aggregation Mechanism", *European Journal of Biochemistry*, 268, 6600–6606, 2001.

[17] Magoshi, J., Magoshi, Y., and Nakamura, S., "Mechanism of Fiber Formation of Silkworm", in *Silk Polymers*, editors Kaplan, D., Adams, W.W., Farmer, B., and Viney, C., ACS Symposium Series, American Chemical Society, 1993.

[18] Meinert, M.C., and Delmer, D.P., "Changes in Biochemical Composition of the Cell Wall of the Cotton Fiber during Development", *Plant Physiology*, 59, 1088–1097, 1977.

[19] Mercer, E.H., "Formation of Silk Fibre by the Silkworm", *Nature*, 168, 792–793, 1951.

[20] Moriya, M., Ohgo, K., Masubuchi, Y., and Asakura, "Flow Analysis of Aqueous Solution of Silk Fibroin in the Spinneret of Bombyx Mori Silkworm by Combination of Viscosity Measurement and Finite Element Method Calculation", *Polymer*, 49, 952–956, 2008.

[21] Naithani, S.C., Rao, N.R., and Singh, Y.D., "Physiological and Biochemical Changes Associated with Cotton Fibre Development. I. Growth Kinetics and Auxin Content", *Physiologia Plantarum*, 54, 225–229, 1982.

[22] Orford, S., Delaney, S., and Timmis, J., "The Genetic Modification of Cotton", in *Cotton: Science and Technology*, editors Gordon S., and Hsieh, Y.L., Woodhead Publishing Limitted, 2007.

[23] Riffer, R., and Broido, A., "Asymmetric Distribution in the Biosynthesis of Cotton Cellulose-[U-14C]", *Journal of Experimental Botany*, 25, 216–218, 1974.

[24] Silva-Zacarin, E.C.M., Silva De Moraes, R.L.M., and Taboga, S.R., "Silk Formation Mechanisms in the Iarval Salivary Glands of Apis Mellifera (Hymenoptera: Apidae)", *Journal of Biosciences*, 28, 753–764, 2003.

[25] Stenn, K.S., and Paus, R., "Controls of Hair Follicle Cycling", *Physiological Reviews*, 81, 449–488, 2001.

[26] Tsuchida, K., Jouni, Z.E., Gardetto, J., Kobayashi, Y., Tabunoki, H., Azuma, M., Sugiyama, H., Takada, N., Maekawa, H., Banno, Y., Fujii, H., Iwano, H., and Wells, M.A., "Characterization of the Carotenoid-Binding Protein of the Y-gene Dominant Mutants of Bombyx Mori", *Journal of Insect Physiology*, 50, 363–372, 2004.

[27] Vollrath, F., Porter, D., and Dicko, C., "The Structure of Silk", in *Handbook of Textile Fibre Structure, Volume II: Natural, Regenerated, Inorganic and Specialist Fibres*, editors Eichhorn, S.J., Hearle, J.W.S., Jaffe, M., and Kikutani, T., Woodhead Publishing Limited, 2009.

[28] Wakelyn, P.J., and Chaudhry, M.R., "Organic Cotton", in *Cotton: Science and Technology*, editors Gordon S., and Hsieh, Y.L., Woodhead Publishing Limitted, 2007.

[29] Wakelyn, P.J., Edwards, J.V., Bertoniere, N.R., Triplett, B.A., Hunter, L., French, A.D., Rousselle, M.A., McAlister, D.D., Thibodeaux, D.P., Goynes, W.R. Jr., and Gamble, G.R., *Cotton Fiber Chemistry and Technology*, Taylor & Francis Group, 2007.

[30] Willcox, P.J., Gido, S.P., Muller, W., and Kaplan, D.L., "Evidence of a Cholesteric Liquid Crystalline Phase in natural Silk Spinning Processes", *Macromolecules*, 29, 5106–5110, 1996.

[31] Worktmann., F.J., "the Structure and Properties of Wool and Hair Fibres", in *Handbook of Textile Fibre Structure, Volume II: Natural, Regenerated, Inorganic and Specialist Fibres*, editors Eichhorn, S.J., Hearle, J.W.S., Jaffe, M., and Kikutani, T., Woodhead Publishing Limited, 2009.

PROBLEMS

(1) What are the four formation and growth stages of cotton fibers?

(2) Describe derivative and direct methods for making manufactured cellulose fibers.

(3) Describe the formation process of wool fibers.

(4) Describe the formation process of silk fibers.

(5) What are the major steps that are needed for making manufactured protein fibers?

CHAPTER 11

Formation of Non-Polymer Fibers

Many different methods can be used to produce non-polymer fibers. For example, carbon fibers are made by high temperature treatment of carbon precursors in an inert atmosphere. Glass fibers and some ceramic fibers can be directly spun from their melts. Ceramic fibers also can be obtained by the calcination of ceramic precursor fibers or by the chemical vapor deposition of precursor gas on a carbon fiber substrate. This chapter discusses the formation of two important non-polymer fibers: carbon and glass fibers.

11.1 CARBON FIBERS

Carbon fibers typically are produced by the high temperature treatment of structurally stable precursor fibers that have been thermally, mechanically, and/or chemically pre-treated. Based on the precursor type, carbon fibers can be divided into four major classes, namely (*i*) polyacrylonitrile (PAN)-based, (*ii*) mesophase pitch-based, (*iii*) cellulose-based, and (*iv*) vapor grown carbon fibers.

11.1.1 PAN PROCESS

PAN currently is the most used precursor for carbon fibers. Figure 11.1 shows the main processes for producing carbon fibers by using the PAN route. PAN can be synthesized from acrylonitrile through a radical polymerization process. During the synthesis of PAN, co-monomers, such as methyl acrylate (up to 5%) can be added to improve the processability of PAN-based precursor fibers. The addition of co-monomers also can improve the mechanical properties of the final carbon fibers by increasing the molecular orientation.

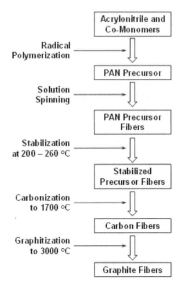

Figure 11.1. Processes to produce carbon fibers by using the PAN route.

PAN precursor fibers often are obtained by solution spinning methods, such as wet spinning and dry spinning. Melt spinning of PAN fibers is not commonly used in commercial production. This is because PAN-based copolymers contain strong polar nitrile groups and experience thermally induced cyclization reaction before melting, which make the melt spinning of PAN impossible unless a large amount of solvent additives are added to lower the melting temperature. In addition to traditional wet spinning and dry spinning, the so-called dry-wet spinning with an air gap between the spinneret and the spinning bath also can be used to produce PAN precursor fibers with high molecular orientation.

The high temperature treatment of PAN precursor fibers starts with a stabilization process between 200 and 260°C. Stabilization can be carried out in the absence of oxygen, but oxygen (from air) typically is used to promote inter- and intramolecular reactions that are important for improving the carbon fiber quality. The main purpose of the stabilization process is to convert the PAN chains into a heteroaromatic structure that is non-meltable and flame-resistant. The stabilization process is complex, in terms of chemical reactions. Many different structures are formed during the stabilization process. For example, a cyclized and dehydrated structure is formed by cyclization and dehydrogenation reactions, and it is widely accepted as the product of low temperature stabilization (Figure 11.2A). An azomethine cross-link structure also may be formed at the same time during stabilization (Figure 11.2B). With the presence of oxygen from air, oxidized structures can be formed (Figures 11.2C, D, and E). The abovementioned structures can be combined in oxidized chains (Figures 11.2F, G, and H). In structures shown in Figures 11.2G and H, non-reacted nitrile (-CN) groups still are present due to the random initiation sites on the PAN chains.

The stabilization process introduces significant volume reduction to the precursor fibers. The longitudinal shrinkage is resisted mechanically, but the diameter of the fibers is allowed to reduce. During that process, the orientation of PAN chains is largely preserved by the strong intermolecular interactions and by the newly-formed rigid ladder chain structure.

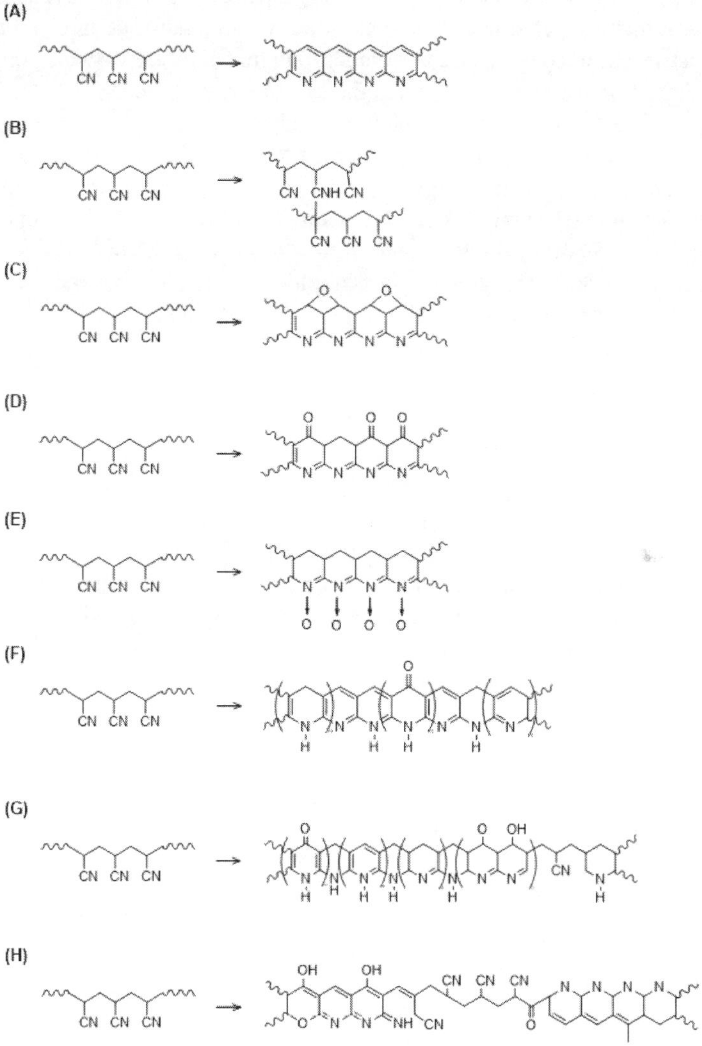

Figure 11.2. Possible chemical reactions and the resultant structures for the stabilization of PAN precursor fibers.

After the stabilization process, the precursor fibers are structurally stable and non-meltable, and the atmosphere for high temperature treatment then is changed from air to an inert medium, such as nitrogen or argon, to carry out the carbonization process. During carbonization, the cyclized and dehydrated precursor crosslinks in the low temperature range, and then condensation reactions follow up to 1700°C. These condensation reactions enable the removal of non-carbon elements from the fibers, leading to the formation a "turbostratic" carbon phase structure. This carbon phase is oriented along the fiber axis, but still has many tetrahedral carbon-type crosslinks between the graphite-type carbon layers. Carbon fibers with this type of structure have high tensile strength. The turbostratic carbon structure has been discussed in Chapter 6. Figure 11.3 shows two examples of the condensation reactions occurred in the carbonization process.

The treatment temperature can be increased to above 1700°C, up to 3000°C. The process above 1700°C is called graphitization. While the carbonization process can be carried out in nitrogen, graphitization must be conducted in argon because carbon reacts with nitrogen at such high temperatures to form cyanogen. The graphitization process heals some of the "defects" in the turbostratic carbon structure and leads to the formation of graphitic structures. The resultant fibers are called graphite fibers, which have higher modulus than regular carbon fibers prepared at temperatures lower than 1700°C.

11.1.2 MESOPHASE PITCH PROCESS

Pitches can be obtained as a byproduct from petroleum or coal industry. Figure 11.4 shows a typical pitch structure. Fibers made from untreated pitches are isotropic and exhibit relatively poor mechanical properties. To make useful carbon precursor fibers, pitches typically are pre-treated between 350–500°C in an inert atmosphere to develop a continuous anisotropic phase (similar to a mesophasic liquid crystal) or a mixture of anisotropic and isotropic phases that can

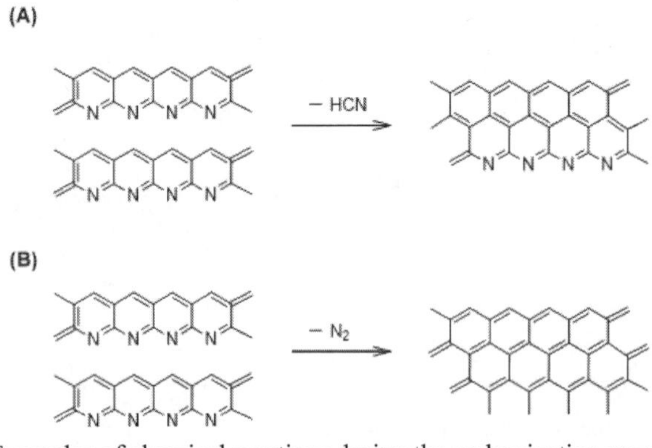

Figure 11.3. Examples of chemical reactions during the carbonization process.

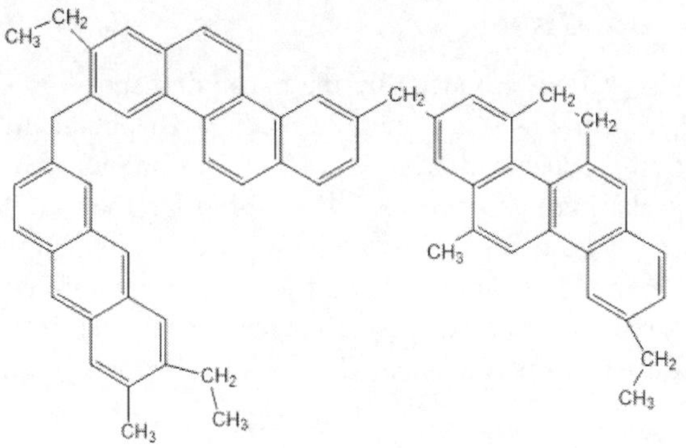

Figure 11.4. Typical pitch structure.

turn into an oriented structure during spinning. The resultant mesophase pitches then are converted to carbon precursor fibers by melt spinning. During spinning, the shear stress developed in the spinneret facilitates the orientation of the disc-shaped molecules, which then is improved by post-spinning drawing.

The stabilization process of mesophase pitch fibers is carried out between 250–350°C in air. During stabilization, pitch molecules form crosslinks and the precursor fibers become non-meltable, ready for carbonization. The stabilized precursor fibers then are carefully pre-carbonized between 700–900°C to remove volatiles without the formation of voids. The pre-carbonized fibers are then carbonized at 1500–2000°C to form carbon fibers. To improve the fiber modulus, a graphitization process up to 3000°C can be applied to obtain graphite fibers.

11.1.3 CELLULOSE PROCESS

Many cellulose fibers, including both natural and manufactured cellulose fibers, can be made into carbon fibers by high temperature treatment. However, carbon fibers made from natural cellulose fibers, such as cotton and ramie, often have high defect contents, which limit the strength of the fibers. Currently, rayon, a manufactured cellulose fiber, is the most used cellulose-based carbon precursor.

The formation of rayon fibers has been discussed in Chapter 10. Rayon fibers have a large number of hydroxyl groups and absorb water molecules easily. Therefore, before the carbonization process, rayon fibers are first heat-treated between 25 and 150°C to carry out the physical desorption of water. The conversion of dried rayon fibers into carbon fibers typically involves a stabilization process between 300 and 400°C in air and a carbonization process up to 1500°C in inert atmosphere. Graphite fibers can be obtained by increasing the temperature up to 3000°C in inert atmosphere.

11.1.4 HYDROCARBON GAS PROCESS

Carbon fibers also can be produced by the pyrolytic deposition of hydrocarbon gases. Many hydrocarbon gases, such as methane, naphthalene, and benzene, have been used to produce carbon fibers with deposition temperatures of 1000–1200°C. During the pyrolysis process, thin tubes of carbon are first formed on ultra-fine particles. The tubes then grow by a surface diffusion mechanism, and the subsequent high temperature treatment with a temperature up to 2500°C results in the formation of carbon fibers with diameters ranging from 10 nm to more than 100 μm. Carbon fibers produced from hydrocarbon gases often have central hollow cores.

11.2 GLASS FIBERS

Raw materials used to make glass fibers include but are not limited to sand, limestone, soda ash, and cullet. These raw materials are melted in a furnace to obtain molten glass. The molten glass then can be made into glass fibers, mainly by three methods: wool process, continuous filament process, and marble process.

11.2.1 WOOL PROCESS

The wool process mainly is used to produce discontinued (short) glass fibers for thermal insulation and filtration applications. These fibers typically are used in the form of batts, blankets or boards, and they often are called fiberglass or glass wool.

Several methods can be used to produce glass wool. Currently, the most popular method is centrifugal spinning, also called rotary spinning. Figure 11.5 shows the schematic of a typical centrifugal spinning process. A stream of molten glass is fed into a spinner, which basically is a metal container with several thousand holes uniformly distributed around on the sidewall. To keep the glass at its liquid state, the temperature in the spinner typically is maintained at 900–1100°C. The spinner rotates at a high speed, ranging from 200 rpm to more than 300 rpm. The centrifugal force created at the high rotating speed causes molten glass to flow through the small holes in the spinner sidewall to form fine streams of glass. The glass streams coming out of the side wall are attenuated by high velocity air (or other gas or steam) and are broken into fine (< 10 μm) glass fibers, which are several centimeters in length. A binder is sprayed on the glass fibers when they are formed. Broken glass fibers move through a "forming hood" placed under the spinner, and they subsequently are collected on a conveyor belt in the form of a mat. The function of the forming hood is to distribute the fibers evenly to form a random alignment across the width and length of the collected glass fiber mat. The conveyor belt delivers the glass fiber mat through a curing oven which dries and cures the binder. The glass fiber mat then can be cut in desired lengths and widths for different uses.

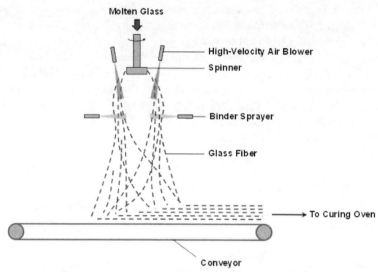

Figure 11.5. Schematic of a typical glass wool process. Forming hood is not shown.

11.2.2 CONTINUOUS FILAMENT PROCESS

Glass fibers can be produced by the continuous filament process with fiber lengths up to 10 kilometers. These continuous glass fibers typically are used for reinforcement purposes. Glass fibers produced with the continuous filament process have nearly uniform diameters, ranging from 5–30 μm, which typically are larger than those (< 10 μm) of discontinued glass fibers produced by the wool process.

Figure 11.6 shows the schematic of a typical continuous glass filament process. Continuous glass filaments are produced by using a direct-melt bushing, i.e., spinneret, which contains a few hundred to several thousand small holes in a flat plate located in the bottom. The bushing typically is made from a platinum-rhodium alloy that can sustain a very high temperature. The temperature in the bushing typically is in the range of 1150–1300°C, depending on the composition of the glass. The molten glass flows out of the bushing under gravity to form filaments with an initial diameter of around 1 mm at a velocity of a few millimeters per second. The final diameter of the glass filaments is a function of the tension applied to the filaments as they are drawn. The linear velocity of the filaments at the winder ranges from a few meters per second to more than 30 meters per second. The huge velocity increase creates a tension that reduces the filament diameter from around 1 mm to 5–30 μm.

On the spinline, a mixture of air and water (i.e., a fine mist) often is sprayed to the newly formed filaments just below the bushing to help remove the heat from the vicinity of the bushing and cool the individual filaments. This often leads to a quick thermal quench rate, ranging from 500,000 to 1,000,000 K s^{-1}. Such a high quench rate makes the resultant glass fibers to exhibit relative low densities.

In addition to the mixture of air and water, a sizing applicator also introduces a mixture of film-forming polymer, lubricant, etc., to provide filament cohesion and protect the glass surface from abrasion.

In industry operations, multiple bushings are placed in parallel immediately under a forehearth, which is connected to a large furnace (Figure 11.7). The furnace and forehearth continuously melt, refine, and homogenize the raw materials and deliver the resultant molten glass into the bushings for fiber formation. This large-scale production is considered as an energy effective process, as compared with the marble process discussed below.

11.2.3 MARBLE PROCESS

Continuous glass fibers also can be produced by re-melting and spinning glass marbles. Figure 11.8 shows the schematic of the marble making process. Raw

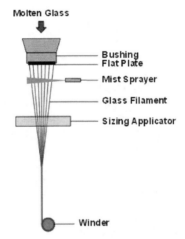

Figure 11.6. Schematic of a typical continuous glass filament process.

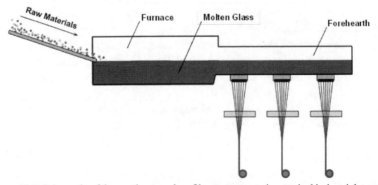

Figure 11.7. Schematic of the continuous glass filament process in a typical industrial operation.

materials are fed into a furnace to be melted to form molten glass, which flows to the forehearth. The still-molten glass is released from the forehearth and the resultant glass stream is cut into individual "gobs" by an automatic cutting device. The gobs travel down a metal ramp to grooved rollers that roll the gobs into sphere-shaped marbles.

The marbles are cooled and shipped to the fiber manufacturing facility, where they are re-melted in specially designed bushings and drawn into continuous filaments. The fiber formation equipment is similar to that used in the continuous filament process described in the previous section. The major difference is the design of bushing. In the continuous filament process, the bushing receives molten glass from the forehearth and ejects glass filaments directly. However, the bushing in the marble process receives glass marbles that are in solid state and need to be re-melted. Therefore, the marble busing has more functions, e.g., melting the marbles and conditioning the glass to the correct fiber-formation temperature. Figure 11.9 shows the schematic of a typical marble bushing. A perforated plate is located within the bushing to retain the glass marbles until they are melted.

In the marble process, the glass first must be melted for making marbles and then is re-melted in the bushing for fiber formation. Due to the re-melting process,

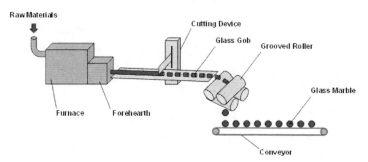

Figure 11.8. Schematic of the marble making process.

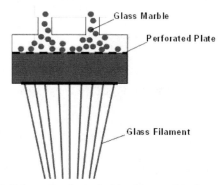

Figure 11.9. Schematic of a typical bushing used in the marble process.

the energy used in the marble process is high, and hence most commercial continuous glass fibers are manufactured by using the more energy-effective continuous filament process. Currently, the marble process is only used for making specialty glass fibers at smaller scales. One advantage of re-melting glass marbles in a smaller scale is the filaments exiting the bushing can be quenched rapidly without the need for mist spray.

REFERENCES

[1] Bahl, O.P., Shen, Z., Lavin, J.G., and Ross, R.A., "Manufacture of Carbon Fibers", in *Carbon Fibers*, Third Edition, Editors Donnet, J.B., Wang, T.K., Rebouillat, S., and Peng, J.C.M., Marcel Dekker, 1998.

[2] Cato, A.D., and Edie, D.D., "Flow Behavior of Mesophase Pitch", *Carbon*, 41, 1411–1417, 2003.

[3] Chand, S., "Review Carbon Fibers for Composites*", Journal of Materials Science*, 35, 1303–1313 (2000).

[4] Donnet, J.B., and Bansal, R.C., *Carbon Fibers*, Marcel Dekker, 1984.

[5] Frank, E., Hermanutz, F., and Buchmeiser, M.R., "Carbon Fibers: Precursors, Manufacturing, and Properties", *Macromolecular Materials and Engineering*, 297, 493–501, 2012.

[6] Hull, D., and Clyne, T.W., *An Introduction to Composite Materials*, Second Edition, Cambridge University Press, 1996.

[7] Johnson, D.J., "Carbon Fibers", in *Structure Formation in Polymeric Fibers*, Editor Salem, D.R., Hanser Gardner, 2000.

[8] Jones, F.R., and Huff, N.T., "The Structure and Properties of Glass Fibres", *Handbook of Textile Fibre Structure. Volume 2: Natural Regenerated, Inorganic and Specialist Fibres*, Editors Eichhorn, S.J., Hearle, J.W.S., Jaffe, M., and Kikutani, T., Woodhead Publishing Limited, 2009.

[9] Lafdi, K., and Wright, M.A., "Carbon Fibers", in *Handbook of Composites*, Editor Peters, S.T., Chapman & Hall, 1998.

[10] Loewenstein, K.L., "The Manufacture of Continuous Glass Fibres—Present Trends in the Use of Platinum Alloys", *Platinum Metals Review*, 19, 82–87, 1975.

[11] Lowenstein, K.L., *The Manufacturing Technology of Continuous Glass Fibres*, Elsevier, 1973.

[12] Matsumoto, T. "Mesophase Pitch and its Carbon Fibers", *Pure and Applied Chemistry*, 57, 1553–1562, 1985.

[13] Morgan, P., *Carbon Fibers and Their Composites*, CRC Press, 2005.

[14] Paris, O., and Peterlik, H., "The Structure of Carbon fibers", *Handbook of Textile Fibre Structure. Volume 2: Natural Regenerated, Inorganic and Specialist Fibres*, Editors Eichhorn, S.J., Hearle, J.W.S., Jaffe, M., and Kikutani, T., Woodhead Publishing Limited, 2009.

[15] Sharma, S.P., and Lakkad, S.C., "Morphology Study of Carbon Nanospecies Grown on Carbon Fibers by Thermal CVD Technique", *Surface and Coatings Technology*, 203, 1329–1335, 2009.

PROBLEMS

(1)   What are the four most important precursors that can be used for making carbon fibers?

(2)   What the main steps for making carbon fibers from polyacrylonitrile? What are the main reactions in each step?

(3)   What are the three major processes for making glass fibers?

(4)   Describe the wool process of glass fibers.

(5)   Describe the continuous filament process of glass fibers.

CHAPTER 12

Formation of Nanofibers by Electrospinning

Electrospinning is the most reported method for producing nanofibers. A literature search using the Web of Science™ database shows that Year 2012 alone had publication of nearly 10,000 journal articles in the electrospinning of nanofibers. Among these publications, more than 50% focused on the investigation of the electrospinning process and the characterization of the resultant nanofibers, and the others mainly address the innovative use of electrospun nanofibers in various applications. Chapter 7 has discussed the main structural characteristics of electrospun nanofibers. This chapter focuses on the fiber formation process and processing-structure relationships of electrospinning.

12.1 ELECTROSPINNING SYSTEMS

The simplest electrospinning system is based on a single nozzle design (Figure 12.1). A typical single-nozzle electrospinning system at least contains a syringe, a metal nozzle, a power supply, and a collector. During electrospinning, the electrically charged fluid forms a conical droplet (i.e., Taylor cone), from which a liquid jet is generated and is elongated. Nanofibers are deposited on the collector or a substrate placed on the collector. The single-nozzle electrospinning system is easy to build and is widely used in academic research. However, the production rate of single-nozzle system is slow, and a single nozzle shown in Figure 12.1 can only produce 1–100 mg nanofibers per hour. The production rate can be improved by connecting a large number of nozzles in parallel. Companies, such as MECC (Japan), Fuence (Japan), Toptec (Korea), Yflow (Spain), have developed and commercialized large-scale electrospinning machines based on various multi-nozzle designs.

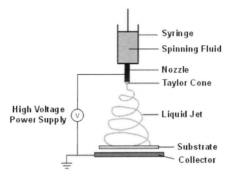

Figure 12.1. Schematic of a single-nozzle electrospinning system.

Nozzle-less electrospinning systems also have been developed for mass-production of nanofibers. Figure 12.2 shows a basic nozzle-less electrospinning system. The spinning fluid is placed in an open bath. To form liquid jets, a cylindrical electrode is rotated in the bath to be wetted by the spinning fluid. When a high voltage is applied to the fluid, multiple jets are ejected from the electrode surface in an "up-spinning" fashion. The resultant nanofibers are deposited onto the grounded collector or a substrate that is moved continuously at a fixed speed passing under the collector. The production rate of the nozzle-less electrospinning system is relatively high since multiple jets are generated simultaneously on the electrode surface. In theory, the production rate can be improved by simply increasing the length and the number of the spinning electrodes. The most well-known nozzle-less electrospinning system is the Nanospider™ developed by Elmarco (Czech Republic).

In the nozzle-less electrospinning system, the structure of the spinning electrode is important. To facilitate the generation of liquid jets, different types of spinning electrodes have been developed. Figure 12.3 compares two electrode designs: smooth cylinder type and patterned wire type. The smooth-cylinder electrode allows the generation of multiple jets from a thin layer of liquid fluid coated on the smooth surface. The patterned-wire electrode generates jets from the fluid drips carried by the specially-designed pattern on the thin wires. The selection of electrodes during nozzle-less electrospinning is mainly dependent on the properties of the spinning fluid.

Although the design of the nozzle-less electrospinning system is different from that of nozzle-based system, both utilize the electrostatic force to generate liquid jets, which elongate to reduce the jet diameter and eventually form nanofibers. The discussion in the following sections will be based on the nozzle-based electrospinning system. However, the fundamental knowledge covered in these sections applies to the nozzle-less system.

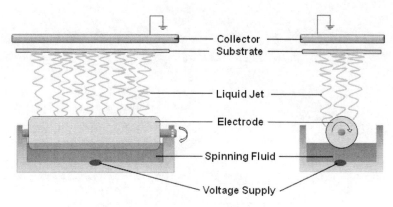

Figure 12.2. Schematic of a nozzle-less electrospinning system.

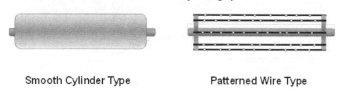

Smooth Cylinder Type   Patterned Wire Type

Figure 12.3. Schematics of two different spinning electrodes: smooth cylinder type and patterned wire type.

12.2 FIBER FORMATION PROCESS

In a nozzle-based electrospinning system, the high voltage is applied to the fluid through the metal nozzle. The charged liquid droplet on the tip of the nozzle experiences two types of electrostatic forces: mutual electrostatic repulsion between the surface charges, and the Coulombic force resulted from the external electric field. Under these electrostatic forces, the liquid droplet elongates into a Talyor cone. When the intensity of the electric field exceeds a certain critical value, the electrostatic forces overcome the surface tension of the fluid and eject the liquid jet from the tip of the Taylor cone.

Figure 12.4 shows the path of the liquid jet after it is ejected from the Taylor cone. The jet path begins with a straight zone. The length of the straight zone increases in response to the electrostatic repulsion between the surface charges. At the end of the straight zone, the bending perturbations begin and grow rapidly to form a three-dimensional coil (i.e., the first bending instability) under the influence of the charges carried by the jet. Figure 12.5 shows the influence of the charges on the formation of bending perturbations. The charged jet is forced $(F_{down-out})$ downward and outward by the charges above, and at the same time, it also is forced (F_{up-out}) upward and outward by the charges below. The sum of the two forces $(F_{sum} = F_{down-out} + F_{up-out})$ is in the radial direction and it causes the formation of the three-dimensional coil. As shown in Figure 12.4, the coil is carried downstream and the diameter of the trajectory increases as both the elongation

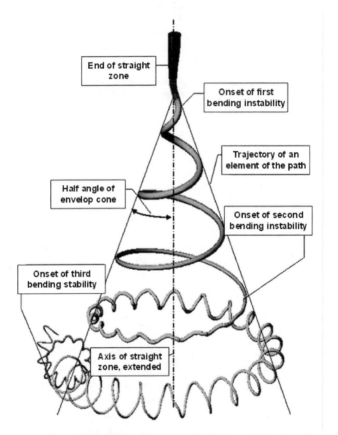

Figure 12.4. Schematic of the path of the liquid jet formed during electrospinning. (Reneker, D.H., et. al., *Polymer*, 49, 2387–2425, 2008.)

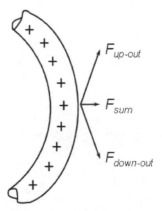

Figure 12.5. Forces acting on a segment of a charged jet.

and the bending continue. The increase in the trajectory diameter is mainly caused by the electrostatic repulsion between the surface charges. When the diameter of the trajectory reaches a certain critical value, the liquid jet transforms to a smaller three-dimensional coil (i.e., the second bending instability), with an axis following the curved path of the first coil. The second coil eventually transforms to an even smaller three-dimensional coil (i.e., the third bending instability). More bending instabilities could occur, and the formation of new and smaller coils could continue until the jet is solidified and reaches the collector. Due to these electrical bending instabilities, the diameter of the liquid jet is reduced significantly and leads to the formation of nanofibers.

In addition to the electrical bending instabilities, other types of instabilities are related to the branching of the jet and the formation of beads. However, the electrical bending instabilities are the most important since they directly determine the diameter of the electrospun nanofibers. The bending instabilities are caused by the electrostatic forces and are influenced by fluid properties and operational conditions. If the electrospinning fluid is a polymer solution, the diameter of the electrospun polymer nanofibers is dependent on: (*i*) intrinsic properties of the polymer solution, such as rheological behavior, conductivity, surface tension, polymer molecular weight, polymer concentration, and additive type and concentration; and (*ii*) operational conditions, such as voltage, solution flow rate, nozzle diameter, nozzle-collector distance, and motion of the collector. However, not all these parameters are fundamental nor are all independent. For example, solution rheology is a function of both polymer molecular weight and solution concentration. In addition, voltage, solution flow rate, and nozzle diameter are interrelated, as are nozzle-collector distance and motion of the collector.

The following two sections discuss the effects of different solution properties and operational conditions on the structure (especially, the diameter) of electrospun polymer nanofibers. Many carbon, ceramic, metal and composite nanofibers are prepared from solutions that contain polymers, and hence the fundamental knowledge covered in the following sections also gives insight to the structure control of these nanofibers.

12.3 SOLUTION PROPERTIES

12.3.1 RHEOLOGICAL BEHAVIOR

Solution rheology has a significant influence on the diameter of electrospun nanofibers; for example, McKee at al. studied the fiber formation process of electrospun linear and branched polyester and found that fiber diameter (D) increases with the zero shear rate viscosity (η_0) of the solution by:

$$D = 0.05\eta_0^{0.8} \tag{12.1}$$

The viscosity of the spinning solutions can be controlled by adjusting the polymer molecular weight and polymer concentration. Typically, the solution viscosity increases with increase in either molecular weight or concentration. Hence, nanofibers with smaller diameters can be obtained by reducing polymer molecular weight and/or solution concentration. However, it also is important to ensure both molecular weight and solution concentration exceed certain critical values to allow the formation of sufficient entanglement of polymer chains during electrospinning. The entanglement of the polymer chains prevents the electrically driven jet from breaking up when the jet is elongated after leaving the nozzle tip. Figure 12.6 shows SEM images of electrospun polyethylene oxide (PEO) nanofibers prepared using two different polymer concentrations. The chain entanglement in the 2 wt% PEO solution is not sufficient and a large amount beads are formed. When the PEO concentration increases to 5 wt%, straight PEO nanofibers are formed and few beads are present.

In addition to polymer molecular weight and polymer concentration, many other approaches can be used to adjust the viscosity of electrospinning solutions. For example, adding nanoparticle fillers and salt additives are two commonly used methods for adjusting the solution viscosity. These two approaches are discussed in sections 12.3.4 and 12.3.5, respectively.

Besides viscosity, it also is found that viscoelasticity particularly relaxation time, plays a significant role in determining the electrospinnability of polymer solutions and the diameter of the resultant nanofibers.

12.3.2 CONDUCTIVITY

The structure of electrospun nanofibers also is influenced by the net charge density carried by the moving jet, which is determined from the electric current and the mass of nanofibers collected on the surface of the grounded collector. The electrostatic repulsion from the excess charge in the liquid jet always tries to increase the surface area, which opposes the formation of spheres and results in thin fibers. Net volume charge density can be described by:

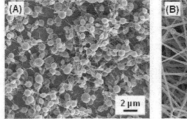

Figure 12.6. SEM images of PEO nanofibers. Polymer concentrations: (A) 2 wt%, and (B) 5 wt%. (Shi, Q., et. al., *Journal of Polymer Science: Part B: Polymer Physics*, 49, 115–122, 2011.)

$$\text{Net volume charge density} = c\rho \int_0^t I dt\, /\, m \qquad (12.2)$$

where I is the jet current, t the collecting time, c the solution concentration, ρ the solution density, and m the mass of electrospun nanofibers. Generally, the net volume charge density is proportional to the conductivity of the spinning solution. Therefore, the solution conductivity can be used as one of the determining parameters to control the diameter of electrospun fibers since it is easy to measure and adjust the solution conductivity. The simplest approach to adjust the solution conductivity is to introduce conductive nanoparticle fillers or soluble salt additives into the solution, as discussed in sections 12.3.4 and 12.3.5.

12.3.3 SURFACE TENSION

In addition to rheological behavior and conductivity, the solution surface tension also plays an important role in the nanofiber formation, and the final structure of electrospun nanofibers strongly depends on the interplay between surface tension, electrostatic repulsion (conductivity), and viscoelastic force (rheological behavior). Surface tension can be defined as the force with which the surface molecules attract each other. Typically, when the surface tension is too high, beads tend to be formed during electrospinning. However, the formation of beads can be avoided by achieving a balance among surface tension, electrostatic repulsion, and viscoelastic force. The surface tension of polymer solutions typically is controlled by adding salts or mixing solvents, as discussed in sections 12.3.5 and 12.3.6, respectively.

12.3.4 NANOPARTICLE FILLER

Adding nanoparticle fillers into the spinning solutions can change the solution properties, and hence the electrospinnability and the diameter of resultant nanofibers. Generally, adding nanoparticle fillers increases the viscosity of spinning solutions although the extent differs from system to system. The viscosity of nanoparticle-added solutions sometimes can be estimated using the following equation:

$$\frac{\eta}{\eta_s} = 1 + 2.5\theta \qquad (12.3)$$

where η is the viscosity of the nanoparticle-added solution, η_s the viscosity of the solution without nanoparticles, and θ the nanoparticle content (or volume fraction). Therefore, adding nanoparticle fillers can increase the fiber diameter by increasing the solution viscosity. However, if the nanoparticle fillers are made of conducting materials, they also can affect the fiber structure by increasing the solution conductivity. Figure 12.7 shows SEM images of Au nanoparticle-added polyvinylpyrrolidone (PVP) nanofibers. The addition of conductive Au nanoparticles actually reduces the fiber diameter due to increased solution conductivity.

In addition to solution viscosity and conductivity, some nanoparticle fillers also can alter the surface tension of the spinning solutions by forming strong interactions with polymer chains and/or solvent molecules. These nanoparticle fillers can affect the structure of electrospun nanofibers by changing the solution surface tension.

12.3.5 SALT ADDITIVE

In addition to nanoparticle fillers, adding salt additives is another means to adjust the solution properties and eventually the nanofiber structure. Figure 12.8 shows SEM images of nanofibers electrospun from $ZnCl_2$-added PAN solutions in dimethylformamide (DMF). The average diameter of the electrospun nanofibers gradually decreases from 290 to 250, 180, and 130 nm when the $ZnCl_2$ salt concentration increases from 0 to 5, 10, and 15 wt%. The decreased fiber diameter is caused by the changes in solution viscosity, conductivity and surface tension. The addition of $ZnCl_2$ salt can significantly increase the solution conductivity since more free ions are available. At the same time, $ZnCl_2$ salt also slightly increases the solution viscosity and surface tension due to the formation of salt-PAN and salt-DMF interactions (Figure 12.9). These changes work together to form a new balance among the viscosity, conductivity and surface tension, which in turn results in the reduction in fiber diameter with the addition of $ZnCl_2$ salt.

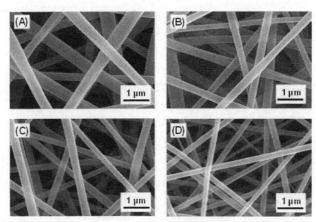

Figure 12.7. SEM images of Au/PVP nanofibers with different Au nanoparticle contents. (A) 0 (pure PVP), (B) 2.6, (C) 3.7, and (D) 7.2 wt%. (Wang, Y., et. al., *Journal of Applied Polymer Science*, 105, 3618–3622, 2007.)

Figure 12.8. SEM images of ZnCl$_2$/PAN nanofibers. ZnCl$_2$ concentration: (A) 0 (pure PAN), (B) 5, (C) 10, and (D) 15 wt%.

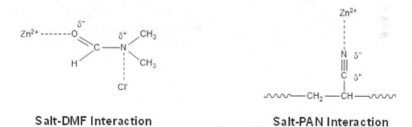

Salt-DMF Interaction   **Salt-PAN Interaction**

Figure 12.9. Salt-DMF and salt-PAN interactions. Dash lines represent intermolecular interactions.

The effect of salt additives on the structure of electrospun nanofibers is dependent on the actual spinning solution used. As discussed above, the addition of ZnCl$_2$ salt in PAN solution results in smaller diameter for the electrospun nanofibers. However, the addition of iron acetylacetonate (IAA) salt to the PAN solution in DMF does not lead to apparent change in the diameter of electrospun PAN nanofibers. The IAA salt also affects the solution viscosity, surface tension and conductivity by forming intermolecular interactions with PAN chains and DMF molecules. However, the changes in these solution properties are not so significant and the resultant nanofibers do not exhibit apparent diameter change.

12.3.6 MIXED SOLVENT

Mixing solvents with different surface tensions is a simple way to adjust the solution properties, especially surface tension. For example, Liu et. al. studied the electrospinning of cellulose acetate. They found neither acetone (surface tension: 23.7 dyne/cm) nor dimethylacetamide (surface tension: 32.4 dyne/cm) allows formation of continuous fibers, but a 2:1 acetone:dimethylacetamide solvent mixture, with a surface tension around 26.6 dyne/cm, enables cellulose acetate to be continuously electrospun into non-woven mats with fiber diameters ranging from 100 nm to 1 μm. Fong et. al., added ethanol to a polyethylene oxide (PEO)/water solution and produced smooth fibers without the formation of beads.

12.4 OPERATIONAL CONDITIONS

In addition to solution properties, the structure (especially, the fiber diameter) of electrospun nanofibers also can be controlled by selectively adjusting the electrospinning operational conditions, such as voltage, nozzle diameter, nozzle-collector distance, solution flow rate, and motion of the collector.

12.4.1 VOLTAGE

One of the crucial operational parameters for electrospinning is the voltage between the nozzle and the grounded collector. A higher voltage indicates larger electric field strength. In general, a voltage of greater than 5 kV is able to cause the spinning solution drop at the tip of the nozzle to elongate into the shape of a Taylor Cone during the initiation of nanofiber electrospinning. A higher voltage often leads to greater stretching of the solution due to the greater Columbic forces in the jet as well as the stronger electric field. As a result, the fiber diameter becomes smaller. In addition, when a solution of lower viscosity is used, a higher voltage favors the branching of the liquid jet, which in turn leads to fibers with smaller diameters.

However, when the voltage is too high, the flight time for the polymer jet will be reduced significantly, which may cause larger fiber diameters due to the reduced time for the fibers to experience the bending instabilities. In addition, higher voltage also leads to larger mass throughput of the jet, and this may further increase the fiber diameter.

12.4.2 NOZZLE DIAMETER

Nozzle diameter also is an important operational parameter in controlling the fiber diameter. A decrease in nozzle diameter typically leads to smaller fiber diameters and fewer beads. However, if the nozzle diameter is too small, it may not be possible to extrude the spinning solution through the nozzle to form nanofibers.

12.4.3 NOZZLE-COLLECTOR DISTANCE

The distance between the nozzle and collector has a direct influence on both the flight time and electric field strength. During the electrospinning of polymer nanofibers, the liquid jet must have enough time for most of the solvents to be evaporated. In general, a smaller nozzle-collector distance provides higher electric field strength, leading to greater jet stretching and elongation, and eventually smaller fiber diameter. On the other hand, with a smaller nozzle-collector distance, the jet has a shorter distance to travel before reaching the collector, which may increase the fiber diameter. Therefore, the actual effect of nozzle-collector distance on the diameter of electrospun nanofibers varies from system to system. In addition, when adjusting nozzle-collector distance, it is very important to ensure the liquid jet has enough flight time for the solvent to evaporate.

12.4.4 SOLUTION FLOW RATE

Changing the solution flow rate is another means to control the nanofiber diameter. When the flow rate is increased, there is a corresponding increase in the fiber diameter simply because a greater volume of spinning solution is drawn away from the nozzle. In addition, when the flow rate is too high, a significant amount of beads may form during electrospinning. The formation of beads at high flow rates may be caused by the reduced charge densities in the liquid jet. To maintain the high charge densities and reduce the formation of beads, higher voltages are needed when high flow rates are used.

12.4.5 OTHER OPERATIONAL CONDITIONS

In addition to the operational conditions described above, many other processing parameters, such as temperature, humidity, pressure, and atmosphere type, can be used to control the diameter of electrospun nanofibers. For example, increasing temperature can reduce the viscosity of the spinning solution, and hence leads to smaller fiber diameter. Increasing humidity can cause water condensation on the fiber surface and influence the surface morphology by improving non-uniformity or even creating surface pore structures. Reducing pressure can increase the tendency of the spinning solution to flow out of the needle, but may cause unstable jet initiation. A very low pressure also may cause direct discharge of the electrical charges and make the electrospinning impossible. Changing air to other gases with higher breakdown voltages, such as Freon-2, also can increase the fiber diameter.

REFERENCES

[1]   Bergshoef, M.M., and Vancso, G.J., "Transparent Nanocomposites with Ultrathin Electrospun Nylon-4,6 Fiber Reinforcement", *Advanced Materials*, 11, 1362–1365, 1999.

[2] Casper, C.L., Stephens, J.S., N.G., T., Chase, D.B., and Rabolt, J.F., "Controlling Surface Morphology of Electrospun Polystyrene Fibers: Effect of Humidity and Molecular Weight in the Electrospinning Process", *Macromolecules*, 37, 573–578, 2004.

[3] Dai, H., Gong, J., Kim, H., and Lee, D., "A Novel Method for Preparing Ultra-Fine Alumina-Borate Oxide Fibres via an Electrospinning Technique", *Nanotechnology*, 13, 674–677, 2002.

[4] Deitzel, J.M., Kleinmeyer, J.D., Hirvonen, J.K., and Tan, N.C.B., "Controlled Deposition of Electrospun Poly(Ethylene Oxide) Fibers", *Polymer*, 42, 8163–8170, 2001.

[5] Du, J., and Zhang, X., "Role of Polymer-Salt-Solvent Interactions in the electrospinning of Polyacrylonitrile/Iron Acetylacetonate", *Journal of Applied Polymer Science*, 109, 2935–2941, 2008.

[6] Fong, H., Chun, I., and Reneker, D.H., "Beaded Nanofibers Formed During Electrospinning", *Polymer*, 40, 4585–4592, 1999.

[7] Huang, C., Chen, S., Lai, C., Reneker, D.H., Qiu, H., Ye, Y., and Hou, H., "Electrospun Polymer Nanofibers with Small Diameters", *Nanotechnology*, 17, 1558–1563, 2006.

[8] Ji, L., Lin, Z., Guo, B., Medford, A.J., and Zhang, "Assembly of Carbon-SnO_2 Core-Sheath Composite Nanofibers for Superior Lithium Storage", *Chemistry—A European Journal*, 16, 11543–11548, 2010.

[9] Ji, L., Lin, Z., Medford, A.J., Zhang, X., "Porous Carbon Nanofibers from Electrospun Polyacrylonitrile/SiO_2 Composites as an Energy Storage Material", *Carbon*, 47, 3346–3354, 2009.

[10] Ji, L., Medford, A.J., and Zhang, X., "Fabrication of Carbon Fibers with Nanoporous Morphologies from Electrospun Polyacrylonitrile/Poly(L-lactide) Blends", *Journal of Polymer Science: Part B: Polymer Physics*, 47, 493–503, 2009.

[11] Ji, J., Saquing, C., Khan, S.A., and Zhang, X., "Preparation and Characterization of Silica Nanoparticulate-Polyacrylonitrile Composite and Porous Nanofibers", *Nanotechnology*, 19, 085605, 2008.

[12] Khil, M.S., Kim, H.Y., Kim, M.S., Park, S.Y., and Lee, D.R. "Nanofibrous Mats of Poly(Trimethylene Terephthalate) via Electrospinning", *Polymer*, 45, 295–301, 2004.

[13] Kim, C., Kim, Y.J., and Kim, Y.A., "Fabrication and Structural Characterization of Electro-Spun Polybenzimidazol-Derived Carbon Nanofiber by Graphitization", *Solid State Communications*, 132, 567–571, 2004.

[14] Li, D., and Xia, Y., "Electrospinning of Nanofibers: Reinventing the Wheel", *Advanced Materials*, 16, 1151, 2004.

[15] Li, Y., Lin, Z., Xu, G., Yao, Y., Zhang, S., Toprakci, O., Alcoutlabi, M., and Zhang, X., "Electrochemical Performance of Carbon Nanofibers Containing an Enhanced Dispersion of Silicon Nanoparticles for Lithium-Ion Batteries by Employing Surfactants", *ECS Electrochemistry Letters*, 1, A31–A33, 2012.

[16] Liang, Y., Ji, L., Guo, B., Lin, Z., Yao, Y., Li, Y., Alcoutlabi, M., Qiu, Y., and Zhang, X., "Preparation and Electrochemical Characterization of Ionic-Conducting Lithium Lanthanum Titanate Oxide/Polyacrylonitrile Submicron Composite Fiber-Based Lithium-Ion Battery Separators", *Journal of Power Sources*, 196, 436–441, 2011.

[17] Lin, Z., Ji, L., Toprakci, O., Krause, W., and Zhang, X., "Electrospun Carbon Nanofiber-Supported Pt-Pd Alloy Composites for Oxygen Reduction", *Journal of Materials Research*, 25, 1329–1335, 2010.

[18] Lin, Z., Ji, L., Woodroof, M.D., Medford, A.J., Shi, Q., Krause, W., and Zhang, X., "Electrocatalytic Interaction of Nano-Engineered Palladium on Carbon Nanofibers with Hydrogen Peroxide and β-NADH", *Journal of Solid State Electrochemistry*, 15, 1287–1294, 2011.

[19] Liu, H., and Hsieh, Y.L., "Ultrafine Fibrous Cellulose Membranes from Electrospinning of Cellulose Acetate", *Journal of Polymer Science Part B: Polymer Physics*, 40, 2119–2129, 2002.

[20] Matthews, J.A., Wnek, G.E., Simpson, D.G., and Bowlin, G.L., "Electrospinning of Collagen Nanofibers", *Biomacromolecules*, 3, 232–238, 2002.

[21] McKee, M.G., Wilkes, G.L., Colby, R.H., and Long, T.E., "Correlations of Solution Rheology with Electrospun Fiber Formation of Linear and Branched Polyesters", *Macromolecules*, 37, 1760–1767, 2004.

[22] Ramakrishna, S., Fujihara, K., Teo, T.C., and Ma, Z., *An Introduction to Electrospinning and Nanofibers*, World Scientific Publishing, 2005.

[23] Reneker, D.H., and Yarin, A.L., "Electrospinning Jets and Polymer Nanofibers", *Polymer*, 49, 2387–2425, 2008.

[24] Shi, Q., Vitchuli, N., Nowak, J., Lin, Z., Guo, B., McCord, M., Bourham, M., and Zhang, X., "Atmospheric Plasma Treatment of Pre-Electrospinning Polymer Solution: A Feasible Method to Improve Electrospinnability", *Journal of Polymer Science: Part B: Polymer Physics*, 49, 115–122, 2011.

[25] Stephens, J.S., Chase, D.B., and Rabolt, J.F., "Effect of the Electrospinning Process on Polymer Crystallization Chain Conformation in Nylon-6 and Nylon-12", *Macromolecules*, 37, 877–881, 2004.

[26] Taylor, G., "Disintegration of Water Drops in an Electric Field", *Proceedings of the Royal Society A: Mathematical, Physical and Engineering Sciences*, 280, 918–924, 1964.

[27] Teo, W.E., Ramakrishna, S., "A Review on Electrospinning Design and Nanofibre Assemblies", *Nanotechnology*, 17, R89–R106, 2006.

[28] Toprakci, O., Toprakci, H.A.K., Ji, L., Lin, Z., Gu, R., and Zhang, X., "LiFePO4 Nanoparticles Encapsulated in Graphene-Containing Carbon Nanofibers for Use as Energy Storage Materials", *Journal of Renewable and Sustainable Energy*, 4, 013121, 2012.

[29] Toprakci, O., Toprakci, H.A.K., Ji, L., Lin, Z., Xu, G., and Zhang, X., "Carbon Nanotube-Loaded Electrospun LiFePO4/Carbon Composite Nanofibers as Stable and Binder-Free Cathodes for Rechargeable Lithium-Ion Batteries", *ACS Applied Materials & Interfaces*, 4, 1273–1280, 2012.

[30] Wang, Y., Li, Y., Sun, G., Zhang, G., Liu, H., Du, J., Yang, S., Bai, J., and Yang, Q., "Fabrication of Au/PVP Nanofiber Composites by Electrospinning", *Journal of Applied Polymer Science*, 105, 3618–3622, 2007.

[31] Wendorff, J.H., Agarwal, S., and Greiner, A., *Electrospinning: Materials, Processing, and Applications*, Wiley-VCH, 2012.

[32] Zhang, S., Lu, Y., Xu, G., Li, Y., and Zhang, X. "LiF/Fe/C Nanofibers as High-Capacity Cathode Material for Li-Ion Batteries", *Journal of Physics D: Applied Physics*, 45, 395301, 2012.

[33] Zhang, X., "Processing-Structure relationships of Electrospun Nanofibers", in *Nanofibers: Fabrication, Performance, and Applications*, editor Chang, W.N., Nova Science Publishers, 2009.

PROBLEMS

(1) Describe the nozzle-based electrospinning process.

(2) How does the nozzle-less electrospinning process work?

(3) How does the bending instability occur during electrospinning?

(4)　Discuss and explain how you would expect the structure of electrospun fibers to vary with the following solution properties:

    (i)　Viscosity
    (ii)　Conductivity
    (iii)　Surface tension
    (iv)　Nanoparticle filler
    (v)　Salt additive

(5)　Discuss and explain how you would expect the structure of electrospun fibers to vary with the following operational conditions:

    (i)　Voltage
    (ii)　Nozzle diameter
    (iii)　Nozzle-collector distance
    (iv)　Solution flow rate

CHAPTER 13

Formation of Nanofibers by Other Methods

Electrospinning is the most well-known method for fabricating nanofibers. However, there are other methods that can be used to produce nanofibers. For example, centrifugal spinning utilizes the centrifugal force generated by a rotating spinneret to produce nanofibers. Melt blowing typically is used to produce fibers with diameters greater than 1 μm by using high-velocity air; however, it can produce nanofibers by using carefully selected materials and processing parameters. Bicomponent fiber separation, phase separation, template synthesis and self-assembly also are useful methods for fabricating nanofibers from different materials.

13.1 CENTRIFUGAL SPINNING

Centrifugal spinning, also called rotational jet spinning or forcespinning, is a useful method for producing nanofibers at high speed and low cost. In general, centrifugal spinning is used to produce polymer nanofibers. However, carbon, ceramic and metal nanofibers can be fabricated by the centrifugal spinning of their precursors, followed by thermal treatments. Composite nanofibers can be produced either by adding nanoparticle fillers directly into the centrifugal spinning fluid or by a post-process, such as electrochemical deposition and chemical deposition, after the centrifugal spinning.

13.1.1 FIBER FORMATION PROCESS

Figure 13.1 shows a basic centrifugal spinning set-up. During fiber formation, a spinning fluid is placed in a rotating spinneret, which contains multiple nozzles on the sidewall. When the rotating speed reaches a critical value, the centrifugal force will overcome the surface tension of the spinning fluid to eject liquid jets from the nozzle tips of the spinneret. Figure 13.2 shows the path of a liquid jet after it is ejected from the nozzle tip. The centrifugal force is accompanied by the air frictional force to elongate the jets, leading to the formation of nanofibers. In addition to the centrifugal force and air friction force, other forces that may affect the nanofiber formation process include rheological force, surface tension, and gravitational force. The as-spun nanofibers are deposited on the surface of the collector. Figure 13.3 shows a SEM image of polyacrylonitrile (PAN) nanofibers centrifugally-spun from a 14 wt% PAN solution. The centrifugal spinning process is simple and scalable, and it avoids the use of high electric voltage and can be used to produce many different materials for various applications.

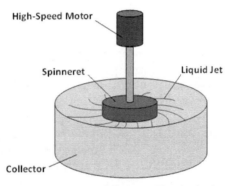

Figure 13.1. Schematic of a basic centrifugal spinning setup.

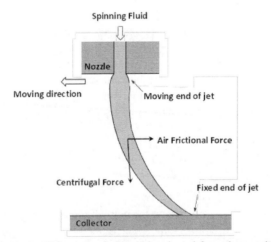

Figure 13.2. Schematic of the path of a liquid jet ejected from the nozzle tip during centrifugal spinning. Rheological force, surface tension and gravitational force may affect the nanofiber formation process, but they are not shown here for the purpose of simplicity.

13.1.2 CENTRIFUGAL SPINNING SYSTEM

Two key components for practical centrifugal spinning systems are carefully designed spinneret and collector. Figure 13.4 shows two cylinder-shape spinneret designs. In Figure 13.4A, the spinneret has two nozzles, which are imbedded on the opposite sides of the cylinder wall. The nozzle diameter and length are important for controlling the fiber diameter. This cylinder-shape spinneret can be used to spin nanofibers directly from a polymer solution. To spin nanofibers directly from a polymer melt, inductive heating coils need to be used to melt the polymer chips. To increase the production rate, multiple nozzles can be introduced (Figure 13.4B). In addition to cylinder spinnerets, other types of spinnerets, with spheroid, oblate spheroid, or trapezoidal shapes, also exist.

Different types of collectors have also been designed to collect nanofibers in different forms. Figure 13.5A shows a circular metal or plastic collector, which can collect nanofibers on the surface of the inner wall. The diameter of the circular collector determines the nozzle-collector distance, which is an important parameter for determining the nanofiber structure. The circular collector is suitable for batch production of nanofibers. A nanofiber sheet collector is shown in Figure 13.5B. In this case, nanofibers are collected onto a porous substrate (such as textile fabric, paper, or other porous membranes) placed on the top of the collector. A suction force is used to assist the formation of a uniform nanofiber sheet (or nonwoven) on the surface of the porous substrate. The sheet collector is suitable for continuous production of nanofibers. Figure 13.5C shows a yarn collector. Nanofibers are collected in a water bath and the use of a rotating roller allows the collection of continuous yarns of nanofibers.

13.1.3 FLUID PROPERTIES

The structure of centrifugally spun nanofibers is affected by the properties of the spinning fluid. Two most important fluid properties that affect the nanofiber structure are viscosity and surface tension. Typically, increasing fluid viscosity can decrease the number of so-called bead defects and increase the diameter of the fibers. On the other hand, surface tension often is the driving force for the formation of beads and beaded fibers because it tends to convert the liquid jet into spherical droplets by making the surface area smaller. During centrifugal spinning, the effect of surface tension is suppressed by the centrifugal force and air frictional force, which tend to elongate the spinning jets and increase the surface area.

The viscosity and surface tension of the spinning fluid can be controlled by selectively adjusting other fluid properties and/or operational conditions. For example, when the spinning fluid is a polymer solution, the viscosity can be changed by adjusting the polymer molecular weight, polymer concentration, solvent type, and additive type and content. The surface tension can be changed by adjusting the solvent type and additive type and content. When the spinning fluid is a polymer melt, polymer molecular weight, additive, and temperature are the main parameters that can be used to control the fluid viscosity and surface tension.

13.1.4 OPERATIONAL CONDITIONS

Operational conditions, such as rotating speed, spinneret diameter, nozzle diameter, nozzle-collector distance, etc., also affect the structure of centrifugally spun nanofibers.

Rotating Speed—The rotating speed of the spinneret is one of the most important operational conditions since it directly affects the centrifugal force and air frictional force. During centrifugal spinning, the centrifugal force combines with the air frictional force to elongate the liquid jet into nanofibers. When the spinning fluid is contained in a rotating nozzle tip, the centrifugal force (F_{centri}) formed on the liquid can be described by:

Figure 13.3. SEM image of PAN nanofibers produced by centrifugal spinning.

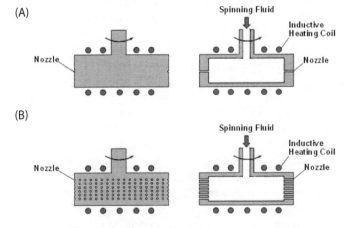

Figure 13.4. Cylinder-shape spinnerets with (A) two nozzles, and (B) multiple nozzles.

(A)

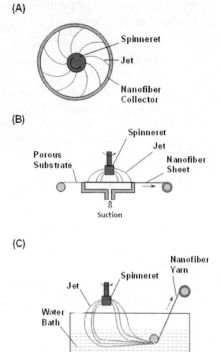

(B)

(C)

Figure 13.5. Schematics of three different nanofiber collectors: (A) circular collector, (B) sheet collector, and (C) yarn collector.

$$F_{centri} = m\omega^2 D / 2 \qquad (13.1)$$

where m is the mass of the fluid, ω the rotating speed of the spinneret, and D the diameter of the spinneret. To eject the liquid jet from the nozzle tip, the rotating speed must exceed a critical value to generate sufficient centrifugal force to overcome the surface tension of the spinning fluid. Therefore, to produce nanofibers, it is important to determine the critical rotating speed of the spinning fluid.

After the liquid jet is ejected from the nozzle tip, the frictional force applied onto the jet still can be calculated by using Equation 13.1, but ω becomes the rotating speed of the jet and D becomes the diameter of the path of the jet. At the same time, the air frictional force (F_{fri}) can be given as:

$$F_{fri} = -\frac{1}{2}\pi C \rho A \omega^2 D^2 \qquad (13.2)$$

where C is a numerical drag coefficient, ρ the air density, A the cross-sectional area of the jet, ω the rotating speed of the jet, and D the diameter of the path of the jet.

While the liquid jet travels toward the collector, the rotating speed of the jet decreases gradually. However, a higher rotating speed of the spinneret always means a higher rotating speed of the jet after it travels a certain distance. Therefore, with increase in rotating speed of spinneret, the centrifugal force and air frictional force applied on the liquid jet also increase, which leads to greater elongation of the liquid jet and favors the reduction of fiber diameter.

However, when the rotating speed is too high, the flight time for the liquid jet to reach the collector becomes shorter, which may cause larger fiber diameter due to the reduced time for the jet to stretch and elongate. In addition, higher rotating speed also leads to larger mass throughput of the jet, which may further increase the fiber diameter. Therefore, it is important to obtain the optimal rotating speed that can result in the smallest fiber diameter.

Spinneret Diameter—The diameter of the spinneret is another important parameter that affects the structure of nanofibers. According to Equation 13.1, if the rotating speed is fixed, the centrifugal force increases with increase in spinneret diameter. As a result, it is easier to eject the liquid jet by using larger spinneret. In addition, a larger spinneret diameter also may lead to greater stretching and elongation of the liquid jet, which is beneficial for forming thinner fibers.

Nozzle Diameter—Changing the nozzle diameter is another means to control the nanofiber structure. A decrease in nozzle diameter typically leads to smaller mass throughput of the liquid jet, which in turn reduces the fiber diameter. However, if the nozzle diameter is too small, it may not be possible to eject the liquid jet and hence nanofibers cannot be formed.

Nozzle-Collector Distance—The distance between the nozzle and collector has a direct influence on the flight time of the liquid jet. When a solution is used as the spinning fluid, a minimum nozzle-collector distance is required so the liquid jet can have sufficient time for most of the solvent to be evaporated before reaching the collector. In addition, when the nozzle-collector distance increases, the liquid jet will have a longer distance to travel and this favors the fiber diameter reduction (This applied to both solution and melt). However, when the nozzle-collector distance is too large, the liquid jet may not be able to reach the collector due to the insufficient centrifugal force.

Temperature—The temperature, at which centrifugal spinning is carried out also plays an important role in controlling the fiber structure. Typically, with increase in temperature, the fluid viscosity decreases. This favors the reduction of fiber diameter, but also may lead to the formation of beads.

Air Flow—During centrifugal spinning, a suction force often is used to collect nanofibers onto a porous substrate (Figure 13.5B). Sometimes, air also is blown onto the liquid jet to assist the spinning process. In both cases, the air flow may enhance the elongation of the liquid jet and lead to smaller fiber diameter.

13.2 MELT BLOWING

Melt blowing was developed in the 1950s at the Naval Research Laboratory in Washington, D.C., and it currently is one of the leading fiber and non-woven manufacturing processes. Fibers produced by melt blowing typically have diameters greater than 1 μm. However, by the careful control of operation conditions, it is possible to produce nanofibers from certain materials.

Figure 13.6 shows a schematic of the melt-blowing process. After the polymer is melt, jets are extruded simultaneously through multiple nozzles, and then attenuated by heated, high-velocity air streams, in which the jet diameters decrease significantly to form fine fibers. The fibers finally are deposited on a collector in random orientations to form a non-woven web. Figure 13.7 shows a SEM image of polybutylene terephthalate (PBT) nanofibers produced by melt blowing.

The structure of melt-blown fibers can be controlled by varying flow rates of polymer melt and air, temperatures of polymer melt and air, nozzle geometry, and intrinsic properties of polymer melt. For example, higher air flow rate can

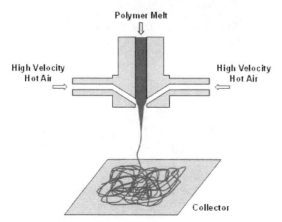

Figure 13.6. Schematic of the melt blowing process. For simplicity, only a single nozzle is shown. In actual production, multiple nozzles are used simultaneously.

enhance the attenuation of jets and favor the formation of smaller-diameter fibers. Increasing the temperature of polymer melt also allows longer attenuation time and leads to smaller fiber diameters.

13.3 BICOMPONENT FIBER SPINNING

Bicomponent fibers that have two immiscible polymers arranged in the cross-section can be used to produce nanofibers by: (*i*) splitting the different components, or (*ii*) removing one of the components. To make nanofibers, at least one of the components has a cross-section with nanosized diameter or thickness. Cross-sectional shapes of bicomponent fibers that can produce nanofibers include, but are not limited to islands-in-the-sea, segmented pie, and hollow segmented pie (Figure 13.8). These bicomponent fibers can be prepared by using two extruders to spin different polymers through specially designed spinneret systems. Some of the bicomponent fibers also can be prepared by spinning fibers directly from polymer blends.

The splitting of bicomponent fibers involves mechanically working with the fibers by drawing, needle-punching, beating, twisting, carding or hydroentangling. When the splitting method is used, a relatively weak bonding between the fiber

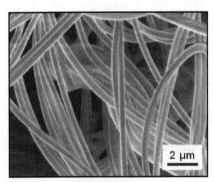

Figure 13.7. SEM image of PBT nanofibers produced by melt blowing. (Ellison, C., et. al., *Polymer*, 48, 3306–3316, 2007.)

Islands-in-the-Sea   Segmented Pie   Hollow Segmented Pie

Figure 13.8. Typical cross-sectional shapes of bicomponent fibers used for producing nanofibers.

components is required to facilitate the splitting process. However, the bonding still should be sufficient to allow the formation of bicomponent fibers during fiber spinning.

The removal of one component from bicomponent fibers typically involves the dissolving of the component using hot water, alkali solution, or other solvents. To use the component removal method, the bicomponent fibers must be composed of one soluble polymer and one un-soluble polymer. The most-commonly used cross-sectional structure for this technology is islands-in-the-sea. Figure 13.9 shows a SEM image of carbon nanotube (CNT)-filled polyacrylonitrile (PAN) composite nanofibers prepared by dissolving the sea component from an islands-in-the-sea bicomponent fiber, in which CNT/PAN is the island component and polymethyl methacrylate (PMMA) is the sea.

13.4 PHASE SEPARATION

Nanofibers can be produced using the phase separation phenomenon of polymer solutions. A typical phase separation process for making nanofibers involves multi-steps: polymer dissolution, gelation, phase separation, solvent removal, and drying. Figure 13.10 shows the nanofiber formation process using the phase

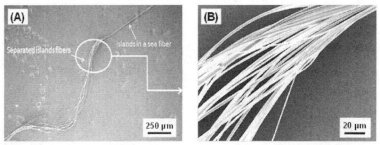

Figure 13.9. SEM images of CNT/PAN composite nanofibers prepared from an islands-in-the-sea bicomponent fiber (island: CNT/PAN, sea: PMMA). (A) Low-magnification image showing the separation of CNT/PAN nanofibers from the islands-in-the-sea fiber after the removal of the sea component by using nitromethane solvent, and (B) high-magnification image showing separated CNT/PAN nanofibers. (Chae, H.G., et. al., *Composites Science and Technology*, 69, 406–413, 2009.)

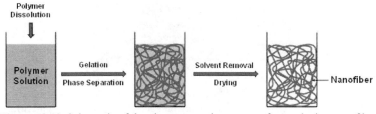

Figure 13.10. Schematic of the phase separation process for producing nanofibers.

separation method. The polymer is first dissolved in a solution at room temperature or an elevated temperature. The homogeneous solution then is kept at the gelation temperature, which is dependent on the polymer type, solvent type, and polymer concentration. At the gelation temperature, the polymer solution forms a gel and phase separate to form a nanofibrous matrix. Nanofibers are obtained after removing the solvent and drying the matrix. Figure 13.11 shows a SEM image of poly(L-lactic acid) (PLLA) prepared by the phase separation method using a tetrahydrofuran solvent.

13.5 TEMPLATE SYNTHESIS

In the template synthesis method, nanofibers are produced in hollow channels of porous ceramic or polymer templates. Figure 13.12 shows the nanofiber formation process using the template synthesis method. The porous template first is filled with monomers. Polymer nanofibers are synthesized from the monomers chemically or electrochemically in the hollow channels of the porous template. Separated nanofibers are obtained after the removal of the template by dissolving or etching. Figure 13.13 shows a SEM image of polypyrrole (PPy) nanofibers prepared by the template synthesis method. Nanofibers produced by template synthesis often have a hollow structure because the synthesized polymer tends to precipitate onto the inner surface of the hollow channels.

In addition to the use of monomers, it is possible to form nanofibers directly from a polymer solution. In this case, the polymer solution is filled into the hollow channels and solidified into nanofibers by removing the solvent. Nanofibers produced from the polymer solution typically have larger diameters than those synthesized from monomers. This is because of the high viscosity of polymer solutions, which does not allow the use of hollow channels with very small diameters. Figure 13.14 shows a SEM image of PAN nanofibers prepared by filling the hollow channels of a porous aluminum oxide template with a PAN solution, followed by polymer solidification and template removal.

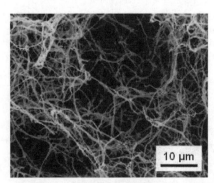

Figure 13.11. SEM image of PLLA nanofibers produced by phase separation. (Ma, P.X., et. al., *Journal of Biomedical Materials Research*, 46, 60–72, 1999.)

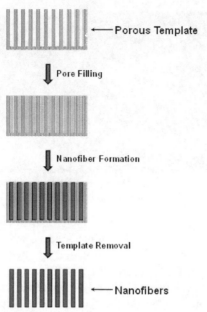

Figure 13.12. Schematic of the template synthesis process for producing nanofibers.

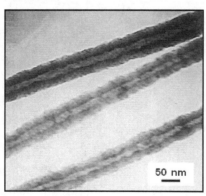

Figure 13.13. SEM image of PPy nanofibers prepared by template synthesis. (Martin, C.R., *Chemistry of Materials*, 8, 1739–1746, 1996.)

13.6 SELF-ASSEMBLY

The self-assembly method produces nanofibers by holding small molecules together via intermolecular interactions. Depending on the chemical structure of the small molecules, there are a few possible mechanisms that can be used to assemble nanofibers. One of the commonly used mechanisms is based on the formation of hydrogels, which contain two interpenetrated phases, i.e., the solid phase and the liquid phase. The liquid phase typically is water, and the solid phase is a network of nanofibers formed by the self-assembly of hydrogelator molecules.

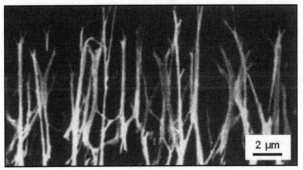

Figure 13.14. SEM image of PAN nanofibers prepared by template synthesis. (Feng, L., et. al., *Angewandte Chemie International Edition*, 41, 1221–1223, 2002.)

Dried nanofibers can be obtained by removing the liquid phase from the hydrogels. Figure 13.15 shows the formation of nanofibers by the self-assembly of hydrogelator molecules that have both hydrophilic and hydrophobic ends. These hydrogelator molecules form nanofibers by weak intermolecular hydrogen bonding and hydrophobic interactions. Figure 13.16 shows an example of such hydrogelator and the nanofibers formed by the hydrogelator molecules.

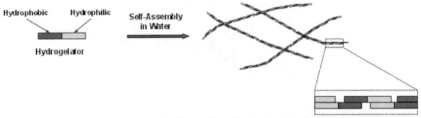

Figure 13.15. Assembly of nanofibers by hydrogelator molecules.

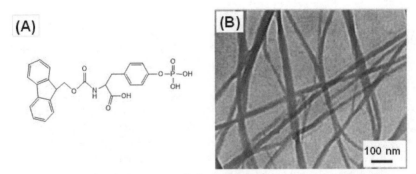

Figure 13.16. (A) Chemical structure of a hydrogelator molecule, and (B) SEM image of nanofibers formed by the self-assembly of the hydrogelator molecules. (Yang, Z.M., et. al., *Chemical Communications*, 2424–2425, 2004.)

REFERENCES

[1] Anantharamaiah, N., Verenich, S., and Pourdeyhimi, B., "Durable Nonwoven Fabrics via Fracturing Bicomponent Islands-in-the-Sea Filaments", *Journal of Engineered Fibers and Fabrics*, 3, 1–9, 2008.

[2] Badrossamay, M.R., McIlwee, H.A., Goss, J.A., and Parker, A.K., "Nanofiber Assembly by Rotary Jet-Spinning", *Nano Letters*, 10, 2257–2261, 2010.

[3] Begenir, A., Michielsen, S., and Pourdeyhimi, B., "Melt-Blowing Thermoplastic Polyurethane and Polyether-Block-Amide Elastomers: Effect of Processing Conditions and Crystallization on Web Properties", *Polymer Engineering and Science*, 49, 1340–1349, 2009.

[4] Chae, H.G., Choi, Y.H., Minus, M.L., and Kumar, S., "Carbon Nanotube Reinforced Small Diameter Polyacrylonitrile Based Carbon Fiber", *Composites Science and Technology*, 69, 406–413, 2009.

[5] Ellison, C., Phatak, A., Giles, D.W., Macosko, C.W., and Bates, F.S., "Melt Blown Nanofibers: Fiber Diameter Distributions and Onset Of Fiber Breakup", *Polymer*, 48, 3306–3316, 2007.

[6] Feng, L., Li, S., Li, H., Zhai, J., Song, Y., Jiang, L., and Zhu, D., "Super-Hydrophobic Surface of Aligned Polyacrylonitrile Nanofibers", *Angewandte Chemie International Edition*, 41, 1221–1223, 2002.

[7] Ikegame, M., Tajima, K., and Aida, T., "Template Synthesis of Polypyrrole Nanofibers Insulated within One-Dimensional Silicate Channels: Hexagonal versus Lamellar for Recombination of Polarons into Bipolarons", *Angewandte Chemie International Edition*, 42, 2154–2157, 2003.

[8] Lee, B., Ko, J., and Han, S., "Characteristics of PP/PET Bicomponent Melt Blown Nonwovens as Sound Absorbing Material", *Advanced Materials Research*, 123, 935–938, 2010.

[9] Josephs, H., and Huston, R., *Dynamics of Mechanical Systems*, CRC Press, 2002.

[10] Ma, P.X., and Zhang, R.Y., "Synthetic Nano-Scale Fibrous Extracellular Matrix", *Journal of Biomedical Materials Research*, 46, 60–72, 1999.

[11] Martin, C.R., "Membrane-Based Synthesis of Nanomaterials", *Chemistry of Materials*, 8, 1739–1746, 1996.

[12] Martin, C.R., "Nanomaterials—A Membrane-Based Synthetic Approach", *Science*, 266, 1961–1966, 1994.

[13] McCulloch, J.G., "The History of the Development of Melt Blowing Technology", *International Nonwovens Journal*, 8, 109–121, 1999.

[14] Mellado, P., McIlwee, H.A., Badrossamay, M.R., Goss, J.A., Mahadevan, L., and Parker, K.K., "A Simple Model for Nanofiber Formation by Rotary Jet-Spinning", *Applied Physics Letters*, 99, 2031107, 2011.

[15] Michielsen, S., Pourdeyhimi, B., and Desai, P., "Review of Thermally Point-Bonded Nonwovens: Materials, Processes, and Properties", *Journal of Applied Polymer Science*, 99, 2489–2496, 2006.

[16] Ohkoshi, Y., "Melt Spinning and Other techniques for the Production of Nanofibers and Microfibres", in Handbook of textile Fibre Structure. Volume 1: Fundamentals and manufactured Polymer Fibres, Editors Eichhorn, S.J., Hearle, J.W.S., Jaffe, M., and Kikutani, T., Woodhead Publishing Limited, 2009.

[17] Pourdeyhimi, B., Fedorova, N., Dondero, W., Gorga, R.E., Michielsen, S., Ghosh, T., Chhaparwal, S., Barrera, C., Rinaldi, C., Satcher, M., and Hinestroza, J.P., "Textile Nanotechnology", in *Handbook of Nanoscience, Engineering, and Technology*, Second Edition, Editors Goddard, W.A.III., Brenner, D.W., Lyshevski, S.E., and Lafrate, G.J., CRC Press, 2007.

[18] Sarkar, K., Gomez, C., Zambrano, S., Ramirez, M., Hoyos, E., Vasquez, H., and Lozano, K., "Electrospinning to Forcespinning", *Materials Today*, 13, 12–14, 2010.

[19] Wang, L., Shi, J., Liu, L., Secret, E., and Chen, Y., "Fabrication of Polymer Fiber Scaffolds by Centrifugal Spinning for Cell Culture Studies", *Microelectronic Engineering*, 88, 1718–1721, 2011.

[20] Wang, X., Yao, J., and Pan, X., "Fiber Splitting of Bicomponent Meltblown Nonwovens by Ultrasonic Wave", *International Journal of Chemistry*, 1, 26–33, 2009.

[21] Weitz, R.T., Harnau, L., Rauschenbach, S., Burghard, M., and Kern, K., "Polymer Nanofibers via Nozzle-Free Centrifugal Spinning", *Nano Letters*, 8, 1187–1191, 2008.

[22] Wu, C.G., and Bein, T., "Conducting Polyaniline Filaments in a Mesoporous Channel Host", *Science*, 264, 1757–1759, 1994.

[23] Yang, Z.M., Gu, H.W., Fu, D.G., Gao, P., Lam, J.K., and Xu, B., "Enzymatic Formation of Supramolecular Hydrogels", *Advanced Materials*, 16, 1440–1444, 2004.

[24] Yang, Z.M., and Xu, B., "A Simple Visual Assay Based on Small Molecule Hydrogels for Detecting Inhibitors of Enzymes", *Chemical Communications*, 2424–2425, 2004.

[25] Yang, Z.M., and Xu, B., "Supramolecular Hydrogels Based on Biofunctional Nanofibers of Self-Assembled Small Molecules", *Journal of Materials Chemistry*, 17, 2385–2393, 2007.

[26] Zhang, Y., Gu, H.W., Yang, Z.M., and Xu, B., "Supramolecular Hydrogels Respond to Ligand-Receptor Interaction", *Journal of the American Chemical Society*, 125, 13680–13681, 2003.

[27] Zhou, F. and Gong, R., "Manufacturing Technologies of Polymeric Nanofibres and Nanofibre Yarns", *Polymer International*, 57, 837–845, 2008.

PROBLEMS

(1)   Describe the fiber formation process of centrifugal spinning.

(2)   Describe the fiber formation process of melt blowing.

(3)   How can nanofibers be formed by bicomponent fiber spinning?

(4)   Describe the phase separation process for making nanofibers.

(5)   Describe the template synthesis process for making nanofibers.

(6)   Describe the self-assembly process for making nanofibers.

PART III

Fiber Properties

CHAPTER 14

Primary and Secondary Properties

Fiber properties can be classified into primary and secondary properties. Primary properties are those that fibers must possess so they can be converted into useful products. Examples of primary properties are aspect ratio, strength, flexibility, cohesiveness, and uniformity. Secondary properties are those that are desirable and can improve consumer satisfaction with the end-products made from the fibers. Secondary properties include, but are not limited to physical shape, density, modulus, elongation, elastic recovery, resilience, thermal properties, electrical properties, color and optical properties, moisture regain, resistance to chemical and environmental conditions, resistance to biological organisms, and resistance to insects. This chapter provides a brief introduction on these primary and secondary properties. Chapters 15–20 give more detailed discussion on some of the important properties.

14.1 PRIMARY PROPERTIES

Primary properties are essential for converting the fibers into useful products. The requirement for primary properties varies from application to application. The following is a brief discussion on five primary properties that often are required in many fiber-based products.

14.1.1 ASPECT RATIO

One important structural characteristic of fibers is their lengths are considerable greater than diameters. Fibers with relatively short lengths, measured in terms of centimeters or inches, are called staple fibers. Long fibers, measured in kilometers or miles, are called filament fibers. The diameters of most fibers range from several micrometers to tens of micrometers. However, nanofibers, i.e., fibers with diameters less than 1 micrometer, also are being produced for certain applications.

Due to the long lengths and small diameters, fibers typically have large aspect ratios, i.e., length-to-diameter ratios. All natural polymer fibers except silk are staple fibers, and the aspect ratios range from 1000 to 5000. Synthetic polymer fibers are produced as filaments, but they can be cut into staple fibers with desired aspect ratios. Inorganic fibers and nanofibers often are produced in continuous filament form. But they also can be made into staple fibers for certain applications.

Aspect ratio has an important effect on the structure and properties of the products made from fibers. For example, in the textile industry, staple fibers are twisted or otherwise assembled together to make continuous yarns. Yarns made from staple fibers often have dull appearance since there are many fiber ends on the yarn surface. On the other hand, filaments can be made into yarns with little or no twisting, and the resultant yarns look smooth and lustrous. In the composite application, filaments can be assembled into preforms, and the introduction of resins leads to the formation of composites with excellent mechanical properties. Staple fibers also can be used to make composites by directly mixing with resins. Composites made from very short staple fibers are often weaker than those made from filaments. However, when the aspect ratio is beyond 100, staple fiber composites could have comparable properties as filament composites.

14.1.2 STRENGTH

Fibers must have adequate strength to survive the fabrication process used for making the end-products. Strength is the ability of a material to withstand an applied stress without failure. In the textile field, fiber strength is defined as tenacity. The tenacity of a fiber basically is the tensile strength expressed as force per unit linear density. A commonly used unit for tenacity is gram per denier, in which denier is a unit of fiber or yarn measurement equal to the weight in grams of 9,000 meters of fiber or yarn. In addition to gram per denier, the unit gram per tex is also often used, in which tex is a unit of fiber or yarn measurement equal to the weight in grams of 1,000 meters of fiber or yarn. In fields other than textiles, the International System (S.I.) unit, i.e., pascal (Pa) or newton per square meter (N/m^2), generally is used.

Table 14.1 shows the strengths of some synthetic polymer, natural polymer, and inorganic fibers. The strength or tenacity of fibers is determined by factors, such as chemical structure, degree of crystallinity, molecular orientation, and uniformity. For example, most polymer fibers have strengths in the range of 2.5–10 grams per denier. However, Kevlar and Spectra fibers can have tenacities greater than 10 grams per denier due to their unique chemical and physical structures. Inorganic fibers also can have very high strengths.

The strength value of fibers provides an importance indication on the potential strength of the resultant fiber-based products. However, the actual strength

Table 14.1. Strengths of some synthetic polymer, natural polymer, and inorganic fibers. Data obtained at 20°C and 65 % relative humidity.

Fiber	Strength (grams per denier)
Synthetic Polymer Fibers	
Polypropylene	2.0–7.8
Polyester, regular	2.5–6.0
Polyester, high-strength	6.0–10.5
Acrylic	2.0–3.6
Nylon 6,6, regular	4.3–6.0
Nylon 6,6, high-strength	6.0–9.0
Nylon 6, regular	5.7–7.7
Nylon 6, high-strength	7.7–9.5
Kevlar	20–25
Spectra	25–43
Natural Polymer Fibers (including regenerated fibers)	
Cotton	3.0–5.0
Flax	2.6–7.7
Hemp	5.8–6.8
Jute	3.0–5.8
Ramie	5.3–7.4
Wool	1.0–1.7
Silk	2.4–6.1
Acetate	1.2–1.5
Triacetate	1.1–1.4
Rayon, regular	1.8–3.0
Rayon, high-strength	3.0–5.0
Inorganic Fibers	
Carbon	8.6–40
Glass	6.3–20

Sources: Hull, D., et. al., *An Introduction to Composite Materials*, Second Edition, Cambridge University Press, 1996.; Morton, W.E., et. al., *Physical Properties of Textile Fibres*, Fourth Edition, Woodhead Publishing Limited, 2008.; Mwaikambo, L.Y., *African Journal of Science and Technology*, 7, 120–133, 2006.; Tortora, P.G., *Understanding Textiles*, Fourth Edition, Macmillian Publishing Company, 1992.

of the end-products also will be affected by many other factors. For example, the twisting of staple fibers plays an important role in determining the actual strength of yarns made from staple fibers. Weak staple fibers could be made into relative strong yarns by selecting appropriate processing parameters. In addition, high-strength fibers are desired in making composites. However, the strength of fiber-reinforced composites also is determined by the arrangement of fibers and the interface between the fibers and the matrix.

14.1.3 FLEXIBILITY

The flexibility of fibers refers to their ability to be bent or folded. In practical applications, fibers often need to be bent or folded to make the end-products. During the use of products, the flexible feature of fibers may also be required. However, different processes and applications have different requirements for the fiber flexibility. For example, wood is composed of cellulose fibers. These fibers lack flexibility and cannot be used as textile fibers, but they can be used for making paper.

The flexibility of fibers is affected by both the chemical and physical structures. For example, most polymer fibers are flexible since they are made of flexible chains. However, the flexibility is reduced with increase in the orientation of polymer chains. The flexibility of fibers can be increased by introducing the crimp structure along the longitudinal direction or changing the circular cross-section to an oval one. Another important and effective method to increase the fiber flexibility is by reducing the fiber diameter. Nanofibers are very flexible due to their nanoscale diameters.

14.1.4 COHESIVENESS

Fibers tend to hold together during processing due to the longitudinal contour or the cross-sectional shape that allows the fibers to stick together. The ability of fibers to stick together during processing is called cohesiveness. The cohesiveness of fibers is required in some applications, but it can be undesirable in others. For example, during yarn manufacturing, the cohesiveness is essential for fibers to be held together and be twisted into yarns, which can be then processed into other products. On the other hand, for composite application, the cohesiveness of fibers could introduce weakness into the structure since it is difficult for resin to wet the entire fiber surface if fibers stick together to form bundles.

Natural polymer fibers have unique structures that allow them to stick together. For example, the crimp nature of cotton and the surface scales of wool provide these fibers with good cohesiveness. However, as-spun synthetic polymer fibers often have smooth surface and simple physical structure. The cohesiveness of synthetic polymer fibers can be improved by increasing the aspect ratio, reducing the fiber diameter, changing the circular cross-sectional shape into a more complex structure, and introducing the crimp shape to the longitudinal direction. Similarly, the cohesiveness of inorganic fibers and nanofibers also can be controlled.

14.1.5 UNIFORMITY

The uniformity of fibers affects the properties and quality of end-products. The strength of an individual fiber is determined by its weakest point. For synthetic polymer fibers, man-made inorganic fibers and nanofibers, the uniformity can be controlled during the fiber formation process to minimize the structural irregularities. However, it is difficult to control the uniformity of natural fibers since the structure of these fibers is affected by many environmental factors. Although the uniformity of an individual natural fiber is uncontrollable, it is possible to improve the overall uniformity of fibers in end-products by blending natural fibers from many different batches.

14.2 SECONDARY PROPERTIES

Secondary properties are not essential for the conversion of fibers into the end-products. However, many of them are needed for the products to be accepted by the customers.

14.2.1 PHYSICAL SHAPE

The physical shape of fibers affects their appearance, luster, hand and feel, cohesiveness, and many other properties. The shape of fibers can be examined both in longitudinal and cross-sectional directions. The simplest longitudinal shape of fibers is straight. But many natural polymer fibers, such as cotton and wool, have crimp longitudinal shape. Synthetic nanofiber fibers can be made to have straight, crimp, coiled, or spiral shape.

The cross-sectional shape of fibers is more complex. Many natural polymer fibers have unique cross-sectional shapes. For example, the cross-section of dry cotton is kidney-shaped, while that of degummed silk is nearly a triangle. These cross-sectional shapes are controlled by genetic codes, and human has limited influence. However, the cross-sectional shapes of synthetic polymer fibers, inorganic fibers, and nanofibers can be manipulated by controlling the fiber formation processes. The cross-sectional shapes of these fibers range from circular to oval, triangular, dog bone, trilobal or multilobal, hollow, etc.

Compared with fibers with other types of cross-sections, circular fibers have the smallest surface area, and can pack closely together into yarns, composites, or other structures. Circular fibers often are lustrous and have soft and smooth handle. On the other hand, dog bone-shaped and flat cross-section fibers have a harsher, less smooth feel. Trilobal and multilobal fibers exhibit an increased luster and have excellent ability to obscure the object placed beneath them because they can reflect the light not only from the surface but also from one lobe to another. Hollow fibers have low packing density and provide greater bulk with less weight. In addition, hollow fibers have high absorbency due to their large surface area.

In addition to the longitudinal and cross-sectional shapes, the surface structure of fibers varies. Many fibers have smooth and even contour. However, some fibers are rough, uneven, or have unique surface features. For example, wool fibers are covered with many scales that make them cling closely together.

14.2.2 DENSITY

The mass density or density of a material is its mass per unit volume:

$$\rho = \frac{m}{V} \tag{14.1}$$

where ρ is the density, m the mass, and V the volume. In some cases, the density is expressed by a dimensionless quantity, specific gravity or relative density, which is obtained by dividing the density of a fiber by that of a standard material, such as water. A specific gravity or relative density of less than one means that the fiber floats on water. Density is an intensive property, which means that increasing the amount of a fiber does not increase its density.

The densities of fibers mainly are determined by the types and packing of the atoms used for forming the fibers. Table 14.2 shows the densities of some synthetic polymer, natural polymer, and inorganic fibers. Polymer fibers have densities ranging from 0.90 to 1.60 g/cm^3 since they are composed of light atoms such as carbon, hydrogen, nitrogen, and oxygen. Polyolefin fibers have the lowest densities. For example, the density of polypropylene fibers is between 0.90–0.91 g/cm^3, which is lower than that of water. Inorganic fibers have higher densities either due to the heavy atoms (e.g., Si in glass fibers) or because of the compactly packed structures (e.g., glass and carbon fibers).

14.2.3 MODULUS, ELONGATION, ELASTIC RECOVERY, AND RESILIENCE

As discussed in Section 14.1.2, strength probably is the most essential mechanical property of fibers. Fibers must have adequate strength to survive the fabrication process and be made into end-products. Other mechanical properties, such as modulus, elongation, elastic recovery, resilience, etc., may be less essential, but they are needed for the products to be accepted by the customers. Most applications have basic requirements for these secondary mechanical properties. In addition, although secondary mechanical properties are less essential than the fiber strength, they still may affect the processing parameters that are important for the production of the end-products.

The modulus of a fiber is a measure of its stiffness. In tensile tests, the fiber modulus is defined as the ratio of the tensile stress over the tensile strain in the range of stress in which Hooke's law holds. Experimentally, the fiber modulus is determined by the slope of a stress-strain curve. The fiber modulus is an intrinsic

Table 14.2. Densities of some synthetic polymer, natural polymer, and inorganic fibers.

Fiber	Density (g/cm^3)
Synthetic Polymer Fibers	
Polypropylene	0.90–0.91
Polyester	1.22–1.39
Acrylic	1.14–1.19
Nylon 6,6	1.14
Kevlar	1.43–1.47
Spectra	0.97
Natural Polymer Fibers (including regenerated fibers)	
Cotton	1.52–1.56
Flax	1.40–1.50
Hemp	1.40–1.48
Jute	1.30–1.50
Ramie	1.51–1.55
Wool	1.30–1.32
Silk	1.25–1.36
Acetate	1.30–1.32
Triacetate	1.30–1.32
Rayon	1.49–1.53
Inorganic Fibers	
Carbon	1.75–2.00
Glass	2.48–2.60

Sources: Hull, D., et. al., *An Introduction to Composite Materials*, Second Edition, Cambridge University Press, 1996.; Mwaikambo, L.Y., *African Journal of Science and Technology*, 7, 120–133, 2006.; Tortora, P.G., *Understanding Textiles*, Fourth Edition, Macmillian Publishing Company, 1992.

property. Most polymer fibers have significantly greater moduli than the corresponding bulk polymers since polymer fibers have higher degrees of crystallinity and molecular orientation. However, the moduli of polymer fibers typically are lower than those of inorganic fibers, such as carbon fibers.

Breaking elongation and elastic recovery are closely related to each other. Elongation measures the percentage change in length when a fiber is stretched. Breaking elongation, also called strain-at-break, is the elongation that occurs to the point when the fiber breaks. Elastic recovery is the ability of a fiber to return to its original length after the removal of stretching force and is measured as the percentage of return from elongation towards the original length. In many applications, breaking elongation and elastic recovery must be considered together. Table 14.3 shows the breaking elongation and elastic recovery of some synthetic

Table 14.3. Breaking elongation and elastic recovery of some synthetic polymer, natural polymer, and inorganic fibers.

Fiber	Breaking Elongation (%)	Elastic Recovery at % Elongation (%)
Synthetic Polymer Fibers		
Polypropylene	15–50	100 @ 2%
Polyester	10–60	85–99 @ 2%
Acrylic	25–55	80–99 @2%
Nylon	15–40	100 @ 8%
Kevlar	2–5	—
Spectra	3–4	—
Natural Polymer Fibers (including regenerated fibers)		
Cotton	5–10	75 @ 2%
Flax	1.3–3.3	65 @ 2%
Jute	1.3–3.0	74 @ 1%
Ramie	3.0–7.0	52 @ 2@
Wool	20–45	99 @ 2%
Silk	10–25	92 @ 2%
Acetate	25–35	94 @ 2%
Triacetate	25–35	90–92 @ 2%
Rayon	15–28	82–98 @ 2%
Inorganic Fibers		
Carbon	0.7–2.5	100 @ 1%
Glass	2–5.4	100 @ 2%

Sources: Hull, D., et. al., *An Introduction to Composite Materials*, Second Edition, Cambridge University Press, 1996; Morton, W.E., et. al., *Physical Properties of Textile Fibres*, Fourth Edition, Woodhead Publishing Limited, 2008.; Mwaikambo, L.Y., *African Journal of Science and Technology*, 7, 120–133, 2006.; Tortora, P.G., *Understanding Textiles*, Fourth Edition, Macmillian Publishing Company, 1992.

polymer, natural polymer and inorganic fibers. In general, polymer fibers exhibit high breaking elongation values. Inorganic fibers have small breaking elongation, but higher elastic recovery.

Resiliency is the ability of a fiber to return to its original shape after bending, compression, or similar deformation. Resiliency is different from elastic recovery, which is the fiber's ability to return to the original length after stretching. Good resiliency is important for some applications such as carpets. Polyester, wool and nylon have good resilience and they often are used for making carpets. However, when soft fabrics are needed, good resilience is not desirable. In this case, low-resilience fibers such as cotton and rayon are the better choice.

14.2.4 THERMAL PROPERTIES

Common thermal properties include glass transition temperature, melting temperature, decomposition temperature, heat capacity, thermal conductivity, dimensional stability, and flammability.

Glass transition temperature is the temperature at which the polymer chain segments in a fiber start to gain mobility. The movement of chain segments only occurs in the amorphous phase. Hence, above the glass transition temperature, polymer fibers still are solid if the temperature still is lower than the melting temperature and decomposition temperature. The melting temperature is the template at which the crystalline phase of the fiber melts. Above melt temperature, the secondary bonds between the polymer chains cannot hold the chains together in the ordered crystalline phase, and polymer fibers can no longer keep their fiber form. The decomposition temperature is the temperature at which the primary bonds break. Above the decomposition temperature, the breaking of primary bonds leads to the formation of nonpolymeric products or a new structure completely different from the original polymer.

Heat capacity is the amount of energy required to raise the temperature of a fiber by one degree, while the thermal conductivity is the property of a fiber's ability to conduct heat. Dimensional stability is the ability of a fiber to keep its dimensions while raising the temperature. Flammability is about how easily a fiber will burn or ignite, causing fire or combustion.

All these properties are important, and different applications have different requirements for them.

14.2.5 ELECTRICAL PROPERTIES

Electrical conductivity is the ability of a fiber to carry or transfer electrical charges. In general, polymer fibers have low conductivities. This is because all electrons are either held to the atom nuclei or shared in the covalent bonds. Polymer fibers with low conductivities can easily build up electrical charges and they cling or even produce electrical shocks. The conductivity of inorganic fibers varies significantly. Glass fibers have low conductivity when they are dry, but carbon fibers are highly conductive.

Although polymer fibers generally are insulators, their conductivity could increase significantly when they absorb moisture. Therefore, in some production processes, the relative humidity is controlled to reduce the buildup of static charges. However, not all polymer fibers absorb moisture. Fibers that do not absorb moisture can be surface-treated to reduce the static charge accumulation by increasing their ability to absorb and hold moisture. Conductive additives also can be added to synthetic polymer fibers to directly increase the electrical conductivity.

14.2.6 COLOR AND OPTICAL PROPERTIES

Synthetic polymer fibers typically are white or off-white when they are manufactured. Some special synthetic polymer fibers have other types of color. For example, as-spun Kevlar fibers typically are yellow. In addition, synthetic polymer fibers with different colors also can be produced by adding pigments during fiber formation or by dyeing after the fibers are formed. Natural cellulose and protein fibers exhibit great color difference by nature, and their color also can be modified by dyeing.

In addition to color, luster also is an important secondary property. Luster refers to the gloss, sheen, or shine that a fiber has and is based on amount of light reflected by the fiber. Lust may be necessary in some applications, but undesirable in others. Synthetic polymer fibers may have bright luster if they have circular cross-section. The luster of synthetic polymer fibers decreases if they are made with complicated cross-sectional or surface features. Synthetic polymer fibers also can have reduced luster by adding pigments including TiO_2. The luster of natural cellulose and protein fibers varies. For example, silk has a very high luster, but cotton has low luster prior to treatments.

14.2.7 ENVIRONMENTAL PROPERTIES

Fibers are exposed to a variety of chemical and environmental conditions during processing (dyeing and other surface treatments), care (laundering and cleaning), and use (air pollution and UV radiation). Among the different chemical and environmental conditions, chemicals such as acids, alkalis and organic solvents have the most rapid effect since they can directly swell, dissolve and degrade some fibers. Table 14.4 shows the comparative resistance of different fibers to acids, alkalis, and organic solvents. Polyester, acrylic and carbon fibers are resistant to most chemicals. However, other fibers can be harmed or weakened by at least some of the chemicals. In addition to chemical conditions, the ultraviolet (UV) radiation can degrade many fibers by breaking their primary bonds. Inorganic fibers typically have good resistance to UV radiation. Among various polymer fibers, polyester and acrylic fibers have relatively good resistance to UV radiation, but wool and silk fibers degrade under UV radiation.

Some fibers such as cotton support the growth of biological organisms, such as molds or mildew. Biological organisms grow fast, especially in warm, dark and damp environments, and they could deteriorate the fibers. However, there are fibers (e.g., synthetic polymer and inorganic fibers) that do not support the growth of biological organisms. Special treatments also can be given to inhibit or kill biological organisms on fibers.

Natural cellulose and protein fibers are food sources for some insects. Carpet beetles, clothes moths, and silverfish are examples of common insect pests that attack these fibers. Insect grubs do not surface on articles that are mobile, frequently washed, or regularly vacuumed and cleaned, and hence one important approach to

regular solid carbon fibers have almost no moisture regain at standard conditions, but activated carbon fibers with micropores and large surface areas can have high moisture regains of greater than 30%.

Another important secondary property is fiber friction. On one hand, without friction, fibers cannot be processed into useful products. On the other hands, fiber friction also could cause equipment failure and/or damage to the fiber surface if it is not controlled. During manufacturing, lubrication often is applied to reduce the fiber friction to protect equipment and fiber surface.

REFERENCES

[1] Bueno, M.A., Aneja, A.P., and Renner, M., "Influence of the Shape of Fiber Cross Section on Fabric Surface Characteristics", *Journal of Materials Science*, 39, 557–564, 2004.

[2] Cook, J.G., *Handbook of Textile Fibres, Volume I—Natural Fibres*, Woodhead Publishing Limited, 2001.

[3] Cook, J.G., *Handbook of Textile Fibers, Vol. II. Man-Made Fibers*, Fifth Edition, Woodhead Publishing Limited, 1984.

[4] Gohl, E.P.H., and Vilensky, L.D., *Textile Science: An Explanation of Fibre Properties*, Longman Group Ltd., 1981.

[5] Jones, F.R., and Huff, N.T., "The Structure and Properties of Glass Fibres", *Handbook of Textile Fibre Structure. Volume 2: Natural Regenerated, Inorganic and Specialist Fibres*, Editors Eichhorn, S.J., Hearle, J.W.S., Jaffe, M., and Kikutani, T., Woodhead Publishing Limited, 2009.

[6] Hull, D., and Clyne, T.W., *An Introduction to Composite Materials*, Second Edition, Cambridge University Press, 1996.

[7] Matsudaira, M., Tan, Y., and Kondo, Y., "The Effect of Fibre Crosssectional Shape on Fabric Mechanical Properties and Handle", *Journal of the Textile Institute*, 84, 376–386, 1993.

[8] Morton, W.E., and Hearle, J.W.S., *Physical Properties of Textile Fibres*, Fourth Edition, Woodhead Publishing Limited, 2008.

[9] Mwaikambo, L.Y., "Review of the History, Properties and Application of Plant Fibres", *African Journal of Science and Technology*, 7, 120–133, 2006.

[10] Paris, O., and Peterlik, H., "The Structure of Carbon fibers", *Handbook of Textile Fibre Structure. Volume 2: Natural Regenerated, Inorganic and Specialist Fibres*, Editors Eichhorn, S.J., Hearle, J.W.S., Jaffe, M., and Kikutani, T., Woodhead Publishing Limited, 2009.

[11] Pizzuto, J., *Fabric Science*, Tenth Edition, Fairchild Publications Inc, 2010.

[12] Tortora, P.G., *Understanding Textiles*, Fourth Edition, Macmillian Publishing Company, 1992.

[13] Warner, S.B., *Fiber Science*, Prentice Hall, 1995.

PROBLEMS

(1) Describe the definitions of primary and secondary properties of fibers.

(2) Why is the aspect ratio of a fiber considered as a primary property?

(3) What is the difference between strength and tenacity?

(4) You are given a filament whose length is 75 cm and mass is 9×10^{-2} mg. Calculate its denier.

(5) Out of tenacity, luster, color, moisture regain, uniformity, density, aspect ratio, elongation, and flexibility, which are secondary properties and why are they considered secondary properties?

(6) Describe the physical shapes of cotton, silk, and wool fibers.

(7) The density of polyolefin fibers is lower than that of water? Is this good or bad?

(8) What is resiliency?

(9) Name five thermal properties.

(10) Describe the benefits and penalties when a fiber has a very high moisture regain.

CHAPTER 15

Mechanical Properties of Fibers

Mechanical properties probably are the most important properties of fibers. Fibers must possess sufficient mechanical properties so they can be converted into useful products, such as textiles, composites, etc. The mechanical properties of fibers also limit the performance potential that can be achieved by these products. There are many different types of mechanical properties, including tensile, torsional, bending, and compressional properties. Among them, tensile properties are the most widely studied for fibers, probably because of their unique shape. However, other types of mechanical properties also are important. This chapter begins with the basic definitions of Hooke's law, stress, strain, and tensile, bulk and shear moduli, followed by a detailed discussion on tensile, torsional, bending, and compressional properties of fibers.

15.1 BASIC DEFINITIONS

15.1.1 HOOKE'S LAW

Fibers are subject to forces or loads when they are processed or in use. It is important to understand how fibers deform (elongate, compress, twist) or break as a function of applied force. When the force is relatively small and does not exceed the elastic limit, fibers obey the Hooke's law, i.e., the law of elasticity. Hooke's law was discovered by the English physicist Robert Hooke in 1660, and it states the deformation of an object is directly proportional to the applied force. In addition, the object returns to its original shape and size upon the removal of the force.

One common form of Hooke's law is the spring equation (Figure 15.1). When a force is applied to a spring, the end of the spring is displaced from its equilibrium position, and at the same time a restoring force is generated and tends to restore the spring back to its equilibrium. The spring equation relates the restoring

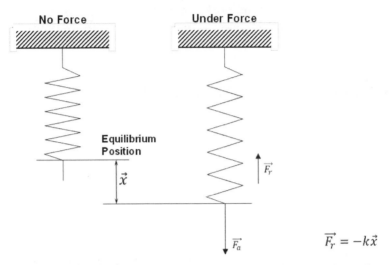

Figure 15.1. Hooke's law describes the relationship between the restoring force of a spring and the displacement of the spring's end from its equilibrium position.

force ($\vec{F_r}$) of a spring to the displacement ($\vec{x}$) of the spring's end from its equilibrium position by a spring constant, k.

$$\vec{F_r} = -k\vec{x} \qquad (15.1)$$

The negative sign indicates the restoring force of the spring is in the opposite direction to the displacement. Similarly, the relationship between the applied force ($\vec{F_a}$) and the displacement can be expressed as:

$$\vec{F_a} = k\vec{x} \qquad (15.2)$$

There is no negative sign in Equation 15.2 because the applied force is in the same direction with the displacement.

Hooke's law is useful in describing how a particular object deforms under a certain force. However, it does not take into consideration the geometrical shape and size of the object and is not convenient for describing the mechanical properties of fibers. For example, under a given force, a long piece of fiber always deforms more than a shorter piece of the same fiber. Similarly, a thicker fiber can sustain a larger force before breaking than a thinner fiber made of the same material. Therefore, to compare the mechanical properties of fibers, stresses and strains are defined to take out the effect of shape and size.

There are three basic types of stresses. If a fiber is stretched or compressed, it is subjected to a tensile stress. If a force is applied over an entire surface of a fiber, changing its volume, the fiber is said to be experiencing a bulk stress. Finally, if the force is acting tangentially to the surface, causing it to twist, the fiber is subject to a shear stress.

15.1.2 TENSILE STRESS, STRAIN AND MODULUS

Figure 15.2 shows a fiber with cross-sectional area A_0 being subject to equal and opposite tensile forces (F) at the ends. The tensile stress (σ) can be defined as the ratio of the force to the cross-sectional area.

$$\sigma = \frac{F}{A_0} \tag{15.3}$$

The SI unit of stress is newton per square meter (N/m^2), which also is called the pascal (Pa). However, a tensile stress of 1 pascal is extremely small, and hence the unit of megapascal (MPa) often is used for convenience.

The tensile stress causes the elongation of the fiber. The fractional amount a fiber elongates when it is subject to a tensile stress is called the tensile strain. Mathematically, the tensile strain (ε) can be written as:

$$\varepsilon = \frac{l - l_0}{l_0} \tag{15.4}$$

where l_0 is the original length of the unstressed fiber, and l is the length of the stressed fiber. Strain is a dimensionless quantity since it is a ratio of length to length, and it often is reported in percentage.

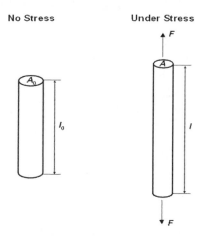

Figure 15.2. Deformation of a fiber under tensile force F.

According to the Hooke's law, the amount of tensile strain experienced by a fiber is directly proportional to the tensile stress. The tensile modulus (E) can then be defined as:

$$E = \frac{\sigma}{\varepsilon} \tag{15.5}$$

Tensile modulus is also called Young's modulus or elastic modulus. The unit of tensile modulus also is pascal, or more often gigapascal (GPa) for the purpose of convenience. Fibers with high tensile modulus are stiff and deform very little under stress, whereas fibers with low tensile modulus are soft and deform significantly.

15.1.3 TRUE STRESS AND TRUE STRAIN

The definitions of tensile stress and tensile strain are based on fixed reference quantities, i.e., the original cross-sectional area and original length, respectively. In many engineering applications, these definitions can be considered to be accurate if the cross-sectional area and length of the fiber do not change substantially while a tensile force is applied. As a result, tensile stress and tensile strain often are called engineering stress and engineering strain. However, in some other situations, the cross-sectional area and the length of the fiber can change substantially. In such cases, the stress and strain calculated based on original cross-sectional area and original length cease to be accurate measures. To address this problem, true stress and true strain are defined.

True stress (σ_T) is the ratio of the tensile force to the instantaneous cross-sectional area:

$$\sigma_T = \frac{F}{A} \tag{15.6}$$

True stress can be related back to the engineering stress by assuming there is no volume change in the fiber. Under this assumption:

$$A \times l = A_0 \times l_0 \tag{15.7}$$

which leads to:

$$\sigma_T = \frac{F}{A} = \frac{F}{A_0} \times \frac{l}{l_0} = \frac{F}{A_0} \times \frac{l_0 + l - l_0}{l_0} = \sigma(1+\varepsilon) \tag{15.8}$$

True strain is the sum of all the instantaneous engineering strains:

$$\varepsilon_T = \int d\varepsilon = \int_{l_0}^{l} \frac{dl}{l} = ln\frac{l}{l_0} \qquad (15.9)$$

True strain also can be related to the engineering strain by:

$$\varepsilon_T = ln\frac{l}{l_0} = ln\frac{l_0 + l - l_0}{l_0} = ln(1+\varepsilon) \qquad (15.10)$$

Under a small strain, true stress and strain are comparable to engineering stress and strain. However, under large strains, the true stress and strain could be significantly different from engineering stress and strain.

15.1.4 SPECIFIC STRESS

The concept of tensile stress is simple and straightforward. However, the cross-sectional areas of many fibers are not well-defined due to their unique cross-sectional shapes. One useful parameter to describe the fiber cross-sectional fineness is the linear density (μ), i.e., mass per unit length. For fibers with comparable bulk densities, their cross-sectional area is proportional to the fiber linear density. Hence, the term specific stress (σ_s) often is used, especially in the textile community:

$$\sigma_s = \frac{F}{\mu} \qquad (15.11)$$

Common units for specific stress are gram per denier or gram per tex. Denier is the unit of fiber or yarn measurement equal to the weight in grams of 9,000 meters of fiber or yarn, while tex is the unit of fiber or yarn measurement equal to the weight in grams of 1,000 meters of fiber or yarn.

When specific stress is used in calculating the tensile modulus, the modulus unit becomes gram per denier or gram per tex.

15.1.5 POISSON'S RATIO

When a fiber is subject to a tensile stress, it does not just deform in the direction of the applied force, but also contracts in directions perpendicular to the force, as shown in Figure 15.2. This phenomenon is called the Poisson effect. Poisson's ratio (v), also called Poisson ratio or Poisson coefficient, is a measure of the Poisson effect. Poisson's ratio is the negative ratio of the transverse contraction strain to longitudinal tensile strain.

$$\nu = -\frac{\varepsilon_T}{\varepsilon_L} \tag{15.12}$$

where ε_T is the transverse contract strain and ε_L the longitudinal tensile strain.

Table 15.1 shows the Poisson's ratios of some materials. An incompressible material that does not change volume when elongates would have a Poisson's ratio of exactly 0.5. For example, rubber has a Poisson's ratio of nearly 0.5. Cork's Poisson ratio is close to 0, indicating very little transverse contract when stretched. Auxetic materials, such as polymer foams, have negative Poisson's ratios, and they become thicker in perpendicular directions when stretched. Most other materials, including metals, ceramics, and polymers, have Poisson's ratios ranging from 0 to 5.

Poisson's ratios shown in Table 15.1 are for isotropic materials that have identical structure and properties in all directions. Fibers, especially polymer fibers, are anisotropic and their Poisson's ratios deviate from the values reported in Table 15.1.

15.1.6 BULK MODULUS

The second basic type of stress is bulk stress, i.e., hydrostatic pressure. Fibers diminish in volume when exposed to a uniform hydrostatic pressure (P), as shown in Figure 15.3. The isotropic compression due to the pressure can be described by the engineering compression ratio (κ).

$$\kappa = \frac{V - V_0}{V_0} \tag{15.13}$$

where V_0 is the original volume of the fiber before applying the pressure, and V the volume of the fiber under pressure.

The bulk modulus (B) is a measure of resistance to the bulk stress or hydrostatic press, and it can be defined as:

$$B = -\frac{P}{\kappa} \tag{15.14}$$

Since the engineering compression ratio is dimensionless, the unit of bulk modulus is the same as the hydrostatic pressure, i.e., pascal.

For isotropic materials, the bulk modulus has a simple relationship with tensile modulus and Passion's ratio:

$$B = \frac{E}{3(1 - 2v)} \tag{15.15}$$

Table 15.1. Poisson's ratios of materials.

Material	Poisson's Ratio
Gold	0.42
Copper	0.33
Magnesium	0.35
Titanium	0.34
Stainless Steel	0.30–0.31
Glass	0.24
Concrete	0.20
Clay	0.30–0.45
Sand	0.20–0.45
Polystyrene	0.33
Polymethyl Methacrylate	0.33
Nylon 6,6	0.33
Rubber	0.50
Cork	ca. 0.00
Auxetics	negative

Sources: Boresi, A.P., et. al., *Advanced Mechanics of Materials*, Fifth Edition, John Wiley & Sons, Ltd., 1993.; Ward, I.M., et. al., *Mechanical Properties of Solid Polymers*, Third Edition, John Wiley & Sons, Ltd., 2013.

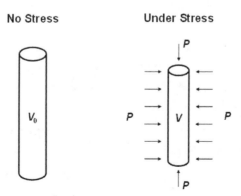

Figure 15.3. Deformation of a fiber under hydrostatic pressure P.

However, fibers are typically anisotropic, and do not follow Equation 15.15. Due to the molecular orientation, the ratio of tensile modulus to bulk modulus for most fibers is greater than what is predicted by Equation 15.15.

15.1.7 SHEAR MODULUS

In addition to tensile stress and bulk stress (hydrostatic pressure), shear stress is another basic type of stress. There are different ways to apply shear stress to a fiber, which will be discussed later in this chapter. Here, for the purpose of simplicity, the deformation of a cubic object under shear stress is discussed. Figure 15.4 shows the deformation that takes place when a shear force is applied parallel to one face of a cubic object while the opposite face is held fixed by another equal force. The face that experiences the shear force is named arbitrarily as the x, y face in a Cartesian system. The shear stress (τ_{xy}) then can be defined as the force (F) applied parallel to the face divided by the area (A_{xy}) of this face:

$$\tau_{xy} = \frac{F}{A_{xy}} \tag{15.16}$$

The shear strain (γ_{xy}) is defined as the deformation (δ) parallel to the direction of the shear force, divided by the original length (l_0) perpendicular to this direction:

$$\gamma_{xy} = \frac{\delta}{l_0} \tag{15.17}$$

Shear modulus is the ratio of shear stress to shear strain:

$$G = \frac{\tau_{xy}}{\gamma_{xy}} \tag{15.18}$$

No Stress   **Under Stress**

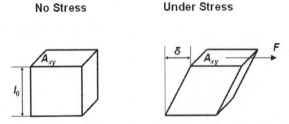

Figure 15.4. Deformation of a cubic object under shear force F.

Similar to bulk modulus, the shear modulus of isotropic materials also has a simple relationship with tensile modulus and Passion's ratio:

$$G = \frac{E}{2(1+v)} \tag{15.19}$$

The relationship between shear modulus, tensile modulus and Poisson's ratio of anisotropic fibers deviates from Equation 15.19. In general, the ratio of tensile modulus to shear modulus for most anisotropic fibers is greater than what is predicted by Equation 15.19.

15.2 TENSILE PROPERTIES

In many practical applications, tensile properties are the most important mechanical properties of fibers since they typically are under tension or complex stress states that include tension. This section focuses on the typical stress-strain behavior and factors that affect the stress-strain behavior of polymer fibers. The elastic recovery of polymer fibers also is discussed.

15.2.1 IDEAL STRESS-STRAIN BEHAVIOR

The relationship between the tensile stress and tensile strain that a fiber displays is known as that fiber's stress-strain behavior. If a fiber obeys the Hooke's law, its tensile stress is directly proportional to the tensile strain, up to the point of failure, where the fiber breaks without yielding or plastic deformation (Figure 15.5). In this case, the fiber exhibits ideal stress-strain behavior.

The ideal stress-strain curve shown in Figure 15.5 provides important information: (*i*) the stress to break, which also is called the strength; (*ii*) the tensile modulus, which is a measure of stiffness and is given by the slope of the curve, i.e., stress divided by strain; and (*iii*) the energy to break, which is proportional to the area under the curve and is a measure of toughness. Strength is an extrinsic property, which means it depends on the weakest point of the fiber. Defects or impurities can significantly reduce the strength of a fiber. However, modulus is an intrinsic property and is less sensitive to defects and impurities. Toughness is a measure of the amount of work required to break a fiber, and tough fibers are the opposite of brittle fibers.

Figure 15.6 shows the ideal stress-strain curves of inorganic and polymer fibers. Inorganic fibers typically have higher strength and modulus, but they break at lower strain and are more brittle.

15.2.2 A SIMPLE MODEL

A simple model can be used to describe the ideal stress-strain behavior. Figure 15.7 shows a one-dimensional array of atoms held together by chemical bonds. This array can be used to represent part of an ideal material that has identical rows of atoms placed adjacent to one another. When a tensile force is applied to this material, the atoms are displaced from their equilibrium positions, creating a restoring force that is equal, but opposite to the applied tensile force. The mechanical response of the material is governed by the internal energy, i.e., the sum of the

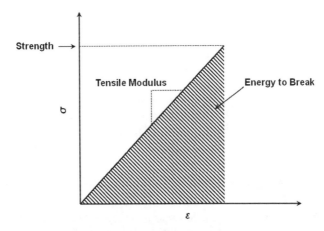

Figure 15.5. Ideal stress-strain behavior.

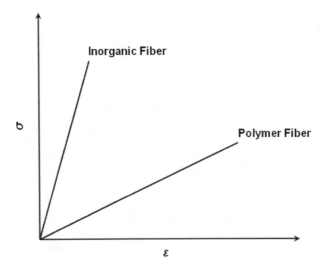

Figure 15.6. Ideal stress-strain curves of inorganic and polymer fibers.

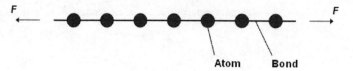

Figure 15.7. An array of atoms under tensile force.

potential energy and the kinetic energy. The kinetic energy is associated with the vibrations of the atoms around their equilibrium positions and can be neglected while considering the tensile properties of the material. The potential energy is associated with the chemical bonds that hold the atoms together in the array, and it determines the mechanical response of the material under the applied tensile force.

Figure 15.8A shows the potential energy for a pair of atoms. There is an equilibrium position, at which the potential energy is the lowest. The two atoms repel strongly when their distance is smaller than the equilibrium distance, but they attract to each other when their distance becomes larger than the equilibrium distance. When three or more atoms are involved, the curve for the potential energy changes. However, the concept of the equilibrium position still is valid (Figure 15.8B). Under the applied tensile stress, the potential energy (U) caused by the displacement (x) of atoms from their equilibrium positions is:

$$U = \frac{1}{2}kx^2 \tag{15.20}$$

where k is the force constant. When the displacement is relatively large, there are some deviations, and Equation 15.20 can be rewritten by using a power series:

$$U = \frac{1}{2}kx^2 + \frac{1}{3}k'x^3 + \frac{1}{4}k''x^4 + \dots \tag{15.21}$$

As a result, the restoring force can be calculated by:

$$force = \frac{dU}{dx} = kx + k'x^2 + k''x^3 + \dots \tag{15.22}$$

When the displacement is small, Equation 15.22 becomes:

$$force = kx \tag{15.23}$$

Therefore, this simple model indicates the mechanical response of the material follows the Hooke's law and exhibits the ideal stress-strain behavior if the tensile strain is small. However, deviations occur under larger strains.

A. Potential energy for a pair of atoms

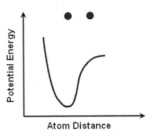

B. Potential energy of the middle atom in an array of three atoms

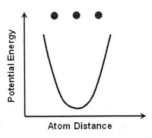

Figure 15.8. Potential energy (A) for a pair of atoms, and (B) of the middle atom in an array of three atoms.

15.2.3 DEVIATIONS FROM IDEAL STRESS-STRAIN BEHAVIOR

According to the simple model described in the previous section, the mechanical response of the material deviates from the ideal stress-strain behavior at large strains since the potential energy needs to be expressed using a power series (Equation 15.21). In fibers, the material structure is far from perfect and the array of atoms shown in Figure 15.7 is not an approximate description of the fiber structure. For example, most polymer fibers have both amorphous and crystalline phases. In each phase, the molecular orientation is not perfect. As a result, at both longitudinal and transverse directions of a polymer fiber, there is a combination of primary and secondary bonds and the potential energy cannot be simply described using Equation 15.21.

Figure 15.9 shows a typical stress-strain curve of a polymer fiber, in which the molecular orientation has not been fully developed. The stress-strain curve is composed of elastic and plastic regions. In the elastic region, the strain is small and the fiber deforms more-or-less elastically. The deformation in the elastic region is largely reversible. The tensile modulus of the fiber is obtained from the initial slope of the stress-strain curve in the elastic region. When the tensile stress reaches the yield strength, the fiber yields and the stress-strain curve enters the

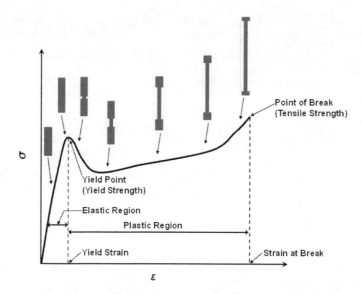

Figure 15.9. Typical stress-strain curve of an un-oriented polymer fiber.

plastic region. At the yield point, a "neck" is formed in the fiber and the deformation becomes irreversible. There is an actual decrease in the tensile stress, i.e., the so-called strain softening, in the initial stage of the plastic region. The deformation then continues with a slow increase in the tensile stress. At the end of the plastic region, the fiber appears to gain resistance to the stress more rapidly and ultimately breaks at a higher stress. The tensile strength basically is the stress at the point of break when the fiber experiences its maximum strain. The maximum strain also is called strain-at-break or breaking elongation.

The stress-strain curve of a polymer fiber depends on its structure. Figure 15.10 compares the stress-strain curves of un-oriented amorphous, semicrystalline, and elastomer polymer fibers. Most polymer fibers are semicrystalline. However, amorphous polymer fibers could be obtained prior to drawing for polymers with slow crystallization kinetics. At temperatures well below the glass-transition temperature (T_g), both amorphous and semicrystalline polymer fibers do not display yielding or plastic deformation. They have high modulus and high strength, but they are brittle. Both amorphous and semicrystalline polymer fibers yield and exhibit plastic deformation at high strains when the temperature is close to or above T_g. Although the modulus and strength decrease, the fibers become tougher because of the yielding and plastic deformation. Elastomer fibers, such as some silicone and polyurethane fibers, have the smallest modulus and strength. But they have the largest strain-at-break. This is not caused by yielding or plastic deformation, but is an inherent non-linear elastic property of elastomeric materials.

The stress-strain curves shown in Figures 15.9 and 10 are for as-spun polymer fibers, in which molecular orientation has not been fully developed. However,

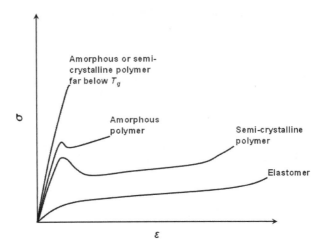

Figure 15.10. Typical stress-strain curves of un-oriented amorphous, semicrystalline, and elastomeric polymer fibers.

commercial polymer fibers have high molecular orientation, and hence more polymer chains are aligned along the fiber longitudinal direction to bear the applied load. These fibers have higher modulus and strength than un-oriented polymer fibers. But their strain-at-break is lower. Figure 15.11 shows a typical stress-strain curve of a polymer fiber with high molecular orientation. The fiber does not present a yield point. However, the stress-strain curve still deviates from the ideal behavior, especially at relatively high strains.

15.2.4 RESPONSE OF POLYMER CHAINS

To understand the stress-strain behavior of polymer fibers, it is important to know how the polymer chains respond to the tensile strain. Figure 15.12 divides the stress-strain curve of an un-oriented amorphous fiber into three stages. Stage I is the same as the elastic region. The plastic region of the curve is divided into Stages II and III. The following is how the polymer chains respond to the tensile strain in these three stages.

Stage I: The strain mainly is caused by the changes in the chain length and angle. The deformation is reversible and approximately follows the Hooke's law.

Stage II: The polymer chain segments start to move and orientation starts to occur. The characteristic of this stage is strain softening, i.e., the stress decreases with increase in strain. (The stain softening phenomenon disappears if true stress and true strain are used in the stress-strain curve. However, the

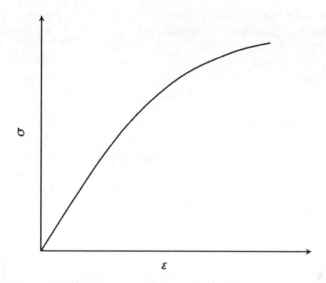

Figure 15.11. Typical stress-strain curve of a molecularly-oriented polymer fiber.

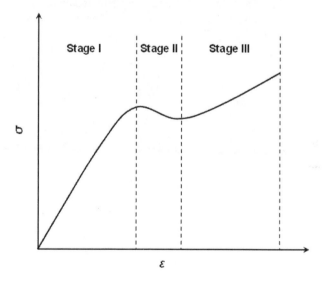

Figure 15.12. Three-stage stress-strain curve of an un-oriented amorphous polymer fiber.

movement and orientation of polymer chains remain the same.) The deformation is largely irreversible since Stage II is in the plastic region.

Stage III: Polymer chain segments continue to move and cold flow occurs. The deformation is irreversible. Due to the molecular orientation and the formation of new interactions such as entanglements, the stress starts to increase again until the fiber breaks.

The stress-strain curve of an un-oriented semicrystalline fiber also can be divided into three stages (Figure 15.13). The following is how the polymer chains respond to the tensile strain in these three stages.

Stage I: The amorphous phase is deformed first and this is realized by changing the chain length and angle (Figures 15.14A and B). The deformation of the crystalline phase occurs when the tie molecules between the adjacent crystallites are highly extended. The deformation of the crystalline phase starts with the increase of the crystallite thickness (Figure 15.14C), followed by the tilting of the crystalline phase (Figure 15.14D). The fiber deformation in this stage is largely reversible and approximately follows the Hooke's law.

Stage II: The polymer chain segments in the amorphous phase start to move and large-scale molecular orientation occurs. Large crystallites may be unraveled under stress to form smaller fibril-like crystallites (Figure 15.14E). These newly formed fibrils still are attached to each other by tie molecules, and they slide against each other to align along the tensile direction (Figure 15.14F). The deformation in Stage II is irreversible.

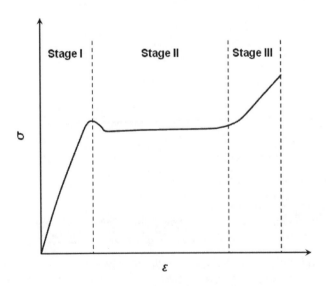

Figure 15.13. Three-stage stress-strain curve of an un-oriented semicrystalline polymer fiber.

Stage III: The sliding and orientation still occur, but are largely limited by tie molecules or entanglements. The stress increases until the fiber breaks. The deformation in this stage is irreversible.

These are just some typical responses that may be observed in an un-oriented semicrystalline fiber while a tensile stress is applied. In reality, the chemical and crystalline structures affect how the polymer chains behave under stress. As a result, for some un-oriented semicrystalline polymer fibers, the responses of polymer chains under tensile stress may be different from what is discussed above.

There may not be significant yielding or plastic deformation in molecularly oriented fibers. However, the stress-strain curve of molecularly oriented fibers still is nonlinear and can be divided into two stages (Figure 15.15):

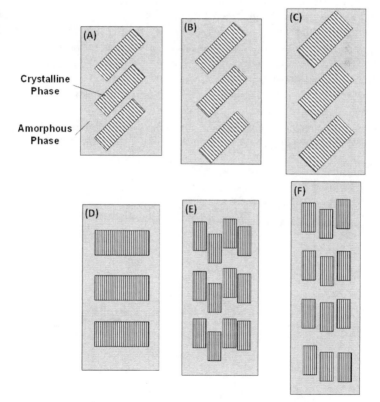

Figure 15.14. Structural evolution of an un-oriented semicrystalline fiber under tensile stress. (A) Before deformation, (B) deformation of amorphous phase, (C) deformation of crystalline phase, (D) tilting of crystalline phase, (E) unraveling and sliding of crystalline phase, and (F) final plastic deformation. For simplicity, tie molecules are not shown.

Stage I: The stress-strain curve in this stage is a straight line and is reversible. The deformation follows the Hooke's law and is caused mainly by the changes in chain length and angle.

Stage II: The stage is not apparent if the degree of molecular orientation is very high. However, Stage II can be clearly observed in polymer fibers that have low or moderate molecular orientation. In this stage, polymer chain segments could move under stress and the sliding between the fibril-like crystallites could occur. However, the tensile stress continues to increase until the fiber breaks.

15.2.5 STRESS-STRAIN BEHAVIOR OF COMMERCIAL FIBERS

Although un-oriented amorphous and semicrystalline polymer fibers are important and they often are the intermediate products of molecularly oriented fibers, most commercial polymer fibers are molecularly oriented, except for a few elastomeric polymer fibers. The molecular orientation in natural polymer fibers occurs by itself under the control of genetic codes. For synthetic polymer fibers, molecular orientation is introduced purposely by high-speed spinning or drawing to enhance the mechanical properties of these fibers so they can be converted into useful final products.

Based on the stress-strain behavior, molecularly oriented polymer fibers can be divided into three groups: high modulus-high tenacity (HM-HT) fibers, tough

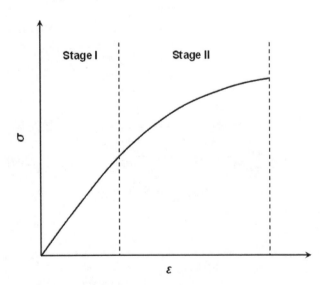

Figure 15.15. Two-stage stress-strain curve of a molecularly-oriented polymer fiber.

fibers, and regular fibers. Figure 15.16 shows the stress-strain curves of these three groups of polymer fibers. For comparison, the stress-strain curves of inorganic and elastomeric polymer fibers also are shown. Inorganic fibers have high modulus and strength, but they are brittle. HM-HT polymer fibers also have high modulus and strength. In Figure 15.16, the modulus of inorganic fibers is higher than that of HM-HT polymer fibers. But that relationship is relative since some commercial HM-HT polymer fibers can have higher modulus than typical inorganic fibers. Tough fibers typically are synthetic and have high strength, but relatively low strain-at-break. Regular fibers, including natural and regenerated polymer fibers and some synthetic polymer fibers, have moderate strength and strain-at-break. Elastomeric polymer fibers have low strength, but extremely high strain-at-break.

Figure 15.17 shows typical stress-strain curves of some commercial synthetic polymer, natural polymer, and inorganic fibers. Carbon and Kevlar have the highest strengths and moduli, but their strains-at-break are the lowest. Polyester and nylon 6,6 fibers with high degrees of molecular orientation and crystallinity are considered as high-strength fibers in certain applications, but their strengths and moduli are lower than those of carbon and Kevlar fibers. Regular polyester and nylon 6,6 fibers have much lower strengths and moduli, but their strains-at-break are much higher. Acrylic fibers often have lower strength than regular polyester and nylon 6,6 fibers, but not necessarily lower modulus or stain-at-break. Among the three natural polymer fibers shown in Figure 15.17, silk and cotton have higher strengths and moduli than wool fibers, but wool fibers have the largest

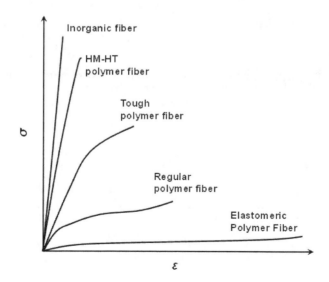

Figure 15.16. Stress-strain curves of commercial inorganic fibers, HM-HT polymer fibers, tough polymer fibers, regular polymer fibers, elastomeric polymer fibers.

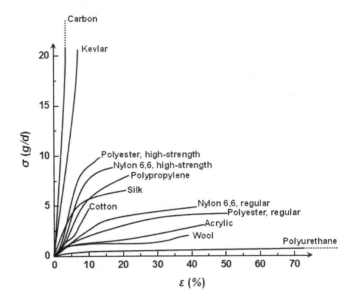

Figure 15.17. Typical stress-strain curves of some synthetic polymer, natural polymer, and inorganic fibers. Data obtained at 20°C and 65% relative humidity. Acrylic fibers are made from copolymers composed of at least 85% by acrylonitrile units, -CH$_2$-CH(CN)-.

strain-at-break. Polyurethane fibers are elastomeric with a strain-at-break up to 500%.

The stress-strain curves shown in Figure 15.17 just present the general property trends. In reality, the curve shapes may vary from fiber to fiber. For example, the stress-strain curves of natural polymer fibers are affected by the farming conditions of the plants or animals. Depending on the applications, the processing conditions of synthetic polymer fibers can be selectively adjusted to produce different physical structures and mechanical properties. Table 15.2 shows typical tensile strength, modulus and strain-at-break values of some commercial fibers.

15.2.6 *External Factors Affecting the Stress-Strain Behavior*

External factors that affect the stress-strain behavior of fibers (especially polymer fibers) include, but are not limited to: moisture, temperature, and strain rate. The discussion in this section focuses on the general trends of regular, molecularly-oriented polymer fibers. For simplicity, the typical stress-strain behavior shown in Figure 15.11 is used in the discussion.

Figure 15.18A shows the effect of moisture, i.e., relative humidity (RH%), on the stress-strain curve of a typical polymer fiber. Water molecules can diffuse into the fiber structure and increases the intermolecular distance between the

Table 15.2. Tensile strengths, moduli, and strains-at-break of synthetic polymer, natural polymer, and inorganic fibers. Data obtained at 20°C and 65% relative humidity.

Fiber	Strength (grams per denier)	Modulus (grams per denier)	Strain-at-Break (%)
Synthetic Polymer Fibers			
Polypropylene	2.0–7.8	50–90	15–50
Acrylic	2.0–3.6	40–75	25–55
Nylon 6,6, regular	4.3–6.0	15–40	15–40
Nylon 6,6, high-strength	6.0–9.0	50–60	13–16
Polyester, regular	2.5–6.0	105–120	10–60
Polyester, high-strength	6.0–10.5	150–160	7–8
Kevlar (HM-HT fiber)	20–25	400–1500	2–5
Spectra (HM-HT fiber)	25–43	850–1800	3–4
Polyurethane (elastomeric fiber)	0.4	0.1	500
Natural Polymer Fibers (including regenerated fibers)			
Cotton	3.0–5.0	45–85	5–10
Flax	2.6–7.7	200–460	1.3–3.3
Jute	3.0–5.8	110–350	1.3–3.0
Ramie	5.3–7.4	175–190	3.0–7.0
Wool	1.0–1.7	25–35	20–45
Silk	2.4–6.1	80–90	10–25
Acetate	1.2–1.5	45	25–35
Triacetate	1.1–1.4	37–40	25–35
Rayon, regular	1.8–3.0	50–70	15–28
Rayon, high-strength	3.0–5.0	100–150	7–10
Inorganic Fibers			
Carbon	8.6–40	1500–2600	0.7–2.5
Glass	6.3–20	350–450	2–5.4

Sources: Hull, D., et. al., *An Introduction to Composite Materials*, Second Edition, Cambridge University Press, 1996.; Morton, W.E., et. al., *Physical Properties of Textile Fibres*, Fourth Edition, Woodhead Publishing Limited, 2008.; Mwaikambo, L.Y., *African Journal of Science and Technology*, 7, 120–133, 2006.; Tortora, P.G., *Understanding Textiles*, Fourth Edition, Macmillian Publishing Company, 1992.

polymer chains. This softens the fiber and causes a reduction in fiber modulus. At the same time, the fiber strength decreases and the strain-at-break increases. However, this softening effect only occurs for nylon, wool, silk, and other polymer fibers that are capable of forming hydrogen bonds with water molecules. Fibers made of polyethylene, polypropylene, or other polymers that do not form

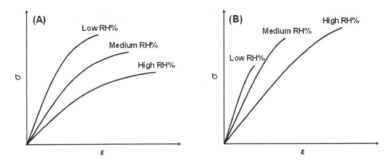

Figure 15.18. Effect of relative humidity on the stress-strain behavior of polymer fibers that are capable of forming hydrogen bonding. (A) Typical polymer fibers, and (B) cotton.

hydrogen bonds are not affected by moisture. Another special case is cotton. As shown in Figure 15.18B, the strength of cotton fibers actually increases when they absorb moisture. One explanation for this is that significant residual stress exists in cotton and the diffusion of moisture helps release the residual stress, leading to increased fiber strength. However, work still is needed to provide strong experimental support for this argument.

The effect of temperature is similar to that of moisture. Figure 15.19 shows the typical stress-strain curves of a polymer fiber at low, medium, and high temperatures. With increase in temperature, the fiber strength and modulus decrease, but the strain-at-break increases. The actual changes in strength, modulus and strain-at-break vary from fiber to fiber. In addition, exposure to high temperatures for prolonged time could lead to permanent degradation of fibers.

The stress-strain behavior of fibers generally is tested by increasing the strain from zero at a fixed rate. The rate of the strain is another factor influencing the stress-strain behavior of fibers. In most cases, increased strain rate leads to increased fiber strength and modulus, but reduced strain-at-break (Figure 15.20). This is because, at high rates, it becomes more difficult to initiate the different types of motions of the polymers, which will be discussed in Chapter 16.

15.2.7 STRUCTURAL FACTORS AFFECTING THE STRESS-STRAIN BEHAVIOR

Many structural factors affect or even determine the stress-strain behavior of fibers. This section focuses on discussing how the different structural factors affect the stress-strain behavior of regular, molecularly oriented polymer fibers.

Polymer chemical structure limits the maximum potential properties that polymer fibers can theoretically achieve. In general, fibers made of rigid polymer chains have higher strength and larger modulus than those of flexible polymer chains. For example, Kevlar is an aramid fiber formed by polyparaphenylene terephthalamide, which contains aromatic rings on the polymer backbone. The presence of aromatic rings makes the polymer chains very rigid, and as a result,

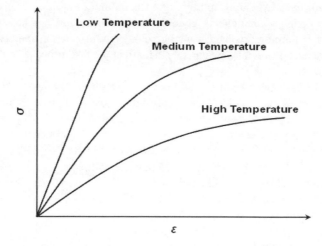

Figure 15.19. Effect of temperature on the stress-strain behavior of polymer fibers.

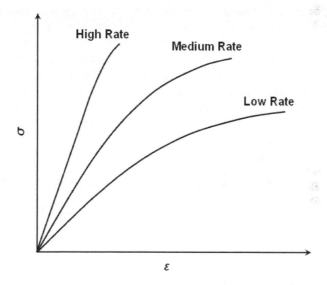

Figure 15.20. Effect of strain rate on the stress-strain behavior of polymer fibers.

Kevlar has excellent tensile properties, i.e., high strength and modulus. Similar to rigid polymer chains, polymers that have strong secondary bonding also can form fibers with high strength and modulus. Although rigid polymer chains and strong secondary bonding can lead to high tensile properties, polymer fibers with high strength and modulus could be obtained by other means. For example, polyethylene chains are flexible and can only form weak secondary bonding (van der Waal force). However, Spectra fibers made from gel-spun ultra-high molecular weight polyethylene have extremely high strength and modulus (Table 15.2), mainly due to the extra-long polymer chains, good molecular orientation, and high degree of crystallinity. Therefore, molecular weight, molecular orientation and crystallinity also are important structural parameters that affect the final properties of polymer fibers.

Figure 15.21 shows the effect of molecular weight on the tensile strength of polymer fibers. At low molecular weights, the tensile strength increases rapidly with increase in molecular weight. However, at high molecular weights, the tensile strength only increases slightly when molecular weight increases. Although it is feasible to improve the fiber tensile strength by increasing the polymer molecular weight, this approach is limited in practice by the polymer viscosity. With increase in molecular weight, the polymer viscosity increases rapidly, especially at high molecular weights, and this makes it difficult to produce fibers from high molecular weight polymers.

Polymer chemical structure limits the maximum potential, but the physical structure of polymers determines the actual tensile properties that can be achieved by fibers in practice. One of the most important physical structural factors for polymer fibers is the molecular orientation along the fiber longitudinal direction. Figure 15.22 shows the effect of molecular orientation on the stress-strain behavior of polymer fibers. When the degree of molecular orientation is low, the fiber exhibits yielding and plastic deformation, and the stress-strain curve can be divided into three stages, as discussed in section 15.2.4. When the molecular orientation increases, the strength and modulus increase, but the strain-at-break decreases. The plastic region reduce quickly, but still may present when the fiber has medium orientation. When the molecular orientation is high, the plastic region disappears, and both the strength and modulus increase significantly. One simple way to understand the effect of molecular orientation is that: while increasing the

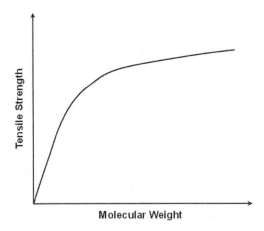

Figure 15.21. Effect of molecular weight on the tensile strength of polymer fibers.

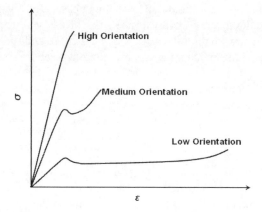

Figure 15.22. Effect of molecular orientation on the stress-strain behavior of polymer fibers.

molecular orientation, more primary bonds are distributed along the fiber longitudinal direction to bear the applied force. This is the main cause of increased strength and modulus since primary bonds along the polymer main chains are significantly stronger and stiffer than the secondary bonds between the polymer chains. Therefore, to improve the tensile properties of polymer fibers, it is essential to achieve high molecular orientation in the fibers. For synthetic polymer fibers, high molecular orientation is achieved by using a take-up speed that is greater than the extrusion speed, and by introducing a post-spinning drawing step. Natural polymer fibers typically have high molecular orientation by themselves. Although high molecular orientation is desired in most cases, fibers with low molecular orientation also are useful in some applications, especially, when large strain-at-break is needed.

Similar to molecular orientation, the degree of crystallinity also is critically important. The crystalline phase has orderly arranged polymer chains and has better mechanical properties than the amorphous phase. As a result, with increase in crystallinity, the strength and modulus of polymer fibers increase, but the strain-at-break decreases. All useful natural polymer fibers have relatively high degrees of crystallinity. The degree of crystallinity of synthetic polymer fibers can be controlled by selectively adjusting the processing conditions used during the fiber formation.

15.2.8 ELASTIC RECOVERY

Elastic recovery is the ability of a fiber to recover from its deformation after the removal of the applied stress. As discussed in the previous sections, the deformation of a fiber includes both elastic and plastic components. The elastic deformation mainly is caused by the changing of chain length and angle under applied stress, and it is recoverable. The plastic deformation is associated with the molecular orientation, unraveling and sliding of crystalline phase, etc., and it is unrecoverable. As a result, the ealstic recovery of fibers is typically less than 100%.

Figure 15.23 shows both the tensile stretching curve and the recovery curve of a typical fiber. The stretching curve shows the typical stress-strain behavior, which includes both elastic and plastic deformations. The recovering curve shows only the elastic deformation (or strain) is recovered after the removal of the applied tensile stress. The elastic recovery, or strain recovery, can then be defined as:

$$Elastic\ Recovery = \frac{Recovered\ Strain}{Total\ Strain} \tag{15.24}$$

Table 15.3 shows the elastic recovery of some fibers under different strains and in different humidities. Nylon, polyester and wool fibers have higher elastic recovery values than most other fibers. Both strain and humidity affect the fiber elastic recovery. In general, the elastic recovery of fibers decreases with increase in strain. However, the effect of humidity is complicated. Polyethylene fibers do not absorb moisture and their elastic recovery is not affected by the humidity. However, for fibers that can absorb moisture, their ability to recover from strain is affected by moisture. In some cases, the elastic recovery increases with increase in humidity. In other cases, the elastic recovery decreases with humidity.

Fibers sometimes are subject to repeated cycles of stretch and recovery. The elastic recovery can change during repeated cycles. Figure 15.24 shows the stretch and recovery curves of a fiber under multi-cycle stretch and recovery tests.

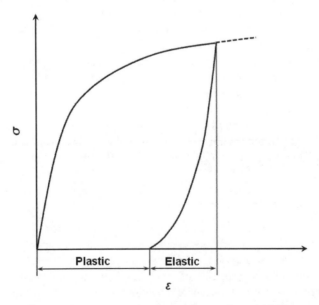

Figure 15.23. Stretch and recovery curves of a typical fiber.

Table 15.3. Elastic recovery of fibers at different strains and humidities.

Fiber	Recovery (%) from					
	1% Strain		5% Strain		10% Strain	
	60 RH%	90 RH%	60 RH%	90 RH%	60 RH%	90 RH%
Synthetic Polymer Fibers						
Polyethylene	80	80	80	83	78	80
Acrylic	92	90	50	48	43	39
Nylon 6,6	90	92	89	90	86	—
Polyester	98	92	65	60	51	47
Natural Polymer Fibers (including regenerated fibers)						
Cotton	91	83	52	59	—	—
Wool	99	94	69	82	51	56
Silk	84	78	52	58	34	45
Acetate	96	75	46	37	24	22
Rayon	67	60	32	28	23	27

Source: Beste, L.F., et. al., *Textile Research Journal*, 20, 441–453, 1950.

For this particular fiber, the elastic recovery at the first cycle is relatively low. However, after a few cycles, the fiber becomes conditioned and the stretch and recovery curves tend to fall on a loop, i.e., 100% elastic recovery. This phenomoum is important for some applications, such as tire cords. However, not all fibers can have 100% elastic recovery in repeated cycles.

In addition to dimensional recovery, work recovery often is studied for tensile deformation. While stretching a fiber, the total work done is either stored in chemical bonds or is lost, typically in the form of heat. The work stored in the chemical bonds is recoverable, but the work lost is not. In Figure 15.23, the area under the stretch curve is the total work per unit volume done during stretching. The area under the recovery curve is the work per unit volume returned during recovery. Work recovery can then be defined as:

$$Work\ Recovery = \frac{Work\ Returned\ during\ Recovery}{Total\ Work\ done\ during\ Stretching} \quad (15.25)$$

Table 15.4 shows the work recovery of some fibers under different strains and in different humidities. Inorganic fibers, such as glass, have very high work recovery at a low strain of 1%. However, they break at moderate and high strains, and no work recovery can be measured. The work recovery of polymer fibers is lower than their elastic (strain) recovery due to the non-linear stress-strain behavior. In addition, the work recovery also is affected by both strain and humidity.

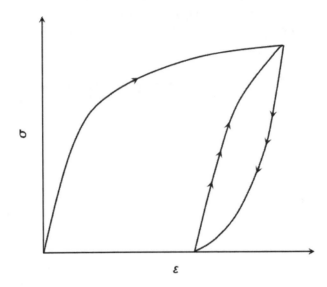

Figure 15.24. Stretch and recovery curves of a fiber under multi-cycle tests.

15.3 COMPRESSIVE PROPERTIES

Compressive properties of fibers also are important. Fibers often experience compressive forces while being made into the final products. The final products also may be under compression when they are in use. Therefore, it is important to understand the compressional properties of fibers.

15.3.1 LONGITUDINAL COMPRESSIVE PROPERTIES

A longitudinal compressive stress basically is a negative tensile stress, while a longitudinal compressive strain is the negative tensile strain. Figure 15.25 shows an ideal longitudinal stress-strain curve of a fiber. The longitudinal compressive modulus is the same as (or comparable to) the tensile modulus. However, the compressive strength typically is lower than the tensile strength. Table 15.5 compares the longitudinal compressive strength and tensile strength of some fibers.

The buckling of fibers under a longitudinal compressive force is a major issue in fiber applications. Figure 15.26 shows the possible response of an unconstrained fiber under longitudinal compression. Under the longitudinal compressive force, the fiber buckles easily even at low strains if there is no lateral support. The critical compressive force ($F_{critical}$), above which the fiber buckling occurs, is given by the Euler's equation:

Table 15.4. Work recovery of fibers at different strains and humidities.

Fiber	Recovery (%) from					
	1% Strain		5% Strain		10% Strain	
	60 RH%	90 RH%	60 RH%	90 RH%	60 RH%	90 RH%
Synthetic Polymer Fibers						
Polyethylene	55	63	50	55	47	51
Acrylic	64	66	23	21	21	16
Nylon 6,6	66	68	55	64	52	—
Polyester	82	76	35	30	24	21
Natural Polymer Fibers (including regenerated fibers)						
Cotton	50	42	31	33	-	-
Wool	83	67	37	45	21	25
Silk	57	47	23	24	17	23
Acetate	80	70	18	14	9	8
Rayon	50	27	11	10	9	11
Inorganic Fiber						
Glass	97	—	—	—	—	—

Source: Beste, L.F., et. al., *Textile Research Journal*, 20, 441–453, 1950.

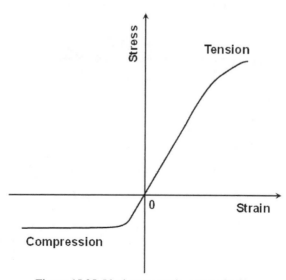

Figure 15.25. Ideal stress-strain curve of a fiber.

Table 15.5. Longitudinal compressive and tensile strengths of
fibers. Data obtained at 20°C and 65% relative humidity.

Fiber	Tensile Strength (GPa)	Compressive Strength (GPa)
Kevlar 149	3.4–3.5	0.32–0.46
Spectra 1000	3.0	0.17
Carbon, polyacrylonitrile-based	1.4–3.9	0.48–1.15
Carbon, pitch-based	1.8–3.8	1.06–2.55
Glass	3.5–4.5	> 0.81

Source: Kumar, S., *Indian Journal of Fiber and Textile Research*, 16, 52–64, 1991.

$$F_{critical} = \frac{\pi^2 EI}{(KL)^2} \tag{15.26}$$

where E is the modulus of the fiber, I the area moment of inertia of the fiber cross-section, K the effective length factor, and L the fiber length. The effective length factor is determined by the conditions of fiber ends: $K = 1.0$ when both ends are pinned (hinged, free to rotate); $K = 0.5$ when both ends are fixed; $K = 0.699$ when one end is fixed and the other end is pinned; and $K = 2.0$ when one end is fixed and the other end is free to move laterally. The KL is the effective length of the fiber.

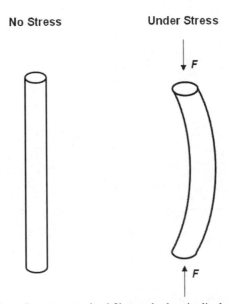

Figure 15.26. Buckling of an unconstrained fiber under longitudinal compressive force.

The Euler's equation then can be rearranged to obtain the critical compressional stress ($\sigma_{critical}$) that is needed for a fiber to buckle:

$$\sigma_{critical} = \frac{F_{critical}}{A} = \frac{\pi^2 E}{\left(KL/R\right)^2} \tag{15.27}$$

Therefore, the fiber's resistance to buckling can be improved by increasing the fiber modulus, increasing the fiber radius, and reducing the fiber length. Providing lateral support is another effective approach to enhance the fiber's resistance to buckling. In composites, the buckling of fibers is limited by the matrix when the compressive force is along the fiber axis (Figure 15.27A).

15.3.2 *Transverse Compressive Properties*

In addition to longitudinal compressive properties, transverse compressive properties also are important. Fibers in composites need have sufficient transverse compressive modulus and strength since the external force sometimes is applied in the transverse direction to the fiber axis (Figure 15.27B). In both woven and nonwoven fabrics, fibers also may experience transverse compressive forces while in use.

Table 15.6 shows compressive moduli of some fibers under the longitudinal and transverse directions. In general, the transverse compressive moduli of polymer fibers are lower than their longitudinal compressive moduli. This is mainly because of high molecular orientation in these polymer fibers. Carbon fibers also have lower transverse compressive modulus than longitudinal compressive modulus since the graphene sheets in these fibers are largely oriented. However, glass fibers are isotropic without any orientation, and hence have comparable transverse and longitudinal compressive moduli. Similar to the moduli, the transverse

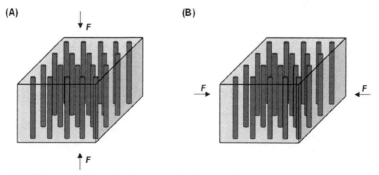

Figure 15.27. A composite under compressive force: (A) along fiber axis direction, and (B) along fiber transverse direction.

Table 15.6. Longitudinal and transverse compressive moduli of fibers. Data obtained at 20°C and 65% relative humidity shows:

Fiber	Longitudinal Modulus (GPa)	Transverse Modulus (GPa)
Polyethylene	89.3	1.21
Kevlar	63.4–179.1	2.31–2.59
Wool	3.55–3.73	0.97–1.01
Carbon, polyacrylonitrile-based	234.6–343.2	6.03–10.08
Carbon, pitch-based	126.2–379.0	3.08–9.95
Glass	77.4	67.87

Source: Muraki, C., et. al., *Journal of the Textile Institute*, 81, 12–21, 1994.; Kawabata, S., *Journal of the Textile Institute*, 81, 432–447, 1990.

compressive strengths of most fibers also are lower than their longitudinal compressive strengths.

15.4 TORSIONAL PROPERTIES

Fibers often are twisted while being converted to useful products. For example, fibers are twisted to form yarns, which then are made into textile fabrics or ropes. The final products made of fibers also may be twisted during use. The torsional properties determine how fibers respond while being twisted.

15.4.1 TORSION OF FIBERS

Torsion basically is shear with a different geometry. Figure 15.28 shows the deformation of a fiber under a torsional force (F). The fiber has a length of L and a radius of R. After the fiber is twisted through an angle θ, line OA on the cross-section of the fiber is displaced to a new position OB. Point O is the center of the fiber cross-section. When θ is small, the displacement (δ) of point A along the torsional force direction is:

$$\delta = r\cos\theta = r\theta \tag{15.28}$$

where r is the length of line OA. The shear strain (γ) and shear stress (τ), respectively, can be obtained by:

$$\gamma = \theta\frac{r}{L} \tag{15.29}$$

and

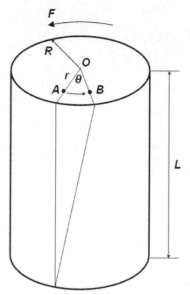

Figure 15.28. Deformation of a fiber under a torsional force *F*.

$$\tau = G\theta \frac{r}{L} \tag{15.30}$$

where *G* is the shear modulus of the fiber. Therefore, the shear stress and shear strain in a fiber are proportional to the radial distance from the fiber center. The maximum shear stress and strain are obtained at the fiber surface. Figure 15.29 shows the shear stress-shear strain curve at the surface of a fiber. Shear stress increases with increase in shear strain. Shear strength is defined as the shear stress when the fiber breaks. Table 15.7 compares the tensile and shear strengths of fibers. It is seen the fiber shear strength is smaller than the fiber tensile strength.

The torque of the fiber often is studied by twisting a fiber. Torque basically is the measure of how much a torsional force acting on a fiber causes that fiber to twist. In mechanics, when the force is applied on a lever arm, the torque can be defined by:

$$Torque = LF \sin \varphi \tag{15.31}$$

where *L* is the length of the lever arm, *F* the magnitude of the force, and φ the angle between the force and the lever arm (Figure 15.30).

While twisting a fiber shown in Figure 15.28, the torque produced on the fiber by the torsional force can be calculated by:

$$Torque = \frac{\pi R^4 G\theta}{2L} \tag{15.32}$$

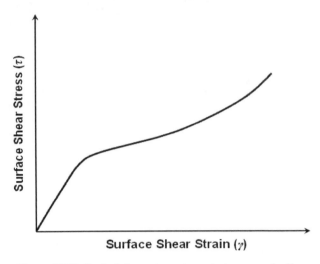

Figure 15.29. Typical shear stress-shear strain curve of a fiber.

Table 15.7. Tensile and shear strengths of fibers. Data
obtained at 20°C and 65% relative humidity.

Fiber	Tensile Strength (grams per denier)	Shear Strength (grams per denier)
Nylon	4.4	1.3
Cotton	2.7	1.0
Flax	2.9	0.91
Silk	3.5	1.3
Rayon	2.0	0.72
Acetate	1.3	0.66

Source: Warner, S.B., *Fiber Science*, Prentice Hall, 1995.

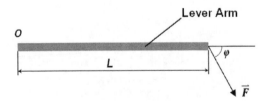

Figure 15.30. Definition of torque.

In most measurements, the torque is plotted against the twist, i.e., the number of turns per unit fiber length (turns/cm or turns/mm). Figure 15.31 shows a typical torque-twist curve of a fiber, which is similar to the shear stress-shear strain curve.

According to Equation 15.32, under a torsional force, the fiber resists the torsional displacement (θ/L) by a factor of $\pi R^4 G/2$. Therefore, the torsional rigidity can be defined as:

$$Torsional\ Rigidity = \frac{\pi R^4 G}{2} \qquad (15.33)$$

The torsional rigidity of a fiber contains a material term (G) and a geometric term ($\pi R^4/2$). The geometric term contains the fiber radius to the fourth power, and hence the radius or diameter of a fiber has a significant effect on its torsional rigidity. Equation 15.33 can only be used for calculating the torsional rigidities of circular fibers, i.e., those with circular cross-sections. When a non-circular fiber is studied, the shape factor (λ_T), i.e., the ratio of the perimeter of the non-circular fiber to that of a circular fiber of the same cross-sectional area, should be used:

$$Torsional\ Rigidity = \lambda_T \frac{\pi R^4 G}{2} \qquad (15.34)$$

15.4.2 SHEAR MODULUS OF FIBERS

As discussed in section 15.4.1, the shear modulus of fibers is important, and it determines the fiber torsional rigidity. The shear modulus of a fiber can be measured by using the torsion pendulum technique. Figure 15.32 shows the schematic of a

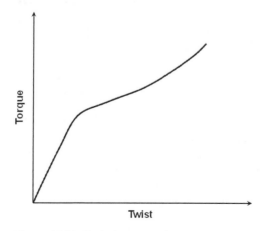

Figure 15.31. Typical torque-twist curve of a fiber.

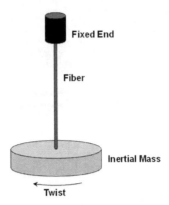

Figure 15.32. Schematic of a basic torsion pendulum. More sophisticated designs are available.

basic torsion pendulum. The fiber is mounted between a fixed end and an inertial mass. The inertial mass should be sufficiently small so the tensile deformation of the fiber can be neglected. At the same time, the inertial mass also should be sufficiently large so it can produce stable oscillation for accurate measurement. During the measurement, the fiber is subject to a shear strain caused by the rotation of the inertial mass. The frequency of oscillation is measured. The shear modulus of the fiber is given by:

$$G = \frac{2LM\omega^2}{\pi R^4} \qquad (15.35)$$

where L is the length of the fiber between the fixed end and the inertial mass, M the moment of inertia of the inertial mass, ω the frequency of the oscillation, and R the radius of the fiber. When the inertial mass (m) is a cylindrical disc, its moment of inertia is:

$$M = \frac{mR_{disc}^2}{2} \qquad (15.36)$$

where R_{disc} is the radius of the inertial mass.

Equation 15.35 only gives accurate shear modulus values of circular fibers, i.e., those with circular cross-sections. When a non-circular fiber is studied, the shape factor should be used. Table 15.8 shows typical shear moduli and shape factors of some fibers.

For fibers, the relationship between shear modulus and tensile modulus is interesting. Earlier in this Chapter, it has been mentioned the shear modulus of isotropic materials has a simple relationship with tensile modulus and Passion's ratio (v). The ratio of tensile modulus to shear modulus is:

$$\frac{E}{G} = 2(1+v) \qquad (15.37)$$

Table 15.8. Shear moduli and shape factors of fibers. Data obtained at 20°C and 65% relative humidity.

Fiber	Shear Modulus (GPa)	Shape Factor
Polypropylene	0.75	1.00
Polyester	0.8	1.00
Acrylic, bilobal	1.3	0.57
Nylon 6,6	0.4	1.00
Kevlar 49	1.4	1.00
Kevlar 149	1.2	1.00
Cotton	2.2	0.71
Flax	1.4	0.94
Wool	1.3	0.99
Silk	2.4	0.84
Rayon	1.0	0.94
Carbon	4.7	1.00

Source: Warner, S.B., *Fiber Science*, Prentice Hall, 1995.

The Passion's ratios of most isotropic polymers are between 0.3 and 0.4, and hence the E/G ratios of isotropic polymers range from 2.5 to 3.0. However, polymer fibers are anisotropic due to the high molecular orientation. With increase in molecular orientation, the tensile modulus increases, but the shear modulus decreases. This is because the molecular orientation is beneficial for increasing the fiber tensile modulus; however, with increased molecular orientation, more fibrils are formed in the fiber and the fibrils are easily separated by twisting although they have excellent tensile properties. Table 15.9 shows the tensile moduli, shear moduli, and their ratios for some fibers. Some fibers have very large E/G ratios due to the high molecular orientation.

15.5 BENDING PROPERTIES

To bend a fabric, composite, or any fiber-containing products, the bending of fibers is required. In each case, the arrangement of fibers is important in determining the bending stiffness of the final product. However, to understand the bending of the final products, the bending properties of fibers must be studied first.

The deformation of a fiber under bending is shown in Figure 15.33. Outer layers of the fiber are stretched and the inner layers are compressed. While being bent, the length of the tensile side of the fiber increases, but the length of the compressive side decreases. However, the neural plane between the tensile and compressive sides remains unchanged in length. In addition to tensile and

Table 15.9. Tensile moduli, shear moduli, and their ratios of fibers. Data obtained at 20°C and 65% relative humidity.

Fiber	Tensile Modulus (GPa)	Shear Modulus (GPa)	Tensile Modulus / Shear Modulus
Polyester, high-speed spun	1.98	0.65	3.05
Polyester, high-speed spun and drawn	8.81	0.85	10.4
Nylon 6	3.41	0.49	6.96
Polypropylene	2.09	0.57	3.67
Polyethylene, gel-spun	93.7	0.84	112
Kevlar 49	94.2	1.60	58.9

Source: Zeronian, S.H., et. al., *Journal of the Textile Institute*, 85, 293–300, 1994.

compressive stresses, shear stress also may be developed, depending on how the bending is carried out.

Figure 15.34 compares the typical tensile and bending stress-strain curves of polymer fibers. In most cases, the bending stress-strain curve lay below the tensile curve. This is because the compressive side of the fiber yields more easily than the tensile side. The bending rigidity (or flexural rigidity) of a circular fiber is given by:

$$\text{Bending Rigidity} = \frac{\pi R^4 E}{4} \tag{15.38}$$

Similar to the torsional rigidity, the bending rigidity also has a material term (E, tensile modulus) and a geometric term ($\pi R^4/4$). The geometric term contains the fiber radius to the fourth power, and hence the fiber radius or diameter has a significant influence on the bending rigidity. For non-circular fibers, the fiber shape factor should be used while calculating the bending rigidity:

$$\text{Bending Rigidity} = \lambda_B \frac{\pi R^4 E}{4} \tag{15.39}$$

The value of the shape factor (λ_B) for bending rigidity may be different from that (λ_T) for the torsional rigidity. However, they have the same tendency to increase or decrease when the cross-sectional shape of fibers changes. According to Equations 15.34 and 39, with increase in shape factors, both bending and torsional rigidities increase (Figure 15.35).

Table 15.10 compares the bending and torsional rigidities of some fibers. The bending rigidities of fibers generally are greater than their torsional rigidities.

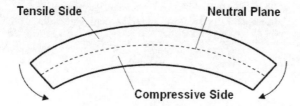

Figure 15.33. Bending of a fiber.

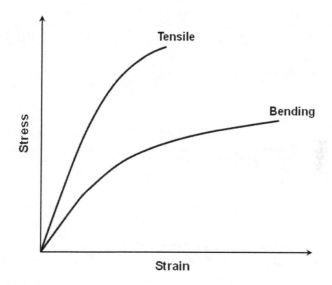

Figure 15.34. Typical tensile and bending stress-strain curves of a fiber.

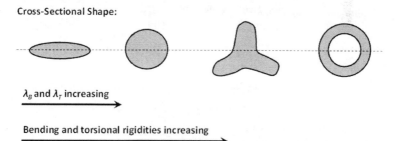

Figure 15.35. Changes in shape factors, and torsional and bending rigidities with cross-sectional shape. The bending direction is defined by the dash line.

Table 15.10. Bending and torsional rigidities of fibers.
Data obtained at 20°C and 65% relative humidity.

Fiber	Bending Rigidity (Pa mm⁴)	Torsional Rigidity (Pa mm⁴)
Polypropylene	143	41.3
Polyester	118–357	25.2–80.0
Acrylic	193–377	67.0–194
Nylon 6	181	61
Nylon 6,6	58.0–209	13.8–81.0
Cotton	194–218	61.0
Wool	600	319
Silk	39.0	10.6
Acetate	125	31.4
Triacetate	220	80.0
Rayon	89.0–800	15.6–191

Source: Owen, J.D., *Journal of the Textile Institute Transactions*, 56, T329–T339, 1965.

REFERENCES

[1]   Beste, L.F., and Hoffman, R.M., "A Quantitative Study of Resilience", *Textile Research Journal*, 20, 441–453, 1950.

[2]   Boresi, A.P., Schmidt, R.J., and Sidebottom, O.M., *Advanced Mechanics of Materials*, Fifth Edition, John Wiley & Sons, Ltd., 1993.

[3]   Cook, J.G., *Handbook of Textile Fibres, Volume I—Natural Fibres*, Woodhead Publishing Limited, 2001.

[4]   Cook, J.G., *Handbook of Textile Fibers, Vol. II. Man-Made Fibers*, Fifth Edition, Woodhead Publishing Limited, 1984.

[5]   Gohl, E.P.H., and Vilensky, L.D., *Textile Science: An Explanation of Fibre Properties*, Longman Group Ltd., 1981.

[6]   Hearle, J.W.S., and Miraftab, M., "The Flex Fatigue of Polyamide and Polyester Fibres", *Journal of Materials Science*, 26, 2861–2867, 1991.

[7]   Hearle, J.W.S., and Wong, B.S., "Flexural Fatigue and Surface Abrasion of Kevlar-29 and Other High-Modulus Fibres", *Journal of Materials Science*, 12, 2447–2455, 1977.

[8]   Hull, D., and Clyne, T.W., *An Introduction to Composite Materials*, Second Edition, Cambridge University Press, 1996.

[9] Kawabata, S., "Measurements of Transverse Mechanical Properties of High-Performance Fibers", *Journal of the Textile Institute*, 81, 432–447, 1990.

[10] Kumar, S., "Advances in High Performance Fibers", *Indian Journal of Fiber and Textile Research*, 16, 52–64, 1991.

[11] Morton, W.E., and Hearle, J.W.S., *Physical Properties of Textile Fibres*, Fourth Edition, Woodhead Publishing Limited, 2008.

[12] Muraki, C., Niwa, M., Amino, N., and Kawabata, S., "Changes in Anisotropic Elastic Moduli of Wool Fibres during Worsted Spinning, Weaving and Finishing", *Journal of the Textile Institute*, 81, 12–21, 1994.

[13] Mwaikambo, L.Y., "Review of the History, Properties and Application of Plant Fibres", *African Journal of Science and Technology*, 7, 120–133, 2006.

[14] Owen, J.D., "The Application of Searle's Single and Double Pendulum Methods to Single Fibre Rigidity Measurements", *Journal of the Textile Institute Transactions*, 56, T329–T339, 1965.

[15] Painter, P.C., and Coleman, M.M., *Fundamentals of Polymer Science: An Introductory Text*, Second Edition, CRC Press, 1997.

[16] Pizzuto, J., *Fabric Science*, Tenth Edition, Fairchild Publications Inc, 2010.

[17] Schultz, J., *Polymer Materials Science*, Prentice-Hall Inc., 1974.

[18] Tortora, P.G., *Understanding Textiles*, Fourth Edition, Macmillian Publishing Company, 1992.

[19] Ward, I.M., and Sweeney, J., *Mechanical Properties of Solid Polymers*, Third Edition, John Wiley & Sons, Ltd., 2013.

[20] Warner, S.B., *Fiber Science*, Prentice Hall, 1995.

[21] Zeronian, S.H., Buschler-Diller, G., Holmes, S., and Inglesby, M.K., "Relationships between the Mechanical Properties of Synthetic Fibers", *Journal of the Textile Institute*, 85, 293–300, 1994.

PROBLEMS

(1) Describe Hooke's law, tensile stress, tensile strain, tensile modulus, Poisson's ratio, bulk modulus, and shear modulus.

(2) What is the difference between true stress and engineering stress? How do you calculate the true stress from engineering stress?

(3)　What is specific stress?

(4)　In general, polymer fibers do not exhibit ideal stress-strain behavior. Why?

(5)　Estimate the modulus, tenacity, true tenacity, and strain-to-break for an unoriented polymer fiber shown below.

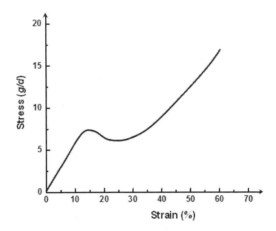

(6)　An as-spun, unoriented, amorphous polymer fiber is stretched until it breaks. Discuss all the possible places the energy might have gone.

(7)　An as-spun, unoriented, semicrystalline polymer fiber is stretched until it breaks. Discuss all the possible places the energy might have gone.

(8)　A molecularly oriented polymer fiber is stretched until it breaks. Discuss all the possible places the energy might have gone.

(9)　Discuss and explain how you would expect the tensile properties of a polymer fiber to vary with:

　　　(i)　　Molecular weight
　　　(ii)　 Molecular orientation
　　　(iii)　Chain rigidity
　　　(iv)　 Intermolecular interaction
　　　(v)　　Moisture
　　　(vi)　 Temperature
　　　(vii)　Strain rate

(10)　Compare elastic recovery with work recovery.

(11)　Which has larger value for polymer fibers, shear tenacity or tensile tenacity? Why?

(12) What kind of deformation is involved when you are bending a fiber?

(13) For commercial polymer fibers, the ratio of tensile modulus (E) to shear modulus (G) is greater than the value predicted by:

$$\frac{E}{G} = 2(1+v)$$

where v is the Passion's ratio. Explain why.

(14) Compare axial compressive modulus with axial tensile modulus. Which is larger? Why?

(15) Compare axial compressive strength with axial tensile strength. Which is larger? Why?

(16) Compare transverse compressive modulus with axial compressive modulus. Which is larger? Why?

CHAPTER 16

Viscoelastic Properties of Fibers

Viscoelasticity is the property of materials that exhibit both viscous and elastic responses under applied stress. Viscoelastic properties haven been observed throughout recorded history. For example, archers in ancient time knew they should never leave their bows strung when not in use because the tension in the bowstring would decrease over time. The first scientific study on the viscoelastic properties of fibers is probably by Weber, who noted in 1835 that silk fibers under tension presented an immediate deformation and a delayed extension that increased with time. As a matter of fact, all materials can exhibit elastic and viscous characteristics simultaneously if the time scale of observation is comparable to the relaxation times needed for large-scale atomic rearrangements in these materials. However, the relaxation times of most non-polymer fibers are significantly greater than the time scale of normal observation, and hence it is hard to observe their viscoelastic behavior at room temperature. On the other hand, polymer fibers have relaxation times that are comparable to the time scale of observation, and then they easily display viscoelastic behavior. This chapter, therefore, focuses on the viscoelastic properties of polymer fibers.

16.1 MOLECULAR MECHANISMS OF VISCOELASTIC BEHAVIOR

Under applied stress, polymer fibers may deform by either or both of two fundamentally different molecular mechanisms.

* In the first mechanism, the bond lengths and angles are altered, moving the atoms to new positions with higher internal energy. This is a small-scale motion and occurs in a time scale of around 10^{-12} seconds.

- The second mechanism is related to larger-scale rearrangements of the atoms. For example, the rotation around the carbon-carbon single bonds on the main chains changes the polymer chain conformations, leading to the development of molecular orientation and crystallinity, the slide of polymer chains over one another, etc. Some of the conformational changes (e.g., the development of molecular orientation) are recoverable, but some other conformational changes (e.g., the slide of polymer chains) are not. However, all conformational changes can decrease the polymer conformational entropy by making the system less "disordered". Compared with the changes in bond lengths and angles, the large-scale rearrangements of atoms associated with the second mechanism require longer time scale.

According to the combined first and second laws of thermodynamics, the mechanical work ($f\,dx$) done on a fiber by applied stress produces an increase in the internal energy (dU) or a decrease in the entropy (dS):

$$f\,dx = dU - T\,dS \qquad (16.1)$$

Equation 16.1 provides a convenient means of determining whether the fiber's stiffness is energetic or entropic in origin.

For polymer fibers, the internal energy-controlled elasticity has an instantaneous nature since it involves the rapid changes of bond lengths and angles. However, the conformational or entropic changes are processes that are sensitive to the local molecular mobility. This molecular mobility is affected by many factors, such as polymer chain structure, temperature, or absorbed moisture or other small molecules, etc. The rates of conformational changes can be described by the *Arrhenius* equation:

$$Rate = Ae^{-\Delta E^*/RT} \qquad (16.2)$$

where A is a structure constant, ΔE^* the activation energy of the conformation change process, R the gas constant, and T the absolute temperature of the polymer. Figure 16.1 shows the temperature dependence of the conformational change rates. When the temperature is significantly greater than the glass transition temperature (T_g), the rates of conformational changes are so fast that polymer fibers are in the rubbery state and exhibit large, instantaneous, and reversible deformation when the stress is applied. Elastomer fibers, such as polyurethane, are used in the rubbery state. However, when the temperature is significantly lower than T_g, the rates are so slow and are negligible. As a result, the polymer chain conformations are frozen, and the fibers are in the glassy state and are able to deform only through the changes in bond lengths and angles. Polymer fibers at the glass state generally are brittle and break easily at low strains. When the temperature is not too far away from T_g, polymer fibers are midway between the glassy and rubbery

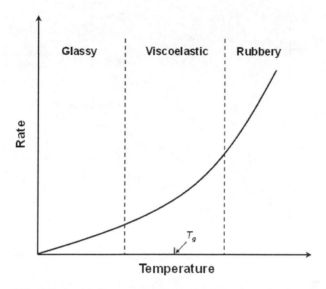

Figure 16.1. Relationship between conformational change rate and temperature.

states, and their response to applied stress is a combination of viscous fluidity and elastic solidity, i.e., in the viscoelastic state. Polymer fibers are often used in their viscoelastic state.

In both glassy and rubbery states, the mechanical properties, such as modulus, of polymer fibers have no or weak dependence on time. But in the viscoelastic state, the mechanical properties of polymer fibers depend strongly on time. For example, the tensile tests take some time, and hence the stress (σ)-strain (ε) behavior of polymer fibers is affected by strain rate (Figure 16.2). At a low strain rate, there is more time available for the polymer chains to change conformations and fibers exhibit higher strain at a given stress. However, at a high strain rate, there is less time for conformational changes and fibers present lower strain at the same stress.

16.2 PHENOMENOLOGICAL ASPECTS OF VISCOELASTIC BEHAVIOR

The viscoelastic behavior of polymer fibers is complex. Experimentally, it is important to perform simple laboratory tests from which information relevant to actual in-use conditions can be obtained. The viscoelastic characterization of polymer fibers often consists of conducting mechanical tests that are similar to those discussed in Chapter 15, but are modified so as to enable the observation of the time dependency of fibers' response. Three most important viscoelastic tests are: creep, stress relaxation, and dynamic mechanical testing.

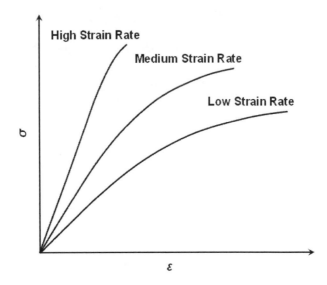

Figure 16.2. Effect of strain rate on the stress-strain behavior of polymer fibers.

16.2.1 CREEP

The creep test consists of observing the change of strain with time under a constant stress (Figure 16.3). The strain of viscoelastic polymer fibers changes with time when a constant stress is applied. Figure 16.4 shows the creep curves of a typical polymer fiber under different constant stresses. On the application of a constant stress, the polymer fiber instantaneously deforms an amount determined by the stress, and then it exhibits the creep behavior, i.e., a delayed deformation that increases gradually with time. Higher constant stress leads to greater creep.

It is important to understand the creep behavior shown in Figure 16.4 is not a simple superposition of linear elastic and viscous responses. Figure 16.5 shows the typical strain-time curves of ideal elastic material, ideal viscous material, and viscoelastic polymer fibers under constant stress. The ideal elastic material deforms instantaneously as the stress is applied and the stain remains constant with time. The removal of the stress causes the ideal elastic material to return to its original dimension. For the ideal viscous material, the strain increases linearly with time as long as the stress is applied. The removal of the stress does not return the ideal viscous material to the original dimension. This is because the energy introduced by the work of the external stress is dissipated in the flow, leading to a permanent deformation. Both the ideal elastic and viscous responses contribute to the creep-recovery curve of the viscoelastic polymer fibers. However, the creep-recovery curve of viscoelastic polymer fibers is not a simple superposition of these two ideal behaviors. In addition to the ideal responses, the creep-recovery curve of the polymer fibers also includes retarded elastic response, in which

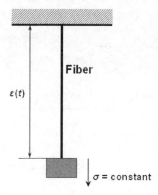

Figure 16.3. Creep test of a viscoelastic fiber.

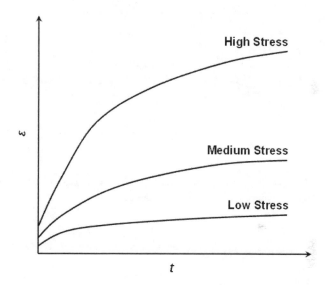

Figure 16.4. Creep of a typical polymer fiber under different constant stresses.

viscous and elastic responses are coupled so the fibers gradually deform in a nonlinear fashion with time.

As discussed above, the creep-recovery curve of viscoelastic polymer fibers includes: elastic, retarded, and viscous responses. Figure 16.6 shows the elastic, retarded, and viscous components of a typical creep-recovery curve of viscoelastic polymer fibers. The contributions of different responses to the creep-recovery curve can be described as below:

- When the time is very short, e.g., shorter than the relaxation time of the polymer chain segments, the polymer chains are "frozen" and the only

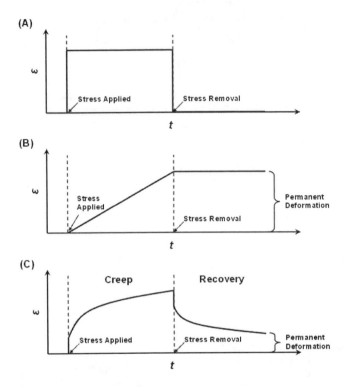

Figure 16.5. Typically strain-time curves of (A) ideal elastic material, (B) ideal viscous material, and (C) viscoelastic polymer fibers under constant stress.

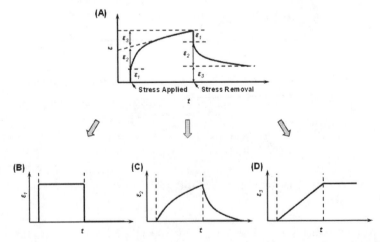

Figure 16.6. (A) Creep-recovery curve of a viscoelastic polymer fiber, and the corresponding (B) elastic, (C) retarded, and (D) viscous components.

possible motions are the changes of bond lengths and angles. As a result, the deformation at the initial stage of the creep test is the result of elastic response. This elastic deformation (ε_1) is recoverable instantaneously after the removal of the applied stress (Figure 16.6B).

- When the time becomes longer and is comparable to the relaxation time of polymer chain segments, the larger-scale rearrangements of the atoms become possible by changes in polymer chain conformations, e.g., molecular orientation, strain-induced crystallization, etc. As discussed in section 16.1, these recoverable conformational changes are rate-controlled and cause retarded deformation (ε_2), which increases gradually with time (Figure 16.6C). Since the elastic deformation remains constant during creep, the total fiber deformation is: $\varepsilon_{total} = \varepsilon_1 + \varepsilon_2$. When the applied stress is removed, the retarded deformation is recovered gradually.

- When the time continues to increase and becomes comparable to the relaxation time of the entire polymer chain, the polymer starts to flow and the viscous deformation (ε_3) makes significant contribution to the total deformation of the polymer fibers (Figure 16.6D). The total fiber deformation is: $\varepsilon_{total} = \varepsilon_1 + \varepsilon_2 + \varepsilon_3$. The viscous deformation is associated with unrecoverable conformational changes, e.g., the slide of polymer chains over one another, and hence such deformation is permanent and cannot be recovered after the removal of applied stress.

Creep can be a serious problem for polymer fibers. In general, the fibers should have good resistance to creep if they are used in applications that require a continuous load. Crosslinking is an effective means to increase the fibers' resistance to creep. Crosslinked polymer fibers do not exhibit permanent viscous deformation since a crosslinked network cannot flow. Crosslinking cannot eliminate the elastic and retarded deformations, but still can reduce them. In general, crosslinking is considered to be effective in reducing the creep behavior as long as over-crosslinking is avoided. In addition to crosslinking, many other factors affect the creep behavior of polymer fibers. In general, the creep of polymer fibers decreases with increases in molecular weight, molecular orientation, molecular polarity, crystallinity, and glass transition temperature, since they all reduce the molecular mobility of polymer chains.

16.2.2 STRESS RELAXATION

In a stress relaxation test, the polymer fiber is deformed to a given value of strain and the stress needed to maintain that strain is monitored as a function of time (Figure 16.7). Stress relaxation tests can be easily conducted on Instron or any displacement-controlled testing instruments, and Figure 16.8 shows typical stress relaxation curves. At a constant strain, the polymer chains change their

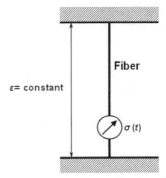

Figure 16.7. Stress relaxation test of a viscoelastic fiber.

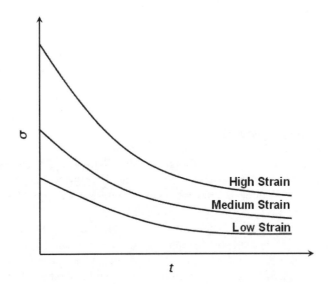

Figure 16.8. Stress relaxation of a typical polymer fiber under different constant strains.

conformations, slide over one another, and so on. As a result, the stress decreases with time. Higher strain leads to higher initial stress, but faster stress relaxation.

Stress relaxation is not desirable in applications where constant strains are required. Crosslinking is effective in increasing the fibers' resistance to stress relaxation. Figure 16.9 shows the stress relaxation of crosslinked and uncrosslinked polymer fibers. Crosslinked polymer fibers do not exhibit permanent viscous flow, and hence the stress does not relax to zero under a constant strain. However, the stress of uncrosslinked polymer fibers could reduce to zero under strain when given a sufficiently long time.

Temperature also affects the stress relaxation of polymer fibers. Figure 16.10 shows the effect of temperature on the stress relaxation of polymer fibers. When the temperature is significantly greater than the glass transition temperature, the

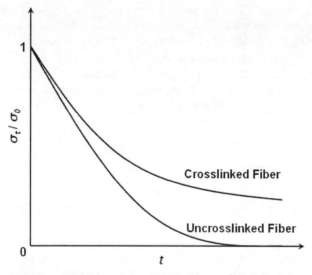

Figure 16.9. Stress relaxation of crosslinked and uncrosslinked polymer fibers.

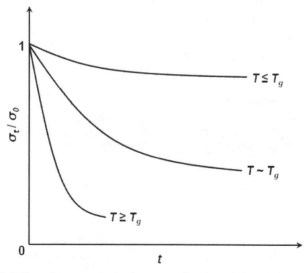

Figure 16.10. Effect of temperature on the stress relaxation of viscoelastic polymer fibers.

polymer chain mobility is high and the stress is relaxed rapidly. When the temperature is significantly lower than the glass transition temperature, the polymer chains are "frozen" and the stress relaxation is slow, and sometimes is negligible. When the temperature is not too far away from the glass transition temperature (e.g., tens of degrees above or below T_g), the stress relaxation is apparent due to the moderate molecular mobility.

Other factors that affect the stress relaxation behavior of polymer fibers include, but are not limited to molecular weight, molecular orientation, molecular polarity, crystallinity, and moisture or other additives. In general, the stress relaxation of polymer fibers decreases with increases in molecular weight, molecular orientation, molecular polarity, crystallinity, and glass transition temperature. However, the introduction of moisture or other small molecules into polymer fibers can facilitate faster stress relaxation since these small molecules can improve the molecular mobility of polymer chains.

16.2.3 Dynamic Mechanical Properties

Creep and stress relaxation tests are convenient for studying fibers' responses in a large time scale (e.g., from minutes to days), but they are less accurate when the time scale is short (e.g., seconds or less). The most useful method for determining the viscoelastic behavior of polymer fibers in short time scales is the measurement of dynamic mechanical properties. In a typical dynamic mechanical test, a sinusoidally varying stress is applied to the fiber sample and the resultant strain is monitored. In a steady state, the strain also is sinusoidal, having the same angular frequency but retarded by a phase angle δ. This is analogous to the retarded strain observed in creep tests.

The sinusoidally varying stress, $\sigma(t)$, in a dynamic mechanical test can be written as:

$$\sigma(t) = \sigma_0 \sin \omega t \qquad (16.3)$$

where σ_0 is the maximum stress, and ω the angular frequency of the applied stress in radians per second. The angular frequency ω is equal to $2\pi f$, where f is the frequency in cycles per second. If this stress is applied to an ideal elastic material, the resultant strain, $\varepsilon(t)$, would be completely in-phase with the applied stress and would be written as:

$$\varepsilon(t) = \frac{\sigma(t)}{E} = \varepsilon_0 \sin \omega t \qquad (16.4)$$

where E is the modulus of the material, and ε_0 the maximum strain. Based on Equations 16.3 and 16.4, the theoretical stress-time, strain-time, and stress-strain curves of an ideal elastic material can be obtained, and they are shown in Figure 16.11. From Figures 16.11A and B, it is seen that the strain can follow the varying stress without any delay. The normalized stress-strain curve shown in Figure 16.11B is linear since an ideal elastic material obeys the Hooke's law. The network (ΔW) done by the varying stress in a loading cycle (e.g., $0 - 2\pi$) can be given by:

$$\Delta W = \int \sigma de = \int_0^{2\pi/\omega} \sigma_0 \sin \omega t d(\varepsilon_0 \sin \omega t) = 0 \qquad (16.5)$$

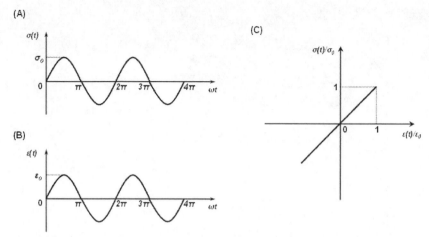

Figure 16.11. (A) stress-time, (B) strain-time, and (C) normalized stress-strain curves of an ideal elastic material.

This indicates the energy consumed during the dynamic mechanical test is completely stored as the internal energy by the ideal elastic deformation, and the energy can be completely recovered.

If the sinusoidally varying stress is applied on an ideal viscous material, the strain rate can be written as:

$$\frac{d\varepsilon(t)}{dt} = \frac{\sigma(t)}{\eta} = \frac{\sigma_0 \sin \omega t}{\eta} \tag{16.6}$$

where η is the viscosity of the material. The resultant strain can then be expressed by:

$$\varepsilon(t) = \int \frac{\sigma_0 \sin \omega t}{\eta} dt = \varepsilon_0 \sin\left(\omega t - \frac{\pi}{2}\right) \tag{16.7}$$

Figure 16.12 shows the stress-time, strain-time, and stress-strain curves of an ideal viscous material, which are based on Equations 16.3 and 16.7. The strain of an ideal viscous material is exactly $\pi/2$ out-of-phase with the stress (Figures 16.12A and B). The normalized stress-strain curve is a perfect circle (Figure 16.12C). The net work done in a loading cycle is equal to the area surrounded by the circle:

$$\Delta W = \int \sigma d\varepsilon = \pi \sigma_0 \varepsilon_0 \tag{16.8}$$

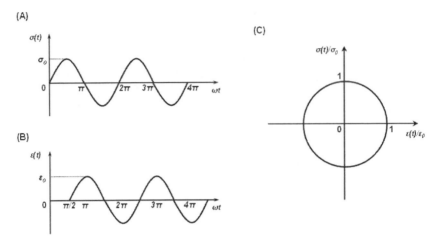

Figure 16.12. (A) stress-time, (B) strain-time, and (C) normalized stress-strain curves of an ideal viscous material.

Since the viscous deformation of an ideal viscous material is unrecoverable, the energy consumed in a cycle is released in the form of heat.

Polymer fibers are viscoelastic. If the sinusoidally varying stress is applied on a viscoelastic polymer fiber, the resultant strain can be given as:

$$\varepsilon(t) = \varepsilon_0 \sin(\omega t - \delta) \tag{16.9}$$

where the phase angle δ is between 0 and $\pi/2$. Figure 16.13 shows the corresponding stress-time, strain-time, and stress-strain curves. The strain of a viscoelastic polymer fiber lags behind the sinusoidally varying stress by a phase angle δ. The normalized stress-strain curve has an oval shape. The net work done in a loading cycle is the area surrounded by the oval:

$$\Delta W = \int \sigma de = \int_0^{2\pi/\omega} \sigma_0 \sin \omega t d\left[\varepsilon_0 \sin(\omega t - \delta)\right] = \pi \sigma_0 \varepsilon_0 \sin \delta \tag{16.10}$$

In the dynamic mechanical test of a viscoelastic polymer fiber, the work is done to: (*i*) alter the bond lengths and angles, (*ii*) induce recoverable changes in polymer chain conformations, e.g., molecular orientation, strain-induced crystallization, etc., and (*iii*) introduce pure viscous flow. The strain caused by changes of bond lengths and angles is a pure elastic response, and the strain involved in the recoverable conformational changes is a retarded response. These two types of responses are reversible and they produce no net work over a loading cycle. However, the work done for the viscous flow is used to overcome the polymer chain friction and is converted irreversibly to heat.

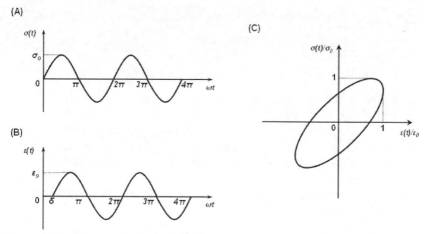

Figure 16.13. (A) stress-time, (B) strain-time, and (C) normalized stress-strain curves of a viscoelastic polymer fiber.

Equations 16.3 and 16.9 are very useful in treating the viscoelastic behavior of polymer fibers. However, in practical applications, they often are rewritten to the following two equations by "resetting the zero" and considering the stress "leading" the strain by a phase angle:

$$\varepsilon(t) = \varepsilon_0 \sin(\omega t) \tag{16.11}$$

and

$$\sigma(t) = \sigma_0 \sin(\omega t + \delta) = (\sigma_0 \cos \delta) \sin \omega t + (\sigma_0 \sin \delta) \cos \omega t \tag{16.12}$$

Equation 16.12 expresses the stress in terms of an in-phase component and an out-of-phase component with respect to the strain. The in-phase component, $(\sigma_0 \cos \delta)$ sin ωt, is the driving force the elastic response, and the out-of-phase component, $(\sigma_0 \sin \delta) \cos \omega t$, is associated with the viscous response. The stress-strain relationship now can be defined in terms of these in-phase and out-of-phase components by:

$$\sigma(t) = \varepsilon_0 (E' \sin \omega t + E'' \cos \omega t) \tag{16.13}$$

where E' and E'' are the storage modulus and loss modulus, defined as:

$$E' = \frac{\sigma_0}{\varepsilon_0} \cos \delta \tag{16.14}$$

and

$$E'' = \frac{\sigma_0}{\varepsilon_0} \sin \delta \qquad (16.15)$$

The storage modulus is a measure of the elasticity of the fiber, and it indicates the fiber's ability to storage energy. Energy storage occurs as polymer chains are distorted from their equilibrium positions by small-scale motions, such as changes of bond lengths and angles. On the other hand, the loss modulus represents the capability of a fiber to dissipate energy as heat, owing to large-scale viscous motions of polymer chains.

Since the modulus of a viscoelastic fiber has two components, it can be written as a complex quantity E^*:

$$E^* = E' + iE'' \qquad (16.16)$$

where $i = \sqrt{-1}$. In addition, the loss factor, $\tan \delta$, also can be obtained:

$$\tan \delta = \frac{E''}{E'} \qquad (16.17)$$

Tan δ is a useful quantity and it is a measure of the ratio of energy lost to the energy stored or recovered. As a result, $\tan \delta$ is an important indication of the viscoelasticity of fibers.

Figure 16.14 shows the idealized frequency dependence of E' and $\tan \delta$ for an amorphous polymer fiber. At low frequencies, the polymer fiber has sufficient time to exhibit the viscous deformation and is in a rubbery state. As a result, the storage modulus E' is low at low frequencies. When the frequency increases and the time scale of experiment (or observation) becomes comparable to the polymer relaxation time, the polymer fiber enters the viscoelastic state and the storage modulus increases rapidly. Eventually, the storage modulus increases by several orders of magnitude and levels off after the polymer fiber enters the glassy state. From Figure 16.14, it also is seen $\tan \delta$ goes through a maximum and exhibits a peak in the frequency range where the storage modulus is changing its value from one characteristic of the rubbery state to that of the glassy state.

The curves shown in Figure 16.14 are idealized for amorphous polymer fibers. Most commercial polymer fibers are semicrystalline and are more complex, due to the superposition of the behaviors of the crystalline and amorphous phases. In general, with increase in degree of crystallinity, the storage modulus increase, but the tan δ value decreases. However, the effect of crystallinity is different in different frequency ranges, and the superposition of the behaviors of the crystalline and amorphous phases is not linear, especially when the degree of crystallinity is high and the amorphous regions are constrained by the crystalline phase. Because of

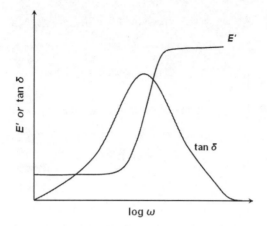

Figure 16.14. Frequency dependence of E' and tan δ for an amorphous polymer fiber.

these factors, the behavior of semi-crystalline polymer fibers is much less uniform than amorphous fibers, and often presents individual idiosyncrasies that have to be treated separately.

In addition to crystallinity, polymer chain rigidity, side groups, molecular weight, molecular weight distribution, and crosslinking also affect the dynamic mechanical properties of polymer fibers. In general, fibers made of rigid polymer chains have smaller tan δ than those of flexible polymer chains. However, flexible polymer chains with side groups can lead to fibers with high tan δ if the side groups increase the intermolecular friction. The tan δ value typically increases by increasing molecular weight and molecular weight distribution, but it often decreases with crosslinking. These are just general trends. In reality, the effects of these structural parameters are complex and may vary from fiber to fiber.

16.3 TIME-TEMPERATURE EQUIVALENCE

16.3.1 TIME-TEMPERATURE EQUIVALENCE

One important feature of the viscoelastic behavior of polymer fibers is that time and temperature are inextricably intertwined. Taking the stress relaxation test as an example, the fiber modulus can be measured as a function of temperature. In such a test, the time scale of experiment is important, and hence the modulus needs to be measured over some arbitrary short time period, e.g., 1 minute. The polymer fiber is, therefore, stretched instantaneously to a given value of strain and after 1 minute, the stress is measured to calculate the modulus. Figure 16.15 shows a plot of this modulus as a function of temperature. When the temperature is lower than T_g, the polymer fiber is at its glassy state and the deformation mainly is caused by the changes in bond lengths and angles, or other local motions. The

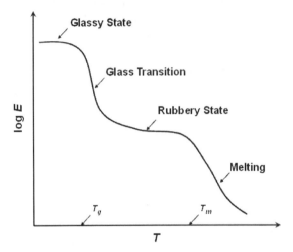

Figure 16.15. Modulus as a function of temperature for a polymer fiber while holding the time constant.

large-scale conformational changes are "frozen", at least at the time scale of observation. As a result, the fiber has very high modulus. As the temperature increases to the vicinity of T_g, there now is sufficient thermal energy that enables the movement of polymer chain segments. The polymer fiber still does not have time to display viscous response, but the retarded deformation becomes possible, leading to a rapid decrease in fiber modulus. At this stage, the polymer fiber presents clear viscoelastic behavior. As the temperature goes beyond T_g, but still is lower than the melting temperature (T_m), the time scale of conformational relaxation processes becomes shorter and the polymer chains can adjust their conformations to orient themselves. The polymer chains in the amorphous phase can stretch out between the entanglement points or crystallites and the fiber exhibits a rubbery plateau, in which the modulus remains constant or decreases slowly. The rubbery plateau could be short if the fiber is highly crystallized. As the temperature continues to increase and reaches the vicinity of T_m, the polymer fiber starts to melt and can no longer hold its shape due to the viscous response. At this stage, the modulus decreases rapidly. The melting of the polymer fiber can be avoided by introducing a chemically crosslinked polymer structure.

Similar results can be obtained if the test is conducted by making time a variable and holding the temperature constant. To be more specific, the polymer fiber now is stretched to a chosen value of strain and the stress is measured as a function of time. The calculated modulus is plotted against time, as shown in Figure 16.16. At short time periods, the modulus is high and the fiber is in the glassy state. As the time becomes longer and reaches a critical value, the modulus decreases rapidly, corresponding to the T_g in the modulus-temperature curve shown in Figure 16.15. As the time goes on, the rubbery plateau is encountered.

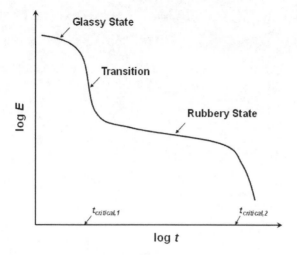

Figure 16.16. Modulus as a function of time for a polymer fiber while holding the temperature constant.

When the time reaches the second critical value, the modulus again decreases sharply, corresponding to the T_m in the modulus-temperature curve. It must be noted if the test is conducted at room temperature, the time needed for obtaining the entire modulus-time curve shown in Figure 16.16 could be very long, of the order of hundreds or even thousands of years. The test can be accelerated by increasing the temperature; however, the beginning part of the curve may be lost at higher temperatures. As a matter of fact, most polymer fibers already are in the transition or rubbery state at room temperature.

Comparing Figures 16.15 and 16.16, it can be concluded that increasing the time has the same effect as increasing the temperature. However, increasing the test time is not practical in many applications. Sometimes, it might take hundreds of years to produce the entire stress relaxation curve shown in Figure 16.16, especially at low temperatures. In cases like this, the viscoelastic tests can be accelerated by using the time-temperature equivalence, expressed in terms of a superposition principle. The time-temperature superposition principle is discussed in the following section.

16.3.2 TIME-TEMPERATURE SUPERPOSITION PRINCIPLE

Figure 16.17 illustrates the time-temperature superposition principle by using stress relaxation curves. To obtain Figure 16.17A, the stress relaxation tests can be carried out in a relatively short time scale at different temperatures: $T_0 < T_1 < T_2 < T_3 < T_4 < T_5$. The stress relaxation becomes faster as the temperature increases. As shown in Figure 16.17B, the effect of increasing the temperature is simply to

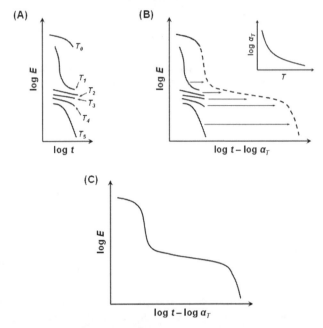

Figure 16.17. Illustration of the time-temperature superposition principle: (A) stress relaxation curves obtained at different temperatures, (B) shifting of stress relaxation curves at different temperatures to the reference temperature T_0 and a plot of the shift factor a_T, and (C) master stress relaxation curve obtained after superimposing the curves obtained at different temperatures.

shift the stress relaxation curves along the horizontal axis without changing the shape. To complete the shifting, a time-temperature shift factor (a_T) is defined as the horizontal shift that must be applied to a response curve measured at an arbitrary temperature (e.g., T_1, T_2, T_3, T_4, or T_5) in order to move it to the curve measured at the reference temperature (e.g., T_0). By shifting the curves obtained at different temperatures, the entire master stress relaxation curve at the reference temperature T_0 can be constructed, as shown in Figure 16.17C. In addition to stress relaxation, creep tests can be superimposed in the same fashion.

For time-temperature superposition, the key is to determine the shift factor required to superimpose stress relaxation or creep curves obtained at one temperature to those obtained at another temperature. If the relaxation time of the polymer fibers obeys the *Arrhenius* relation, the shift factor may be expressed as:

$$\log a_T = \frac{\Delta E^*}{2.303R}\left(\frac{1}{T} - \frac{1}{T_{ref}}\right)$$

(16.18)

where ΔE^* is the activation energy of the process, R the gas constant, and T the temperature of interest, T_{ref} the reference temperature, and the factor $2.303 = \ln 10$ is the conversion between natural and base-10 logarithms.

Another popular approach to obtain the shift factor is to use the empirical WLF equation developed by Williams, Landel, and Ferry:

$$\log \alpha_T = \frac{-C_1\left(T - T_{ref}\right)}{C_2 + T - T_{ref}} \qquad (16.19)$$

where C_1 and C_2 are constants whose values depend on the polymer structure and choice of reference temperature. For many polymers, the C_1 and C_2 values are 17.44 and 51.6, respectively, if the reference temperature is T_g. In this case, the WLF equation can be rewritten as

$$\log \alpha_T = \frac{-17.44\left(T - T_g\right)}{51.6 + T - T_g} \qquad (16.20)$$

16.4 MODELS OF VISCOELASTIC BEHAVIOR

One convenient way to describe the viscoelastic behavior of polymer fibers and to visualize the corresponding molecular motions is to employ "spring-dashpot" mechanical models.

16.4.1 IDEAL SPRING AND IDEAL DASHPOT

Mechanical models consist of various combinations of ideal springs and ideal dashpots. Springs show linear elastic behavior (Figure 16.18A):

$$\sigma_s = E\varepsilon_s \qquad (16.21)$$

where σ_s is the stress applied on the spring, ε_s the resultant strain, and E the spring modulus. The spring models the instantaneous bond deformation in the polymer fiber, and its magnitude is related to the fraction of energy stored reversible in the fiber. On the other hand, dashpots show linear viscous behavior (Figure 16.18B):

$$\sigma_d = \eta \dot{\varepsilon}_d \qquad (16.22)$$

where σ_d is the stress applied on the dashpot, $\dot{\varepsilon}_d$ the strain rate (*i.e.*, $d\varepsilon_d / dt$) produced by the stress, and η the dashpot viscosity. The dashpot models the entropic conformational changes in the polymer fiber.

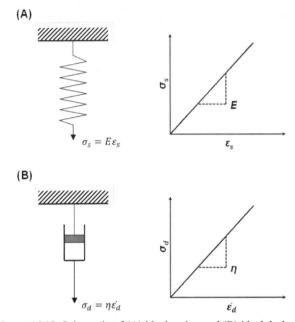

Figure 16.18. Schematic of (A) ideal spring and (B) ideal dashpot.

16.4.2 MAXWELL MODEL

The Maxwell model consists of an ideal spring and an ideal dashpot connected in series (Figure 16.19). The spring can be visualized as representing the elastic or energetic component of the viscoelastic behavior, while the dashpot represents the conformational or entropic component. In the Maxwell model, the stresses on the spring and dashpot are the same, and they equal to the applied stress (σ), while the resultant total strain (ε) is the sum of the strains of the spring and dashpot:

$$\sigma = \sigma_s = \sigma_d \tag{16.23}$$

and

$$\varepsilon = \varepsilon_s + \varepsilon_d \tag{16.24}$$

The stress and strain can be related by differentiating the strain equation and writing the spring and dashpot strain rates in terms of the stress:

$$\frac{d\varepsilon}{dt} = \frac{d\varepsilon_s}{dt} + \frac{d\varepsilon_d}{dt} = \frac{1}{E}\frac{d\sigma}{dt} + \frac{\sigma}{\eta} \tag{16.25}$$

This is the so-called "governing equation" for the Maxwell model.

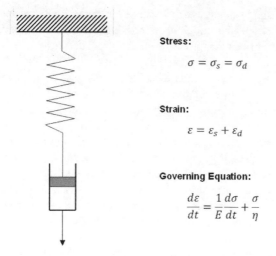

Stress:

$$\sigma = \sigma_s = \sigma_d$$

Strain:

$$\varepsilon = \varepsilon_s + \varepsilon_d$$

Governing Equation:

$$\frac{d\varepsilon}{dt} = \frac{1}{E}\frac{d\sigma}{dt} + \frac{\sigma}{\eta}$$

Figure 16.19. Schematic of the Maxwell model.

In a stress relaxation test, the polymer fiber is stretched to a constant strain ε_0, i.e.,

$$\frac{d\varepsilon}{dt} = 0 \tag{16.26}$$

The governing equation then can be integrated to obtain:

$$\int_0^t \frac{E}{\eta} dt = -\int_{\sigma_0}^{\sigma} \frac{d\sigma}{\sigma} \tag{16.27}$$

where σ_0 is the initial stress at $t = 0$. As a result, the stress needed to maintain the constant strain can be written as a function of time:

$$\sigma(t) = \sigma_0 \exp\left(-\frac{E}{\eta}t\right) = \sigma_0 \exp\left(-\frac{t}{\tau}\right) \tag{16.28}$$

where τ is equal to η/E and is called the relaxation time. The relaxation time is strongly dependent on the temperature and other factors that affect the molecular mobility. In general, with increase in temperature, the relaxation time decreases. Based on Equation 16.28, the modulus of the fiber during the stress relaxation test also can be obtained:

$$E(t) = \frac{\sigma(t)}{\varepsilon_0} = \frac{\sigma_0}{\varepsilon_0}\exp\left(-\frac{t}{\tau}\right) = E_0 \exp\left(-\frac{t}{\tau}\right) \tag{16.29}$$

where E_0 is the initial modulus at $t = 0$.

Figure 16.20A shows the stress-time curve for the Maxwell model in a stress relaxation test. At $t = 0$, the initial stress σ_0 is the result of the elastic response (represented by the spring). As time goes on, the stress decreases due to the contribution of viscous response (represented by the dashpot). Therefore, the Maxwell model gives a reasonable approximation of the stress relaxation behavior of viscoelastic polymer fibers in a relative short period of time. However, when the time scale of experiment become longer, the Maxwell model is no longer able to reproduce the entire stress relaxation curve (e.g., Figure 16.16). In a real polymer fiber, many different types of conformational changes could occur at different temperatures, and each conformational change is characterized by a different relaxation time. The Maxwell model only contains one relaxation time, and hence it cannot reproduce the entire stress relaxation curve over a long period of time. Nevertheless, the Maxwell model is a classical initial treatment of the viscoelastic behavior and often is used to describe the stress relaxation of polymer fibers in a relatively short time period.

Another major drawback of the Maxwell model is that it cannot be used to describe the creep behavior. In a creep test, the constant stress σ_0 is applied to the polymer fiber and the governing equation becomes:

$$\frac{d\varepsilon}{dt} = \frac{\sigma}{\eta} \qquad (16.30)$$

As a result, the strain-time curve of the Maxwell model is a straight line (Figure 16.20B) and this does not represent the creep behavior of polymer fibers.

16.4.3 KELVIN-VOIGT MODEL

The Maxwell model is incapable of describing the creep behavior because it cannot model the retarded response under a constant stress. The Kelvin-Voigt model (Figure 16.21), consisting of an ideal spring and an ideal dashpot connected in

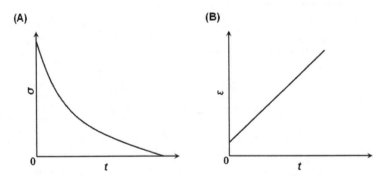

(A)   **(B)**

Figure 16.20. Behavior of the Maxwell model in (A) stress relaxation and (B) creep tests.

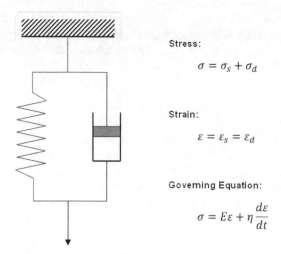

Stress:

$$\sigma = \sigma_s + \sigma_d$$

Strain:

$$\varepsilon = \varepsilon_s = \varepsilon_d$$

Governing Equation:

$$\sigma = E\varepsilon + \eta \frac{d\varepsilon}{dt}$$

Figure 16.21. Schematic of the Kelvin-Voigt model.

parallel, can represent the retarded response and hence it can describe the creep behavior of polymer fibers. In the Kelvin-Voigt model, the total stress is the sum of the stresses of the spring and dashpot, while the strains on the spring and dash-pot are the same and they equal to the applied strain:

$$\sigma = \sigma_s + \sigma_d \tag{16.31}$$

and

$$\varepsilon = \varepsilon_s = \varepsilon_d \tag{16.32}$$

This gives the following governing equation:

$$\sigma = E\varepsilon + \eta \frac{d\varepsilon}{dt} \tag{16.33}$$

In a creep test, a constant stress σ_0 is applied onto a fiber at $t = 0$. The governing equation can be rewritten as:

$$\frac{d\varepsilon}{dt} + \frac{\varepsilon}{\tau} = \frac{\sigma_0}{\eta} \tag{16.34}$$

Solving this linear differential equation, the strain during creep can be described as a function of time:

$$\varepsilon(t) = \frac{\sigma_0}{E}\left[1 - \exp\left(-\frac{t}{\tau}\right)\right] \tag{16.35}$$

Here, τ is called retardation time, instead of relaxation time, since this is a creep test. If the constant stress is released at $t = t'$, the elastic component (i.e., the spring) would retard the fiber and the strain decreases according to the following equation:

$$\varepsilon(t > t') = \varepsilon(t')\exp\left(-\frac{t-t'}{\tau}\right) \tag{16.36}$$

Figure 16.22A shows the strain-time curve of the Kelvin-Voigt model. After applying a constant stress σ_0, the strain increases exponentially and approaches to the maximum value (σ_0/E) at a rate that depends on the retardation time τ. However, if the stress is released at $t = t'$, the strain starts to decrease exponentially and the rate of decrease also is dependent on the retardation time. The Kelvin-Voigt model does not include the contribution of permanent viscous deformation. As a result, the Kelvin-Voigt model gives a reasonable approximation of the creep behavior only in a relatively short time period, when the permanent viscous deformation is not apparent. In addition, like Maxwell model, the Kelvin-Voigt model also is a single relaxation (or retardation) time type of model.

Another disadvantage of Kelvin-Voigt model is that it cannot be used to describe the stress relaxation behavior of polymer fibers. Under a constant strain ε_0, the governing equation of the Kelvin-Voigt model becomes:

$$\sigma(t) = E\varepsilon_0 + \eta\frac{d\varepsilon_0}{dt} = E\varepsilon_0 \tag{16.37}$$

This means in the Kelvin-Voigt model, the stress is constant during the stress relaxation test (Figure 16.22B), which is not true for real polymer fibers.

16.4.4 FOUR-ELEMENT MODEL

The Maxwell model does not represent the creep behavior, while the Kelvin-Voigt does not describe the stress relaxation behavior. This problem can be addressed by

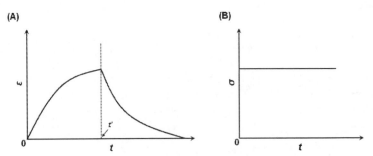

Figure 16.22. Behavior of the Kelvin-Voigt model in (A) creep and (B) stress relaxation tests.

combining more springs and dashpots in various ways to create models that can describe both creep and stress relaxation behaviors. One example is the so-called "four-element model", consisting of one Maxwell sub-model and one Kelvin sub-model connected in series, as shown in Figure 16.23A. The four-element model has four parameters: Maxwell spring modulus E_M and dashpot viscosity η_M and the Kelvin-Voigt spring modulus E_{K-V} and dashpot viscosity η_{K-V}. This simple four-element model can be used to describe both the creep and stress relaxation behaviors of polymer fibers. Taking the creep test as an example, the strain produced by the constant stress σ_0 can be obtained by simply summing the terms for the Maxwell and Kelvin sub-models:

$$\varepsilon(t) = \frac{\sigma_0}{E_M} + \frac{\sigma_0}{E_{K-V}}\left[1 - \exp\left(-\frac{t}{\tau}\right)\right] + \frac{\sigma_0}{\eta_M}t \qquad (16.38)$$

Equation 16.38 is basically the sum of elastic (ε_1), retarded (ε_2), and viscous (ε_3) responses, as illustrated in Figure 16.23B.

16.4.5 MULTI-RELAXATION TIME MODEL

The mechanical models discussed above are based on single relaxation (or retardation) time. Real polymer fibers have a spectrum or distribution of relaxation and retardation times due to the existence of different types of conformational changes. One convenient way to introduce a range of relaxation times into the problem is to construct models consisting of a number of Maxwell and/or Kelvin-Voigt sub-models connected in parallel and/or series. Figure 16.24 shows a Maxwell-Wiechert model, which is constructed by connecting an arbitrary number of

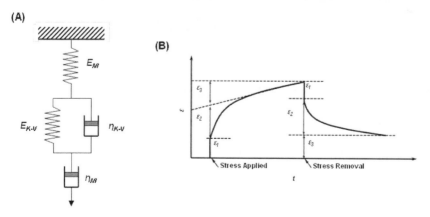

Figure 16.23. Schematics of (A) the four-element model, and (B) the corresponding creep-recovery curve.

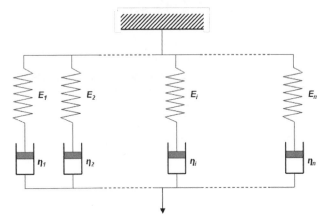

Figure 16.24. Schematic of the Maxwell-Wiechert model.

Maxwell sub-models in parallel. In this model, the total stress is the sum of the stresses experienced by each Maxwell sub-model, while the total strain is the same in each of the sub-models, i.e.:

$$\sigma = \sigma_1 + \sigma_2 + \ldots + \sigma_n = \sum_{i=1}^{n} \sigma_i \qquad (16.39)$$

and

$$\varepsilon = \varepsilon_1 = \varepsilon_2 = \ldots = \varepsilon_i = \ldots = \varepsilon_n \qquad (16.40)$$

where σ_i and ε_i are the stress and strain of the ith Maxwell sub-model, respectively. The governing equations for each sub-model are:

$$\frac{d\varepsilon}{dt} = \frac{1}{E_1}\frac{d\sigma_1}{dt} + \frac{\sigma_1}{\eta_1}$$

$$\frac{d\varepsilon}{dt} = \frac{1}{E_2}\frac{d\sigma_2}{dt} + \frac{\sigma_2}{\eta_2}$$

$$\ldots$$

$$\frac{d\varepsilon}{dt} = \frac{1}{E_i}\frac{d\sigma_i}{dt} + \frac{\sigma_i}{\eta_i}$$

$$\ldots$$

$$\frac{d\varepsilon}{dt} = \frac{1}{E_n}\frac{d\sigma_n}{dt} + \frac{\sigma_n}{\eta_n} \tag{16.41}$$

where E_i and η_i are the modulus and viscosity of the ith Maxwell sub-model, respectively. In a stress relaxation test, the strain is constant ($d\varepsilon/dt = 0$) and hence the stress-time relationship for each sub-model can be given as:

$$\sigma_1(t) = \varepsilon_0 E_1 \exp\left(-\frac{t}{\tau_1}\right)$$

$$\sigma_2(t) = \varepsilon_0 E_2 \exp\left(-\frac{t}{\tau_2}\right)$$

$$\cdots$$

$$\sigma_i(t) = \varepsilon_0 E_i \exp\left(-\frac{t}{\tau_i}\right)$$

$$\cdots$$

$$\sigma_n(t) = \varepsilon_0 E_n \exp\left(-\frac{t}{\tau_n}\right) \tag{16.42}$$

where τ_i is the relaxation time of the ith Maxwell sub-model. The total stress of the Maxwell-Wiechert model now can be written as:

$$\sigma(t) = \varepsilon_0 \sum_{i=1}^{n} E_i \exp\left(-\frac{t}{\tau_i}\right) \tag{16.43}$$

The total modulus of the Maxwell-Wiechert model also can be obtained:

$$E(t) = \frac{\sigma(t)}{\varepsilon_0} = \sum_{i=1}^{n} E_i \exp\left(-\frac{t}{\tau_i}\right) \tag{16.44}$$

Research shows by selectively adjusting the relaxation times of appropriate number of sub-models, Equations 16.43 and 16.44 can give a reasonably good representation of the stress relaxation behavior of polymer fibers over a wide time period. This indicates the stress relaxation of polymer fibers can be described as a superposition of a large number of independent modes of relaxation. Each relaxation mode is associated with a certain type of conformational change and is represented by a characteristic relaxation time τ_i. If there is a continuous distribution of relaxation times in the studied polymer fibers, the summations in Equations 16.43 and 16.44 can be replaced with integrals, i.e.:

$$\sigma(t) = \varepsilon_0 \int_0^\infty E(\tau) \exp\left(-\frac{t}{\tau}\right) d\tau \qquad (16.45)$$

and

$$E(t) = \int_0^\infty E(\tau) \exp\left(-\frac{t}{\tau}\right) d\tau \qquad (16.46)$$

The Maxwell-Wiechert model also can be used to describe the creep behavior of polymer fibers. However, for the creep behavior, it is mathematically more convenient to create a model involving a range of retardation times by connected a number of Kelvin-Voigt sub-models in series.

The simple mechanical models discussed above only allow us to describe the viscoelastic behavior phenomenologically. The in-depth fundamental understanding of the viscoelastic behavior of polymer fibers still requires more complex microscopic or molecular models. The interested reader is referred to the works by De Gennes (1971), Ferry (1980), and Rouse (1953).

REFERENCES

[1]   Aklonis, J.J., and MacKnight, W.J., *Introduction to Polymer Viscoelasticity*, Second edition, Wiley Interscience, 1983.

[2]   Boresi, A.P., Schmidt, R.J., and Sidebottom, O.M., *Advanced Mechanics of Materials*, Fifth Edition, John Wiley & Sons, 1993.

[3]   De Gennes, P.G., "Reptation of a Polymer Chain in the Presence of Fixed Obstacles", *Journal of Chemical Physics*, 55, 572–579, 1971.

[4]   Elias, H.G., *An Introduction to Polymer Science*, VCH Publishers, 1997.

[5]   Ferry, J.D., *Viscoelastic Properties of Polymers*, Third Edition, John Wiley & Sons, 1980.

[6]   Leaderman, H., *Elastic and Creep Properties of Filamentous Materials and Other High Polymers*, the Textile Foundation, 1943.

[7]   Morton, W.E., and Hearle, J.W.S., *Physical Properties of Textile Fibres*, Fourth Edition, Woodhead Publishing Limited, 2008.

[8] Painter, P.C., and Coleman, M.M., *Fundamentals of Polymer Science: An Introductory Text*, Second Edition, CRC Press, 1997.

[9] Rouse, P.E., "A Theory of the Linear Viscoelastic Properties of Dilute Solutions of Coiling Polymers", *Journal of Chemical Physics*, 21, 1272–1280, 1953.

[10] Schultz, J., *Polymer Materials Science*, Prentice-Hall Inc., 1974.

[11] Sperling, L.H., *Introduction to Physical Polymer Science*, Fourth Edition, John Wiley & Sons, 2006.

[12] Ward, I.M., and Sweeney, J., *Mechanical Properties of Solid Polymers*, Third Edition, John Wiley & Sons, Ltd., 2013.

[13] Warner, S.B., *Fiber Science*, Prentice Hall, 1995.

PROBLEMS

(1) Why do polymer fibers show viscoelastic behavior?

(2) Describe creep, stress relaxation, and dynamic mechanical testing.

(3) Is the creep behavior of a polymer fiber a simple superposition of linear elastic and viscous responses? Why?

(4) Discuss and explain how you would expect the creep behavior of a polymer fiber to vary with:

   (i)   Crystallinity
   (ii)   Molecular orientation
   (iii) Molecular polarity
   (iv)   Glass transition
   (v)   Molecular weight
   (vi)   Crosslinking

(5) Discuss and explain how you would expect the stress relaxation behavior of a polymer fiber to vary with:

   (i)   Crystallinity
   (ii)   Molecular orientation
   (iii) Molecular polarity
   (iv)   Glass transition
   (v)   Molecular weight
   (vi)   Crosslinking

(6)   What are storage modulus, loss modulus, and tan δ? What are their relationships?

(7)   Discuss and explain how you would expect the dynamic mechanical properties of a polymer fiber to vary with:

   (i)   Crystallinity
   (ii)   Molecular orientation
   (iii)   Molecular polarity
   (iv)   Glass transition
   (v)   Molecular weight
   (vi)   Crosslinking

(8)   Describe the time-temperature superposition principle.

(9)   Can Maxwell model be used to predict stress relaxation? How about creep? Why?

(10) Can Kelvin-Voigt model be used to predict stress relaxation? How about creep? Why?

(11) The four-element model shown below is subject to a creep experiment. Show how the length increases with time. At time = t, the stress is removed. Show how the length recovers.

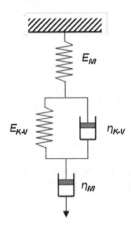

CHAPTER 17

Thermal Properties of Fibers

Thermal properties are important in many applications. For example, the main function of textile fabrics is to protect the wearer from cold or heat, and to ensure appropriate heat transfer between the human body and the environment in order to maintain the physiological thermal balance of the wearer. Composites also need appropriate thermal properties so they can be useful in aerospace and space industries. The thermal properties of fibers are the starting point for understanding the final properties of these products, although many other factors also play important roles. This chapter deals with the most basic thermal properties of fibers, including heat capacity, specific heat, thermal conductivity, thermal expansion and contraction, glass transition, melting, and degradation and decomposition.

17.1 HEAT CAPACITY AND SPECIFIC HEAT

17.1.1 HEAT CAPACITY AND SPECIFIC HEAT

Heat capacity is the amount of energy required to raise the temperature of a substance by one degree. Specific heat, or specific heat capacity, is the heat capacity divided by the mass of the substance. The unit of specific heat is J/kg·K. According to the definition of specific heat, the relationship between heat (Q) and temperature change (ΔT) can be expressed as:

$$Q = Cm\Delta T \tag{17.1}$$

where C and m are the specific heat and mass of the material. It must be noted this equation does not apply when a phase change, such as melting, is encountered since the heat added or removed during a phase change does not change the temperature.

Specific heat indicates the ability of a material to store energy in the form of heat. The specific heats of some fibers and other materials are shown in Table 17.1. In general, polymer fibers have higher specific heats than non-polymer fibers and most other materials (except for water, ice, and organic solvents) because a large amount of energy is needed to excite the vibrational, rotational, and translational motions of polymer chains in order to raise the temperature. As a result, textile fabrics could give serious burns when they melt and are in contact with skin.

17.1.2 EFFECTS OF TEMPERATURE AND HUMIDITY

The specific heat of polymer fibers typically increases with increase in temperature. When the temperature approaches the melting temperature of a polymer fiber, a large amount of heat is needed to melt the polymer, and hence the fiber exhibits a significantly increased specific heat at the vicinity of the melting temperature (Figure 17.1).

As shown in Table 17.1, liquid water has an extremely high specific heat of 4180 J/kg·K, and hence the absorption of moisture increases the specific heat of fibers. During the absorption of moisture, the specific heat of fibers is very high due to the heat of sorption associated with the moisture absorption. If the moisture regain of fibers remains constant, the specific heat (C_{wet}) of wet fibers can be related to the moisture regain (MR) by a simple mixture law:

$$C_{wet} = \frac{C_{dry} + 4.2MR}{1 + MR} \tag{17.2}$$

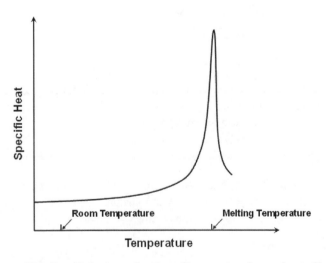

Figure 17.1. Specific heat as a function of temperature for a polymer fiber.

Table 17.1. Specific heats of fibers and non-fibrous materials.
Fibers were dried and tested at room temperature.

Material	Specific Heat (J/kg·K)
Synthetic Polymer Fibers	
Polyester	1030
Nylon 6,6	1460
Nylon 6	1430
Kevlar	1465
Natural Polymer Fibers	
Cotton	1220–1350
Wool	1360
Silk	1380
Rayon	1350–1590
Inorganic Fibers	
Carbon	710
Glass	800–850
Other Non-Fibrous Materials	
Aluminum	903
Steel	434
Acetone	2180
Ethanol	2720
Glycerol	2427
Water	4180
Ice	2050
Snow	240
Air	1007

Sources: Morton, W.E., et. al., *Physical Properties of Textile Fibres*, Fourth Edition, Woodhead Publishing Limited, 2008.; Warner, S.B., *Fiber Science*, Prentice Hall, 1995.

where C_{dry} is the specific heat of dried fibers. Equation 17.2 does not consider the state of water and the structural change of polymer fibers caused by the absorption of moisture. In reality, the absorbed water molecules exist in different states and some of them have a specific heat that is similar to that of ice (2050 J/kg·K). In addition, the absorbed water molecules can increase the intermolecular distance between polymer chains, which also affect the specific heat of wet fibers. Therefore, corrections are needed for Equation 17.2 to give more accurate specific heat values for wet fibers.

17.2 THERMAL CONDUCTIVITY

17.2.1 LONGITUDINAL AND TRANSVERSE THERMAL CONDUCTIVITIES

Thermal conductivity is a measure of the ability of a material to transfer heat. Figure 17.2 shows the transfer of heat through a material between a cold surface (T_1) and a hot surface (T_2). The material thickness, i.e., the distance between the hot and cold surfaces, is Δx. According to the law of heat conduction, also known as Fourier's law, the thermal conductivity (K) is the proportionality constant between heat flux and temperature gradient:

$$Q = K \frac{T_2 - T_1}{\Delta x} = K \frac{\Delta T}{\Delta x} \tag{17.3}$$

where Q is the heat flux, and $\Delta T/\Delta x$ is the temperature gradient. Equation 17.3 can be rewritten to give:

$$K = Q / \frac{\Delta T}{\Delta x} \tag{17.4}$$

Table 17.2 shows thermal conductivities of some fibers and other materials. Except for glass fibers, all polymer and carbon fibers are anisotropic due to molecular orientation. For these anisotropic fibers, the thermal conductivity (K_L) along the longitudinal direction is greater than that (K_T) on the transverse direction. The ratio of K_L to K_T is a good indication of the degree of molecular orientation. For the same type of fibers, higher K_L/K_T ratio indicates greater molecular orientation.

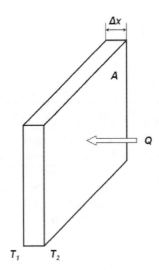

Figure 17.2. Transfer of heat through a material between a cold surface and a hot surface.

Table 17.2. Thermal conductivities of fibers and non-fibrous materials.

Material	Thermal Conductivity (W/m·K)		Anisotropy
	Longitudinal K_L	Transverse K_T	K_L/K_T
Synthetic Polymer Fibers			
Polypropylene	1.241	0.111	11.18
Polyester	1.26	0.157	8.01
Acrylic	1.028	0.172	5.93
Nylon	1.43	0.171	8.38
Kevlar			
Kevlar 29	3.05	0.192	15.9
Kevlar 49	3.34	0.212	15.8
Kevlar 149	4.74	0.230	20.6
Natural Polymer Fibers			
Cotton	2.88	0.243	11.85
Flax	2.851	0.344	8.23
Wool	0.48	0.165	2.91
Silk	1.49	0.118	12.64
Inorganic Fibers			
Carbon			
Torayca T-300	6.69	0.530	12.6
Torayca M-308	18.33	0.667	27.5
Torayca M-408	58.81	1.215	48.4
Glass	0.04		
Other Non-Fibrous Materials*			
Aluminum	205		
Steel	16–60		
Water	0.58		
Ice	2.22		
Snow	0.05–0.25		
Air	0.024		

* Most non-fibrous materials are isotropic and only have one thermal conductivity value.
Sources: Morton, W.E., et. al., *Physical Properties of Textile Fibres*, Fourth Edition, Woodhead Publishing Limited, 2008.; Warner, S.B., *Fiber Science*, Prentice Hall, 1995.

From Table 17.2, it also is seen that carbon fibers are thermally conductive, but polymer and glass fibers are good thermal insulators. Among the polymer fibers shown in Table 17.2, Kevlar fibers have the highest thermal conductivities probably because of the close sequence of benzene rings along the polymer main chains.

17.2.2 THERMAL CONDUCTIVITIES OF FIBER-BASED PRODUCTS

Polymer and glass fibers are thermal insulators. They often are assembled to form products, such as bats in sleeping comforters, winter coats, and building insulation, for thermal protection. The thermal conductivity (K_{total}) of these fiber assemblies can be estimated by:

$$K_{total} = f_{fiber} K_{fiber} + f_{air} K_{air} \qquad (17.5)$$

or

$$1 / K_{total} = f_{fiber} / K_{fiber} + f_{air} / K_{air} \qquad (17.6)$$

where K_{fiber} and K_{air} are the thermal conductivities of fiber and air, and f_{fiber} and f_{air} the volume fractions of fiber and air, respectively. Equation 17.5 gives the upper limit of the thermal conductivity of fiber assemblies, while Equation 17.6 gives the lower limit. According to Table 17.2, air has a significantly lower thermal conductivity than polymer and glass fibers, and hence the actual thermal conductivity of fiber assemblies is largely determined by the amount of air entrapped within them. In general, the assembly that can trap the most air provides the best thermal insulation.

Fibers also can be used in composites to adjust their thermal properties. Similar to fiber-based thermal protection products, the thermal conductivity (K_{comp}) of fiber-added composites is between the upper and lower limits determined by the following two equations:

$$K_{comp} = f_{fiber} K_{fiber} + f_{matrix} K_{matrix} \qquad (17.7)$$

and

$$1 / K_{comp} = f_{fiber} / K_{fiber} + f_{matrix} / K_{matrix} \qquad (17.8)$$

where K_{matrix} and f_{matrix} are the thermal conductivity and volume fraction of the matrix, respectively. Due to fiber's anisotropic nature, the length and orientation of fibers also influence the actual thermal conductivity of composites.

17.3 THERMAL EXPANSION AND CONTRACTION

17.3.1 COEFFICIENT OF THERMAL EXPANSION

Most materials expand when heated. However, many fibers contract when heated. This fiber behavior is called thermal contract, or negative thermal expansion.

The coefficient of linear thermal expansion, α_L, of a fiber is defined as:

$$\alpha_L = \frac{1}{L_0}\frac{dL}{dT} \qquad (17.9)$$

where L_0 is the initial length of the fiber, and dL/dT the rate of change of fiber length per unit temperature change. Similarly, the area thermal expansion coefficient (α_A) and volumetric thermal expansion coefficient (α_V) of a fiber are defined as:

$$\alpha_A = \frac{1}{A_0}\frac{dA}{dT} \qquad (17.10)$$

and

$$\alpha_V = \frac{1}{V_0}\frac{dV}{dT} \qquad (17.11)$$

where A_0 is the initial fiber cross-sectional area, V_0 the initial fiber volume, dA/dT the rate of change of fiber cross-sectional area per unit temperature change, and dV/dT the rate of change of fiber volume per unit temperature change, respectively.

For isotropic materials, these three thermal expansion coefficients are related to each other by:

$$\alpha_A = 2\alpha_L \qquad (17.12)$$

and

$$\alpha_V = 3\alpha_L \qquad (17.13)$$

However, most fibers are anisotropic and they do not follow these two relationships.

For most fiber applications, the linear thermal expansion coefficient of fibers is the most important one among the three expansion coefficients. Table 17.3 shows the linear thermal expansion coefficients of some fibers and non-fibrous materials. Polymer fibers have negative coefficients of linear thermal expansion although their corresponding non-fibrous materials have positive coefficients. The negative coefficients of polymers fibers are caused by the molecular orientation of polymer chains. Oriented polymer chains have the tendency to increase the entropy of the system and return to coiled conformations. However, oriented polymer chains are "frozen" at room temperature. When heated, the increased thermal vibrations allow the polymer chains to coil on themselves, resulting in negative coefficients

Table 17.3. Linear thermal expansion coefficients of fibers and non-fibrous materials.

Material	Linear Thermal Expansion Coefficient (1/°C)
Polymer Fibers	
Polyethylene (Spectra® 1000)	-0.1×10^{-4}
Polyester	-10×10^{-4}
Nylon	-3×10^{-4}
Kevlar® 49	-0.04×10^{-4}
Inorganic Fibers	
Carbon	-1.2×10^{-4}
Glass	0.05×10^{-4}
Other Non-Fibrous Materials	
Polyethylene	2×10^{-4}
Polyester	0.2×10^{-4}
Nylon	1×10^{-4}

Sources: Clark, J.F., *et. al., Journal of the Textile Institute Transactions*, 44, T596-T608, 1953.; Kumar, S., *Indian Journal of Fiber and Textile Research*, 16, 52–64, 1991.; Roff, W.J., et. al., *Fibres, Films, Plastics and Rubbers: Handbook of Common Polymers*, Butterworths, 1971.; Warner, S.B., *Fiber Science*, Prentice Hall, 1995.

of linear thermal expansion. Although most polymer fibers have negative coefficients of linear thermal expansion, their area and volumetric thermal expansion coefficients still are positive since polymer chains take up more space at higher temperatures when they are vibrating more vigorously.

Like polymer fibers, carbon fibers have a negative coefficient of linear thermal expansion since these fibers also have an oriented structure. However, glass fibers do not have an oriented structure and have a positive coefficient of linear thermal expansion.

17.3.2 DIMENSIONAL STABILITY AND HEAT SETTING

Dimensional stability of fibers is critically important in many applications. The linear thermal expansion coefficient discussed above can be used to describe the dimension stability of fibers. However, in practical applications, the thermal stability of fibers is commonly evaluated by boiling water shrinkage (*BWS*) measurement. During the measurement, fibers are placed in boiling water and the *BWS* value is obtained at equilibrium by using the following equation:

$$BWS = -\frac{L - L_0}{L_0} \qquad (17.14)$$

where L_0 is the initial fiber length, and L the final fiber length in boiling water. This is a simple and fast measurement of fiber dimensional stability. The presence of water accelerates the equilibrium of fiber shrinkage since water molecules can penetrate into the fiber structure and serve as a plasticizer. In general, tension is not applied during the measurement. However, in some cases, tension is applied to control the relaxation of polymer chains.

Most fibers shrink when heated, and hence their *BWS* values are positive. A higher *BWS* value indicates greater fiber shrinkage. To minimize the shrinkage of fibers, it is a common practice to intentionally expose the fibers to at least their use temperature and allow a small amount of relaxation to occur. This process is called "heat setting" and has been discussed in Chapter 9. Heat setting of fibers can be carried out after the fiber drawing process by using dry air, water vapor, solid heating elements, or heated liquid baths. Figure 17.3 shows an example of drawing and heat setting processes conducted with heated rolls. The speed of draw roll is greater than that of feed roll so the fibers can be drawn to obtain high molecular orientation. The speed of the relax roll is slightly lower (or comparable) to that of draw roll, allowing the relaxation (i.e., heat setting) of the fibers. During heat setting, a small portion of the orientation developed during spinning and drawing is lost. However, heat setting is a necessary process for achieving good thermal stability for orientated fibers.

17.4 GLASS TRANSITION

In addition to heat transfer and dimensional changes, fibers may experience glass transition, melting, degradation, and decomposition when they are heated. For non-polymer fibers, these phenomena do not occur or only occur at relatively high temperatures. However, these phenomena can be easily observed in polymer fibers. Sections 17.4–17.6 discuss the glass transition, melting, degradation, and decomposition of polymer fibers, respectively.

17.4.1 GLASS TRANSITION TEMPERATURE

Polymer fibers typically are semicrystalline. The amorphous phase of polymer fibers exhibits glass transition, i.e., a reversible transition from a hard, glassy state

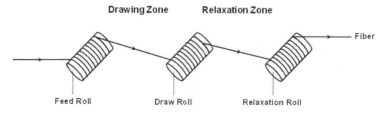

Figure 17.3. Schematic of drawing and heat setting processes of fibers.

to a soft, rubbery state. At the glass transition temperature (T_g), there is large-scale movement of polymer chain segments in the amorphous phase of polymer fibers. Figure 17.4 shows the modulus (E)-temperature (T) relationship of polymer fibers. When the temperature is lower than T_g, the relaxation time of the polymer chain segments is greater than the time scale of observation and the polymer chain segments do not have sufficient time to move. As a result, the fibers have high modulus and are in the glassy state. When the temperature is in the vicinity of T_g, the relaxation time is comparable to the time scale of observation and polymer chain segments start to move, and as a result, the fibers start to enter the rubbery state and their modulus decreases rapidly. The modulus of some fibers decreases by three orders of magnitude in the vicinity of T_g. When the temperature is greater than T_g, the structural integrity of polymer fibers mainly is maintained by the physical crosslinking effect of the crystalline phase.

In addition to fiber modulus, polymer fibers experience many other structure and property changes at T_g. Figure 17.5 shows the typical volume (V)-T and enthalpy (H)-T relationships of polymer fibers. Both the volume and enthalpy of polymer fibers increase with increase in temperature. The slopes of V-T and H-T curves become larger at temperatures greater than T_g. It must be noted there is no discontinuity at T_g for both curves. This is an important characteristic of a second-order transition. In section 17.5, we will discuss the melting of polymer fibers, which is a first-order transition. In a first-order transition, both the volume and enthalpy change rapidly at transition temperature, and there are discontinuities in the V-T and H-T curves.

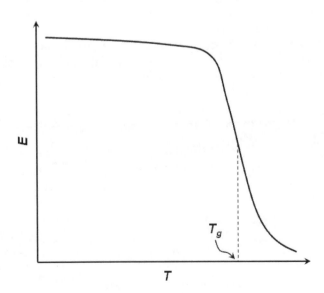

Figure 17.4. Modulus-temperature relationship of polymer fibers.

Figure 17.6 shows the variations in volumetric thermal expansion coefficient (α_V) and specific heat (C) as a function of temperature for polymer fibers. Volumetric thermal expansion coefficient and specific heat are, respectively, the first derivatives of volume and enthalpy with respective to temperature. Both the expansion coefficient and specific heat increase rapidly and are discontinued at T_g.

17.4.2 FREE VOLUME THEORY

Many theories have been developed to explain the glass transition phenomenon. Among them, the free volume theory proves to be very useful and applicable for a theoretical description of the glass transition of polymer fibers. According to this theory, a polymer fiber can be considered to be made up of occupied volume and free volume. Glass transition is a point at which there is sufficient free volume for polymer chain segments to move and change their positions (Figure 17.7).

Figure 17.8 shows occupied volume (V_o) and free volume (V_f) as a function of temperature for the amorphous phase of polymer fibers. The occupied volume increases with increase in temperature, and the expansion rate of occupied volume

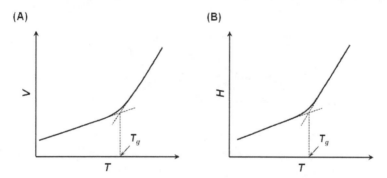

Figure 17.5. Variations in (A) volume and (B) enthalpy in the vicinity of the T_g of polymer fibers.

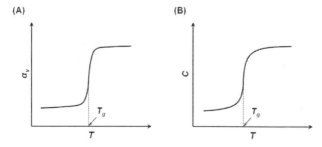

Figure 17.6. Variations in (A) volumetric thermal expansion coefficient and (B) specific heat in the vicinity of the T_g of polymer fibers.

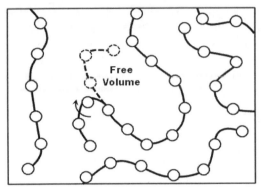

Figure 17.7. Schematic of free volume in the amorphous phase of polymer fibers.

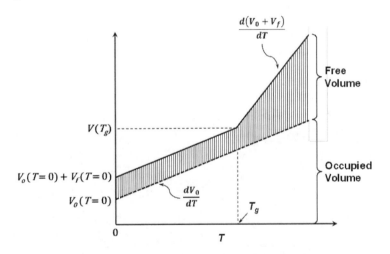

Figure 17.8. Schematic of the free volume theory.

remains constant (i.e., dV_o/dT = constant) both below and above T_g. As a result, the occupied volume can be written as:

$$V_o(T) = V_o(T = 0) + \frac{dV_0}{dT} T \tag{17.15}$$

where $V_o(T = 0)$ is the occupied volume at absolute zero.

The temperature dependence of free volume is more complex than that of occupied volume. Below T_g, the polymer chain segments are "frozen" and the free volume does not change with temperature, i.e., $dV_f/dT = 0$ ($T < T_g$). As a result, the free volume below T_g and at T_g can be written as:

$$V_f(T \leq T_g) = V_f(T = 0) = constant \tag{17.16}$$

where $V_f(T=0)$ is the free volume at absolute zero. Above T_g, polymer chain segments are able to move and the free volume increases with a fixed expansion rate, i.e., $dV_f/dT > 0$ ($T > T_g$). The free volume becomes:

$$V_f\left(T > T_g\right) = V_f\left(T_g\right) + \frac{dV_f}{dT}\left(T - T_g\right) \tag{17.17}$$

where $V_f(T_g)$ is the free volume at T_g. The fraction of free volume (f) can then be expressed as:

$$f\left(T\right) = \frac{V_f}{V_o + V_f} = f\left(T_g\right) + \alpha_f\left(T - T_g\right) \tag{17.18}$$

where $f(T_g)$ is the fraction of free volume at T_g, and α_f the thermal expansion coefficient of free volume. α_f is equal to the difference between the thermal expansion coefficient above and below T_g. For most polymer fibers, $f(T_g)$ and α_f are around 0.025 and 4.8×10^{-4} 1/K, respectively.

Many fiber properties are related to the free volume available in the amorphous phase of the fibers. For example, according to free volume theory, viscosity can be related to the fraction of free volume by the *Doolittle* equation:

$$\ln \eta\left(T\right) = A + \frac{B}{f\left(T\right)} \tag{17.19}$$

where A and B are constants. The *Doolittle* equation states when the fraction of free volume increases, the viscosity decreases. This equation can be rewritten to give:

$$\ln \frac{\eta\left(T\right)}{\eta\left(T_g\right)} = B\left(\frac{1}{f\left(T\right)} - \frac{1}{f\left(T_g\right)}\right) \tag{17.20}$$

Substituting Equation 17.18 into Equation 17.20 leads to:

$$\ln \frac{\eta\left(T\right)}{\eta\left(T_g\right)} = B\left(\frac{1}{f\left(T_g\right) + \alpha_f\left(T - T_g\right)} - \frac{1}{f\left(T_g\right)}\right)$$

$$= -\frac{B}{f\left(T_g\right)}\left[\frac{T - T_g}{\left\{f\left(T_g\right)/\alpha_f\right\} + T - T_g}\right] \tag{17.21}$$

Equation 17.21 also can be written as:

$$\log \frac{\eta(T)}{\eta(T_g)} = \frac{-\left(\dfrac{B}{2.3 f(T_g)}\right)(T - T_g)}{\left(\dfrac{f(T_g)}{\alpha_f}\right) + (T - T_g)}$$

(17.22)

or

$$\log \frac{\eta(T)}{\eta(T_g)} = \frac{-C_1(T - T_g)}{C_2 + (T - T_g)}$$

(17.23)

where C_1 and C_2 are constants. Equation 17.23 is the famous WLF equation. Universal constants ($C_1 = 17.4$ and $C_2 = 51.6$) often are used for polymer fibers. Using the universal constants, Equation 17.23 can be rewritten as:

$$\log \frac{\eta(T)}{\eta(T_g)} = \frac{-17.4(T - T_g)}{51.6 + (T - T_g)}$$

(17.24)

Figure 17.9 shows the log $\eta(T)/\eta(T_g)$–T relationship predicted by Equation 17.24. With increase in temperature, the free volume expands and the viscosity decreases.

The universal C_1 and C_2 constants are obtained by fitting the WLF equation to a wide variety of polymers. It must be noted the variation from polymer to polymer

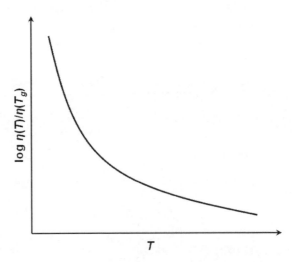

Figure 17.9. Log $\eta(T)/\eta(T_g)$–T relationship predicted by WLF equation.

could be significant. In practice, it is better to determine the C_1 and C_2 constants experimentally. The universal constants should only be used as a last resort when there are no sufficient experimental data for the specific fiber of interest.

17.4.3 FACTORS AFFECTING THE GLASS TRANSITION TEMPERATURE

Table 17.4 shows the T_g values of some fibers. It has been discussed that at T_g, the large-scale movement of polymer chain segments becomes possible. It is, therefore, expected any structural or external factors that influence polymer chain mobility also will affect the value of T_g. Structural factors include chain flexibility, intermolecular interaction, molecular weight, crystallinity, and crosslinking. External factors include additives, pressure, and tensile stress.

Chain flexibility affects the ease of rotation around the primary bonds of the polymer main chains. Polyethylene fibers are made of flexible polymer chains, which rotate easily and have excellent mobility. Hence, polyethylene fibers have a low T_g of around –80°C. The main chains of nylon fibers contain amide groups, which form strong intermolecular hydrogen bonds. The formation of hydrogen bonds significantly limits the rotation of primary bonds and leads to increased T_g values of 75 and 57°C, for nylon 6 and nylon 6,6 fibers, respectively. The bulky benzene rings on the main chains also can introduce a high energy barrier to bond rotations, and as a result, polyester fibers have a relatively high T_g of 80°C.

Side groups attached to the main chains have important impacts on the T_g of polymer fibers. Flexible side groups, including long branches, push polymer chains further apart, which in turn increases the free volume and lowers the T_g.

Table 17.4. Glass transition temperatures of fibers.

Fiber	Glass Transition Temperature (°C)
Polyethylene	–80
Polypropylene	–20
Polystyrene	100
Polyester	80
Nylon 6	75
Nylon 6,6	57
Polyacrylonitrile	90
Cotton	230
Wool	170
Silk	175
Glass	630 – 785

Sources: Kumar, S., *Indian Journal of Fiber and Textile Research*, 16, 52–64, 1991.; Warner, S.B., *Fiber Science*, Prentice Hall, 1995.

However, polymers with long flexible side groups or branches are difficult to form molecular orientation, and hence they are seldom used to make polymer fibers. Side groups found in polymer fibers typically are rigid and they can raise the T_g through steric hindrance to bond rotations. For example, polypropylene fibers have the same type of main chains as polyethylene, but their methyl side groups hinder the rotation of primary bonds and reduce the mobility of main chains. As a result, polypropylene fibers have higher T_g (–20°C) than polyethylene fibers.

The size and polarity of the side groups play important roles in determining the T_g. Compared with polypropylene fibers, polystyrene contains larger side groups (*i.e.*, benzene rings), which are rigid and have better ability to hinder the movement of polymer chain segments, leading to a higher T_g of 100°C. The nitrile side groups attached to polyacrylonitrile main chains are polar and can form strong intermolecular bonds, and hence polyacrylonitrile fibers also have a relatively high T_g of 90°C. Natural polymer fibers, such as cotton, wool and silk, have large numbers of side groups that can form strong intermolecular bonds and they have high T_g values of 230, 170, and 175°C, respectively. Among these fibers, cotton also has rigid glucose rings on the main chains, and hence it has the highest T_g.

The chain segments on the two ends of the main chain are restricted only at one end, and they have more freedom of motion than the internal segments, which are constrained at both ends. With increase in molecular weight, the number of chain ends per unit volume decreases and the free volume of the system decreases, which in turn increases the T_g. Figure 17.10 shows the effect of molecular weight on the T_g of polymer fibers. For relatively short chains, the T_g of polymer fibers increases rapidly with increase in molecular weight, but it eventually levels off

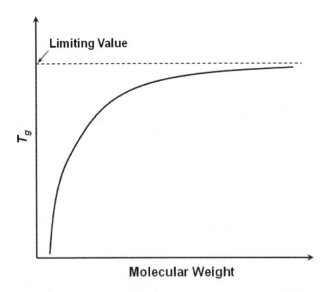

Figure 17.10. T_g as a function of molecular weight for polymer fibers.

and asymptotically approaches a limiting value at high molecular weights. According to the free volume theory, the following equation can be used to describe the relationship between T_g and number average molecular weight ($\bar{M}_n$) of polymer fibers:

$$T_g = T_g^\infty - \frac{K}{\bar{M}_n} \tag{17.25}$$

where K is a constant related to the excess free volume per chain end, and T_g^∞ the glass transition temperature obtained from a polymer of infinite molecular weight, i.e., the limiting value shown in Figure 17.10.

Most polymer fibers are semicrystalline. The presence of the crystalline phase limits the mobility of the polymer chain segments in the amorphous region. As a result, the T_g increases with increase in degree of crystallinity. There also is a simple empirical relationship between the T_g and the melting temperature (T_m):

$$T_g = \frac{1}{2}T_m, \text{ for symmetrical polymers} \tag{17.26}$$

or

$$T_g = \frac{2}{3}T_m, \text{ for unsymmetrical polymers} \tag{17.27}$$

where T_g and T_m are in degrees Kelvin.

The T_g of polymer fibers can be reduced by the addition of low-molecular-weight organic additives, such as plasticizers. This is because these organic additives increase the intermolecular distance and weaken the intermolecular bonds between neighboring polymer chains. On the other hand, inorganic additives (e.g., TiO_2 and SiO_2) can increase the T_g of polymer fibers since they reduce the mobility of polymer chain segments.

The effect of pressure on the T_g is straightforward. The mobility of polymer chain segments is reduced at high pressures, and hence the T_g of polymer fibers increases with increase in pressure. In general, T_g increases with pressure at a rate of 20°C/1000 atm. However, the effect of tensile stress is complex. In some cases, applying a tensile stress can increase the free volume and reduce the T_g. The relationship between the T_g and the tensile stress (σ) can be simply expressed as:

$$T_g = A - B\sigma \tag{17.28}$$

where A and B are constants. In some other cases, the tensile stress increases the T_g because of the development of stress-induced molecular orientation. Whether the applied tensile stress increases or decreases the T_g depends on the initial structure of polymer fibers.

17.4.4 OTHER TRANSITIONS

In addition to glass transition, polymer fibers exhibit a number of other transitions that are associated to different types of molecular motions. Figure 17.11 shows examples of small-scale molecular motions of polymer fibers. The crankshaft motion involves the rotation of a small number of carbon atoms around the polymer main chain (Figure 17.11A). The transition associated with main chain crankshaft motion often is referred to as the "glass II transition". This transition occurs at around $-128°C$ for polystyrene, $-120°C$ for polyethylene, and $5°C$ for polyvinyl chloride. In addition to the small-scale motion along the main chain, the side groups also display rotational vibration around the main chain and/or oscillation around its bond with the main chain (Figure 17.11B). For example, the transitions associated with the rotation and oscillation of the benzene rings in polystyrene are at around 50 and $-215°C$, respectively. These small-scale molecular motions provide polymer fibers with good toughness since a significant amount of energy is consumed to excite these motions.

17.5 MELTING

At temperatures greater than T_g, the integrity of polymer fibers is largely maintained by the physical crosslinking effect of the crystalline regions. When the

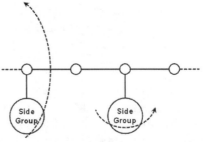

(A) Crankshaft Motion of Main Chain:

(B) Rotation and Oscillation of Side Groups:

Figure 17.11. Examples of small-scale molecule motions in polymer fibers: (A) crankshaft motion of main chain, and (B) rotation and oscillation of side groups.

temperature continues to increase and becomes higher than the melting temperature (T_m), the crystalline phase of polymer fibers melts. The polymer fibers become sticker, and eventually lose the integrity and contract to molten globules. Therefore, the melting of polymer fibers is an "irreversible" process. The structure of polymer fibers can only be reproduced by repeating the fiber formation process.

17.5.1 MELTING TEMPERATURE

The melting of polymer fibers is a first-order transition, which involves a latent heat. During such a transition, the crystalline phase absorbs a fixed amount of energy. Because energy cannot be instantaneously transferred between the crystalline phase and its environment, the melting process is associated with "mixed-phase regions", in which some parts of the crystalline phase have completed the transition and others have not.

As a first-order transition, the melting of polymer fibers can be characterized by discontinuities in properties such as volume, enthalpy, transparency, etc. Figure 17.12 shows V-T and H-T relationships of polymer fibers in the vicinity of T_m. Both the volume and enthalpy of polymer fibers undergo discontinuous changes at T_m, which are completely different from the continuous V and H changes at T_g (Figure 17.5). The α_V-T and C-T curves of polymer fibers in the vicinity of T_m are shown in Figure 17.13. As mentioned in section 17.4.1, volumetric thermal expansion coefficient and specific heat are, respectively, the first derivatives of volume and enthalpy with respective to temperature. It is seen from Figure 17.13 that both the α_V-T and C-T curves exhibit peaks at T_m, which also is a characteristic of first-order transition.

As discussed above, the melting of polymer fibers is a first-order transition and is associated with discontinuities in many fiber properties. As a result, any property whose values are different below and above T_m provides a potential method for measuring the melting temperature of polymer fibers. In reality, methods that

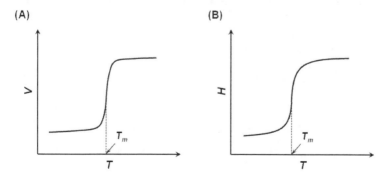

Figure 17.12. Variations in (A) volume and (B) enthalpy in the vicinity of the T_m of polymer fibers.

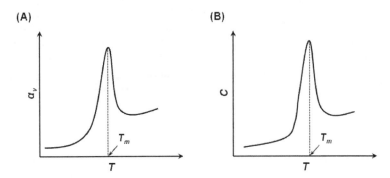

Figure 17.13. Variations in (A) volumetric thermal expansion coefficient and (B) specific heat in the vicinity of the T_m of polymer fibers.

have been used to measure the melting temperature of polymer fibers include dilatometry, calorimetry, dynamic mechanical testing, stress relaxation, creep, nuclear magnetic resonance, etc. Compared with the T_m of low-molecular-weight materials, the observed melting temperature of polymer fibers has some unique features:

- Low-molecular-weight materials often melt at a single well-defined temperature. During the entire melting process, the temperature of these materials does not change until a fixed amount of energy is absorbed. However, polymer fibers generally melt over a range of temperatures. The main reason is that the crystals in polymer fibers span a range of size and perfection. The smaller and less perfect crystals melt at lower temperatures, and the larger and more perfect crystals melt at higher temperatures. As a result, the temperature of polymer fibers continues to increase during the melting process.
- The crystalline structure of polymer fibers is imperfect, and hence the experimentally measured melting temperature of polymer fibers is lower than the equilibrium melting temperature. For example, the equilibrium melting temperature of polypropylene is 187°C, but the measured melting temperature of polypropylene fibers is around 170°C.
- The melting of polymer fibers is more rate sensitive than that of low-molecular-weight materials.

17.5.2 FACTORS AFFECTING THE MELTING TEMPERATURE

Table 17.5 shows the experimentally-measured T_m values of some fibers. One simple way to understand the effects of different factors on the T_m of polymer fibers is to consider the change of Gibbs free energy (G_m) upon melting. The G_m

Table 17.5. Melting temperatures of polymer fibers.

Fiber	Melting Temperature (°C)
Polyethylene	130
Polypropylene	170
Polyester	260
Nylon 6	215
Nylon 6,6	260
Polyacrylonitrile	none
Cotton	none
Wool	none
Acetate	250
Triacetate	300

Sources: Kumar, S., *Indian Journal of Fiber and Textile Research*, 16, 52–64, 1991.; Morton, W.E., et. al., *Physical Properties of Textile Fibres*, Fourth Edition, Woodhead Publishing Limited, 2008.; Warner, S.B., *Fiber Science*, Prentice Hall, 1995.; Wiedemann, H.G., et. al., *Thermochimica Acta*, 169, 1–13, 1990.

value of polymer fibers is related to the enthalpy (H_m) and the entropy (S_m) by the following equation:

$$G_m = H_m - TS_m \qquad (17.29)$$

Thermodynamically, the equilibrium T_m is the temperature at which the G_m values in the crystalline and molten states are the same:

$$\Delta G_m = \Delta H_m - T_m \Delta S_m = 0 \qquad (17.30)$$

where Δ refers to the difference between the crystalline and molten states. Equation 17.30 can be rewritten to give the equilibrium T_m value:

$$T_m = \frac{\Delta H_m}{\Delta S_m} \qquad (17.31)$$

This indicates the T_m of polymer fibers is related to the ratio of the enthalpy change ΔH_m to the entropy change ΔS_m upon melting. It must be noted the equilibrium T_m obtained by Equation 17.31 is always higher than the experimentally-measured T_m. However, this equation still is useful since it gives important qualitative insight on the measured T_m of polymer fibers, as discussed below.

The enthalpy change ΔH_m is related to the difference in the forces of attraction between polymer chains in the crystalline phase and the forces between those same chains when randomly intertwined in the melt. The closely packaged polymer chains in the crystalline phase allow the attractive forces to be maximized. As a result, polymer fibers with stronger intermolecular bonds between neighboring polymer chains would have higher T_m than those with weaker intermolecular bonds. For example, polyethylene fibers only have weak van der Walls forces between the polymer chains, and hence they have a relatively low T_m value of around 130°C. In contrast, nylon fibers have amide groups on the main chains and these groups form strong intermolecular hydrogen bonds. As a result, nylon fibers have much higher T_m than polyethylene fibers. Attaching polar side groups onto the main chains also can lead to the formation of strong intermolecular bonds, which in turn results in high T_m values. One good example is polyacrylonitrile fibers, in which the nitrile side groups form strong dipole-dipole forces between polymer chains. The equilibrium T_m of polyacrylonitrile fibers is greater than 300°C, but various chemical reactions, including cyclization and dehydrogenation, occur below 300°C. Hence, the melting of polyacrylonitrile fibers cannot be observed in common conditions. Wool fibers have various side groups that can form strong intermolecular bonds. Among these groups, the cysteine side groups can form covalent disulfide bonds that have similar strength to the primary bonds in the main chains, and as a result wool fibers do not melt.

The entropy change ΔS_m represents the difference in the degree of disorder between polymer chains in the crystalline and molten states. The ΔS_m term can be written as:

$$\Delta S_m = k \left(\ln \Omega_{melt} - \ln \Omega_{crystal} \right) \tag{17.32}$$

where k is the Boltzmann constant (1.38×10^{-23} J K^{-1}), and Ω_{melt} and $\Omega_{crystal}$ are, respectively, the numbers of conformations available in the molten and crystalline states. In the crystalline state, polymer chains are in a single ordered conformation (e.g., the planar zig-zag conformation of polyethylene) and hence the $\Omega_{crystal}$ value is very small. Upon melting, the polymer chains are able to change their conformations through bond rotations, and the number of available conformations becomes significantly greater (*i.e.*, $\Omega_{melt} \gg \Omega_{crystal}$). Therefore, the ΔS_m term is mainly determined by the number of conformations available in the molten state. In general, compared with flexible polymer chains, rigid polymer fibers have a smaller number of conformations available in the molten state, and hence they have smaller ΔS_m. As a result, rigid polymer chains have higher T_m than flexible polymer chains. For example, polypropylene fibers have methyl side groups, which make the main chains less flexible than those in polyethylene fibers due to their steric hindrance to bond rotations. As a result, polypropylene fibers have a T_m of 170°C, which is much higher than that (130°C) of polyethylene fibers.

Both the ΔH_m and ΔS_m terms are affected by introducing rigid benzene rings or glucose rings. For example, the benzene rings on the main chains of polyester fibers can increase the ΔH_m value by forming intermolecular aromatic ring association and decrease the ΔS_m value by introducing energy barrier to bond rotations. As a result, polyester fibers have a relatively high T_m of 260°C. For cotton and acetate fibers, the glucose rings decrease the ΔS_m value by limiting the bond rotations and increase the ΔH_m value by forming intermolecular hydrogen bonds through hydroxyl groups. The theoretical T_m of cotton fibers is so high these fibers decompose before melting. Acetate and triacetate fibers have some of the hydroxyl groups acetylated and can form fewer hydrogen bonds than cotton fibers. Hence, acetate and triacetate fibers have observable T_m values of 250 and 300°C, respectively, which still are relatively high as compared to many other polymers.

Molecular weight is an important factor affecting the T_m of polymer fibers. In general, molecular weight does not influence the ΔH_m term, which is related to the attractive forces between polymer chains. However, increasing the molecular weight can reduce the ΔS_m value by decreasing the number of chain ends per volume. As a result, with increase in molecular weight, the T_m of polymer fibers increases mainly because of the reduced ΔS_m value. It must be noted the effect of chain ends on the freedom of bond rotations becomes insignificant at very high molecular weights. Therefore, when the molecular weight exceeds a critical value, the T_m of polymer fibers becomes relatively constant with continuous increase in molecular weight.

17.6 DEGRADATION AND DECOMPOSITION

17.6.1 DEGRADATION VS. DECOMPOSITION

The degradation of polymer fibers involves several physical and/or chemical processes accompanied by small structure changes, which could lead to significant deterioration of the fiber properties. The decomposition of polymer fibers, on the other hand, defines the chemical process occurring under the action of heat, oxygen, chemical agents, etc., and results in the formation of a new structure completely different from the original. Decomposition can be considered as the advanced stage of degradation. In many literature reports, the distinction between the degradation and decomposition is not made. This section focuses on the decomposition of fibers.

Non-polymer fibers typically are more thermally stable than polymer fibers. For example, glass fibers can maintain their structure integrity until the T_g, which ranges from 630 to 785°C. Above T_g, glass fibers lose their physical shape although their chemical structure does not change. Therefore, for most applications, the maximum use temperature of glass fibers is their T_g. Carbon fibers can keep their mechanical properties unchanged upon heating to 1600 – 2000°C in the absence of oxygen. This allows carbon fibers to be used in many high-temperature applications. The presence of oxygen significantly reduces the thermal stability of carbon fibers. In air or oxygen, carbon fibers can be oxidized and eventually burned into carbon dioxide gas. The maximum use temperature of carbon fibers in air medium typically is 300–350°C, which is still higher than regular polymer fibers. Compared with non-polymer fibers, most polymer fibers start to decompose at much lower low temperatures, typically ranging from 150 to 250°C.

17.6.2 DECOMPOSITION OF POLYMER FIBERS

The decomposition process of polymer fibers is complex. In most cases, polymer fibers break down into a variety of smaller molecular fragments made up of different chemical species. The lighter molecular fragments vaporize immediately upon their formation, but heavier molecules remain in the condensed phase. While remaining in the condensed phase, these heavier molecules undergo further decomposition to lighter fragments that are more easily vaporized. Some polymer fibers break down completely so that eventually no solid residue remains. However, some polymer fibers produce solid residues which can be carbonaceous (char), inorganic (originating from heteroatoms contained in the polymer chains or additives), or a combination of both. Carbonaceous chars can be burned by oxidation in air at higher temperatures. Figure 17.14 show possible mechanisms of the decomposition of polymer fibers. Decomposition mechanisms can be divided into reactions involving atoms in the polymer main chains and reactions involving side groups. The decomposition of most fibers involves the combination of two or more reactions.

The most common decomposition mechanism involves the breaking of primary bonds in the polymer main chains. Such chain scission reactions may occur at chain ends or at random locations along the main chains. End-chain scissions often result in the formation of monomers, and the process often is known as unzipping. Random chain scissions inside the main chains generate monomers and oligomers, as well as a variety of other chemical species. Crosslinking is another important reaction involving the polymer main chains and creates bonds between two adjacent chains. Crosslinking is important for the formation of chars because it generates a network structure that is less easily volatilized.

The main mechanisms involving side groups are elimination and cyclization reactions. In elimination reactions, the bonds connecting side groups to the main

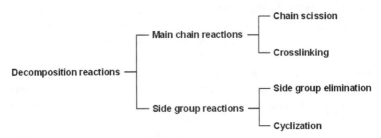

Figure 17.14. Possible mechanisms of the decomposition of polymer fibers.

chains are broken, with the side groups often reacting with other eliminated side groups. The products of elimination reactions typically are small enough to be volatile. In cyclization reactions, adjacent side groups react to form covalent bonds between them, resulting in the formation of a cyclic structure. This process also is important for char formation.

17.6.3 THERMALLY STABLE POLYMER FIBERS

There are several approaches to fabricate thermally stable polymer fibers. One traditional approach to increase the thermal stability of polymer fibers is to apply coatings of retardants and stabilizers, such as halides and hydrates. Most flame retardant/stabilizer coatings have one or more of the following functions: (*i*) directing the thermal decomposition reactions to low-rate paths, (*ii*) coating the fiber surfaces to exclude oxygen, (*iii*) forming a barrier to prevent release of small molecules that are combustible, (*iv*) releasing inert gasses to dilute combustible molecules, and (*v*) lowering the temperature by absorbing a large amount of energy.

Another approach to obtain thermally stabile polymer fibers is to form ladder-type structures through high temperature treatment. One good example is the high temperature treatment of polyacrylonitrile fibers between 200 and 260°C in air. This high temperature treatment also is called the stabilization process. As discussed in Chapter 11, the stabilization of polyacrylonitrile fibers can convert the linear polymer chains into ladder structures that are non-meltable and flame-resistant. Figure 17.15 shows one possible ladder structure that is formed through the stabilization process of polyacrylonitrile fibers.

Thermally-stable polymer fibers also can be obtained directly from polymers that have high decomposition temperatures. Table 17.6 shows a few examples of such polymer fibers. The aromatic and/or heterocyclic structures on the polymer main chains make these fibers thermally stable. The maximum use temperatures of these thermally stable polymer fibers are greater than 300°C, or even 400°C. Some of these fibers only lose 20 to 30% of their original weight at temperatures up to 900°C.

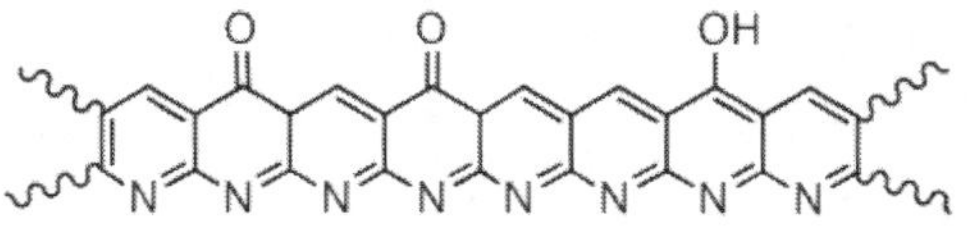

Figure 17.15. Possible ladder structure of stabilized polyacrylonitrile fibers.

Table 17.6. Chemical structures of thermally stable polymer fibers.

Fiber	Chemical Structure
Polyparaphenylene terephthalamide (Kevlar®)	
Polymetaphenylene isophthalamide (Normax®)	
Polybenzimidazole (PBI)	
Polyparaphenylene benzobisoxazole (PBO)	
Polyparaphenylene benzobisthiazole (PBT)	
Polyhydroquinone-diimidazopyridine (M-5)	

REFERENCES

[1]   Beyler, C.L., and Hirschler, M.M., "Thermal Decomposition of Polymers", in *SFPE Handbook of Fire Protection Engineering*, Editor-in-Chief DiNenno, P.J., Third Edition, National Fire Protection Association, 2002.

[2]   Clark, J.F., and Preston, J.M., "Thermoelastic Properties of Synthetic Fibres", *Journal of the Textile Institute Transactions*, 44, T596–T608, 1953.

[3]   Ebewele, R.O., *Polymer Science and Technology*, CRC Press, 2000.

[4]   Elias, H.G., *An Introduction to Polymer Science*, VCH Publishers, 1997.

[5]   Fu, S.Y., and Mai, Y.W., "Thermal Conductivity of Misaligned Short-Fiber-Reinforced Polymer Composites", *Journal of Applied Polymer Science*, 88, 1497–1505, 2003.

[6]   Fujishiro, H., Ikebe, M., Kashima, T., and Yamanaka, A., "Thermal Conductivity and Diffusivity of High-Strength Polymer Fibers", *Japanese Journal of Applied Physics*, 36, 5633–5637, 1997.

[7] Hsu, C.K., "Thermal Decomposition Properties of Polymer Fibers", *Thermochimica Acta*, 392–393, 163–167, 2002.

[8] Kumar, S., "Advances in High Performance Fibers", *Indian Journal of Fiber and Textile Research*, 16, 52–64, 1991.

[9] Losi, G.U., and Knauss, W.G., "Free Volume Theory and Nonlinear Thermoviscoelasticity", *Polymer Engineering and Science*, 32, 542–557, 1992.

[10] Mei, Z., and Chung, D.D.L., "Thermal History of Carbon-Fiber Polymer-Matrix Composite, Evaluated by Electrical Resistance Measurement", Thermochimica Acta, 369, 87–93, 2011.

[11] Morton, W.E., and Hearle, J.W.S., *Physical Properties of Textile Fibres*, Fourth Edition, Woodhead Publishing Limited, 2008.

[12] Nechitailo, V.S., "About the Polymer Free Volume Theory", *International Journal of Polymeric Materials*, 16, 171–177, 1992.

[13] Painter, P.C., and Coleman, M.M., *Fundamentals of Polymer Science: An Introductory Text*, Second Edition, CRC Press, 1997.

[14] Roff, W.J., and Scott, J.R., *Fibres, Films, Plastics and Rubbers: Handbook of Common Polymers*, Butterworths, 1971.

[15] Rosenbaum, S., "Polyacrylonitrile Fiber Behavior. I. Mechanisms of Tensile Response", *Journal of Applied Polymer Science*, 9, 2071–2084, 1965.

[16] Rosenbaum, S., "Polyacrylonitrile Fiber Behavior. I. Dependence on Structure and Environment", *Journal of Applied Polymer Science*, 9, 2085–2099, 1965.

[17] Schultz, J., *Polymer Materials Science*, Prentice-Hall Inc., 1974.

[18] Shlenskii, O.F., Goncharuk, N.I., and Gal'tsov, V.Y., "Determination of the Coefficient of Thermal Conductivity of Glass and Polymer Fibers", *Glass and Ceramics*, 26, 523–526, 1969.

[19] Sperling, L.H., *Introduction to Physical Polymer Science*, Fourth Edition, John Wiley & Sons, 2006.

[20] Warner, S.B., *Fiber Science*, Prentice Hall, 1995.

[21] Wiedemann, H.G., McKarns, T., and Bayer, G., "Thermal Characteristics of Polymer Fibers", *Thermochimica Acta*, 169, 1–13, 1990.

[22] Wróbel, G., Pawlak, S., and Muzia, G., "Thermal Diffusivity Measurements of Selected Fiber Reinforced Polymer Composites Using Heat Pulse Method", *Archives of Materials Science and Engineering*, 48, 25–32, 2011.

PROBLEMS

(1) What are heat capacity, specific heat, thermal conductivity, coefficient of thermal expansion, glass transition temperature, melting temperature, and degradation and decomposition?

(2) Compare the longitudinal thermal conductivity with transverse thermal conductivity. Why are they different from each other?

(3) How does moisture affect the heat capacity of polymer fibers?

(4) How can you design a textile fabric that can effectively keep the wearer warm with a given fiber?

(5) Describe the free volume theory.

(6) What are first-order and second-order transitions?

(7) Discuss and explain how you would expect the glass transition temperature of a polymer fiber to vary with:

    (i)   Chain flexibility
    (ii) Intermolecular interaction
    (iii) Molecular weight
    (iv) Crystallinity
    (v) Crosslinking

(8) In addition to glass transition, there are other types of important second-order transitions. Give two examples and explain why these second-order transitions are important.

(9) Discuss and explain how you would expect the melting temperature of a polymer fiber to vary with:

    (i)   Chain flexibility
    (ii) Intermolecular interaction
    (iii) Molecular weight
    (iv) Crystallinity
    (v) Crosslinking

(10) What are the differences between degradation and decomposition?

(11) What are the possible mechanisms of the decomposition of polymer fibers?

(12) What are the common features of the thermally-stable polymer fibers shown in Table 17.6?

CHAPTER 18

Electrical Properties of Fibers

The electrical behavior of non-polymer fibers is varied from excellent electrical conductors (e.g., carbon fibers) to good insulators (e.g., glass fibers). With only a few exceptions, pure polymer fibers are insulators with electrical conductivities in the order of 10^{-16} S cm^{-1}. Static charges easily can be generated and accumulated on the surface of polymer fibers. This could lead to serious consequences, such as handling problems during fiber processing, breaking down of sensitive electronic devices, ignition of flammable vapors and dusts in certain environments, and clinging tendency and annoying electrical shocks during consumer use. This chapter focuses on the electrical conductivity and static charging of polymer fibers.

18.1 ELECTRICAL CONDUCTIVITY

18.1.1 BASIC CONCEPTS

While applying a voltage to a polymer fiber, the current can be carried by either electrons or ions. Normally, the conductivity associated to the movement of electrons is called electronic conductivity. The conductivity caused by the movement of ionic species is called ionic conductivity. Both electronic and ionic conductivities contribute to the so-called electrical conductivity.

A simple way to understand the electronic conductivity is to examine the available energies for electrons in the materials. Instead of having discrete energies, the available energy states form bands. Figure 18.1 shows the schematic of the electronic band structures of conductors, semiconductors, and insulators. The lower band is called the valence band, by analogy with the valence electrons of individual atoms. Electrons in the valence band are bound to individual atoms. The upper band is called the conduction band because only when electrons are

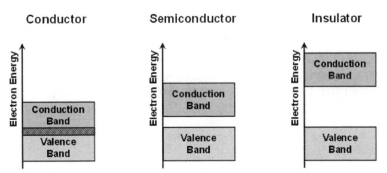

Figure 18.1. Schematic of the electronic band structures of conductors, semiconductors, and insulators.

excited to the conduction band can current flow in the material. In conductors like carbon fibers, the valence band overlaps the conduction band and at least a fraction of the valence electrons can move through the material. The conductivities of conductors are in the range of 10^{-3} to 10^{6} S cm^{-1}. In semiconductors, there is a small gap between the valence and conduction bands. This gap can be bridged by thermal or other excitations. The conductivities of semiconductors range from 10^{-8} to 10^{-3} S cm^{-1}. In insulators like polymer fibers, the electrons in the valence band are separated by a large gap from the conduction band, and the gap is so large that it is difficult to excite the valence electrons to the conduction band. Insulators have conductivities ranging from 10^{-18} to 10^{-8} S cm^{-1}. Pure polymer fibers are excellent insulators and their electronic conductivities are in the order of 10^{-16} S cm^{-1} when dried.

Since polymer fibers have low electronic conductivities, their ionic conductivities cannot be ignored. Depending on the chemical structure of polymer fibers, ions can be dissociated from the polymer chains by different mechanisms. For example, in nylon fibers, the momentary ionization of the hydrogen bonds can generate protons to serve as charge carriers (Figure 18.2). In addition to the ions generated from the polymer chains, impurities, residues (e.g., catalysts) and additives all contribute to the ionic conductivity of polymer fibers. This is why pure polymer fibers typically have conductivities in the order of 10^{-16} S cm^{-1}, but impure polymer fibers can have higher conductivities. However, the mobility of ions typically is low, and as a result most polymer fibers still are insulators even with the presence of impurities, residues, and additives.

In theory, the overall conductivity (σ) of a polymer fiber is governed by the following equation:

$$\sigma = nq\mu \tag{18.1}$$

where n is the number of charge carriers per unit volume, q the charge per charge carrier, and μ the mobility of the charge carrier. This equation states conductivity

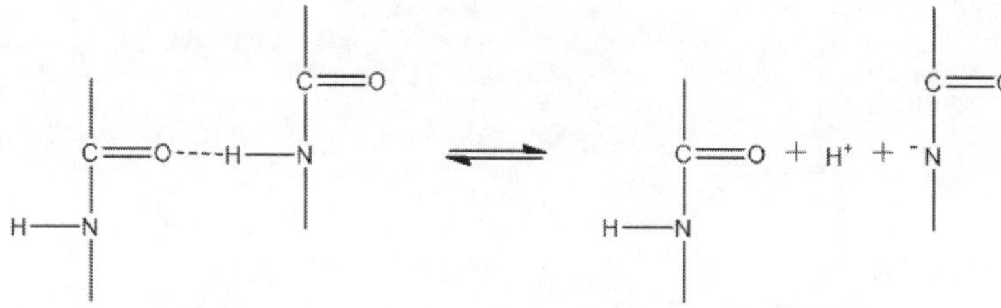

Figure 18.2. Ionization of hydrogen bond in nylon fibers.

is associated to the concerted motion of charge carriers. In polymer fibers, the charge carriers can be either electrons or ionic species.

In practice, it is difficult to calculate the conductivity of polymer fibers by using Equation 18.1. The conductivity of polymer fibers can be obtained by carrying out the electrical resistance measurement. According to the Ohm's law, the electrical resistance (R) of a fiber can be obtained by:

$$R = \frac{U}{I} \tag{18.2}$$

where U is the voltage in volts, and I the current in amperes. The fiber resistivity (ρ), a geometry-independent material property, can then be calculated by:

$$\rho = R\frac{A}{L} \tag{18.3}$$

where A is the cross-sectional area of the fiber, and L the length of the fiber. The fiber conductivity is the reciprocal of resistivity:

$$\sigma = \frac{1}{\rho} \tag{18.4}$$

18.1.2 ELECTRICAL CONDUCTIVITIES OF POLYMER FIBERS

In most polymer fibers, all electrons are bound to the atom nuclei or shared in the covalent bonds. These electrons are not free to move without being excited over the large band gap shown in Figure 18.1. Indeed, even if the electrons are excited to the conduction band, they still are not perfectly free since the trap density along the polymer chain can be sufficiently large to inhibit the motion of the excited electrons.

Figure 18.3 shows the conductivity-temperature relationship of polymer fibers. Below the glass transition temperature (T_g), the fiber conductivity increases slowly with increase in temperature. However, above T_g, the fiber conductivity increases much faster with temperature. This probably is because the mobility of

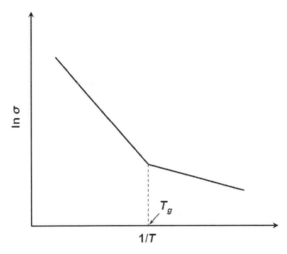

Figure 18.3. Electrical conductivity-temperature relationship of polymer fibers.

the entire system is enhanced when the temperature is greater than T_g. Both below and above T_g, the conductivity-temperature relationship follows the *Arrhenius* equation:

$$\sigma = \sigma_0 e^{-\Delta E/kT} \qquad (18.5)$$

where ΔE is the activation energy, k the Boltzmann's constant, and T the absolute temperature. For many polymer fibers, the activation energies lie between 5 and 15 kcal/mole below T_g and between 30 and 80 kcal/mole above T_g. The high activation energies indicate the conductivities in polymer fibers may occur mainly by the ionic mechanism, especially above T_g. However, evidence also shows the contribution of electronic conductivity, especially at low temperatures.

As discussed above, the electrical conductivities of pure polymer fibers are in the order of 10^{-16} S cm^{-1}, which is approximately 10^8 times lower than that of pure water and 10^{11} times lower than that of water containing impurities capable of transporting charges such as ions. The relatively high conductivity of water explains why the introduction of even small amount of water molecules can result in a significant conductivity increase for many polymer fibers, especially those with hydrophilic nature. The presence of water molecules provides transport carriers for electrical charges by facilitating the migration of ions in moisture-absorbed fibers. In general, hydrophobic fibers, such as polyethylene and polypropylene fibers, do not absorb moisture and their conductivities show little or no moisture sensitivity. However, the conductivities of hydrophilic cotton, wool and rayon fibers could increase by more than 10 orders of magnitude through moisture absorption. For many hydrophilic polymer fibers, the conductivity between 30 and 90% relative humidity can be related to the moisture content (*MC*) by:

$$\log \sigma = n \log MC - \log K \qquad (18.6)$$

where *n* and *K* are constants.

The moisture sensitivity of hydrophilic fibers is affected by the degree of crystallinity. In general, with increase in crystallinity, the moisture sensitivity of hydrophilic polymer fibers decreases. This is because the amorphous phase of polymer fibers is more amenable to both penetration and motion of ions than the crystalline phase.

18.1.3 ELECTRICALLY CONDUCTIVE POLYMER FIBERS

Although most polymer fibers are insulators, electrically conductive polymer fibers can be obtained by different approaches. One of the simplest approaches is to incorporate conductive materials, such as carbons, metals, and metal oxides, directly into polymer fibers. One advantage of this approach is that the conductivities of the resultant fibers are independent of humidity. The introduction of carbons, metals and metal oxides can be realized by: (*i*) dispersing their particulates directly into synthetic fibers before or during the fiber extrusion, and (*ii*) using them to coat the fiber surface. The challenge of extruding conductive particulate-added synthetic fibers is the difficulty in achieving homogenous dispersion of particulates. However, this could be solved by selectively controlling the extrusion condition and/or appropriately modifying the particulate surface. The coating of fiber surface with conductive materials may involve hazardous chemicals, depending on the coating method used, and this problem is being addressed by new research and development.

Another approach to obtain conductive polymer fibers is to spin them directly from electronically conductive polymers. Most conductive polymers have extended π-bonded, fully conjugated structures, such as fused aromatic rings, double bonds, lone electron pairs, etc. These polymers in their pure state still are electrical insulators since they do not have intrinsic charge carriers. The required charge carriers can be provided by partial oxidation (p-doping) of the polymer chains with electron acceptors (e.g., AsF_5, I_2) or by partial reduction (n-doping) with electron donors (e.g., Li, Na, K). Through the doping process, charged defects (e.g., polarons, bipolarons and solitons) are introduced and are available as the charge carriers. Table 18.1 shows examples of conductive polymers and the conductivities that they can achieve after being doped. So far, fibers made from these conductive polymers are in their early research stage and significant efforts are needed before they can be developed into commercial products.

Table 18.1. Structures and conductivities of conductive polymers.

Polymer	Chemical Structure	Doping Materials	Conductivity $(S\ cm^{-1})$
Polyacetylene	(structure)	AsF_5, I_2, Br_2, Li, Na	$10^3 - 10^4$
Polypyrrole	(structure)	BF_4^-, ClO_4^-, tosylate	$500 - 7.5 \times 10^3$
Polythiophene	(structure)	BF_4^-, ClO_4^-, FeO_4^-, tosylate	$10 - 10^3$
Polyphenylene	(structure)	AsF_5, Li, K	$10^2 - 10^3$
Polyphenylene vinylene	(structure)	AsF_5	$3 - 5 \times 10^3$
Polyaniline	(structure)	HCl	$30 - 200$

Source: Kumar, D., and Sharma, R.C., *European Polymer Journal*, 34, 1053–1060, 1998.

18.2 STATE ELECTRICITY

18.2.1 BASIC CONCEPTS

All materials are composed of atoms containing positive charges in the nuclei and an equal amount of negative charges orbiting the nuclei in the form of electrons. The contact of two materials allows the transfer of electrons across the interface. The re-distribution of electrons causes the formation of charges on both materials after they are separated. One material has negative charge (i.e., excess electrons) and the other material has positive charge (i.e., insufficient electrons). If the materials are conductive, the charges can equalize themselves by the backflow of electrons immediately after the separation of two surfaces. However, for most polymer fibers, electrons are not free to flow because they are bound to the nuclei or shared in the covalent bonds. As a result, charges can survive on polymer fibers for a measurable length of time and they are named static charges.

The effects of static charges are familiar to most people because we can feel, hear, and even see the sparks as excess charges are neutralized when brought close to a grounded conductor, or a region with excess charges of the opposite polarity. The familiar phenomenon of a static "shock" is caused by the neutralization of charges. In reality, the generation of static charges on the surface of polymer fibers can lead to serious consequences. For example, charged fibers may repel from each other, which makes further processing difficult or even impossible. Charges generated on fibers may interfere with the operation of sensitive electronic devices, and sometimes overload and break down these devices. In addition, discharges of sufficient magnitude may cause fires or explosion in an operating room since the spark generated during discharging can ignite flammable vapors and dusts. Therefore, in many applications, it is important to take actions to either avoid the formation of static charges or dissipate them quickly during the processing and consumer use of polymer fibers.

18.2.2 MECHANISMS OF STATIC CHARGE GENERATION

Many mechanisms can lead to the formation of static charges. The following are some common mechanisms. Any one of these mechanisms can lead to static charging on polymer fibers, but in many cases, more than one mechanism may work together to generate static charges.

The most important mechanism is contact-induced charge separation (i.e., triboelectric effect). As mentioned in section 18.2.1, electrons can be exchanged between materials on contact. Materials with sparsely filled outer shells tend to gain excess electrons, while materials with weakly bound electrons tend to lose them. This causes one material being negatively charged and the other positively charged. In addition to electrons, other charged species also can be exchanged between materials. For example, in fibers made of acidic or basic polymers, or polymers with space charge layers, ions can be exchanged at the interface of two contacted fibers. During the contact-induced charge separation, charges redistribute according to Boltzmann statics, i.e., charges move between the two contact materials in numbers (n) that depend on the activation energy ΔE:

$$n = n_0 e^{-\Delta E / kT} \tag{18.7}$$

where n_0 is the pre-exponential constant, k the Boltzmann's constant, and T the absolute temperature.

In contact-induced charge separation mechanism, the polarity of static charges generated on the materials depends on their relative positions in the triboelectric series. The triboelectric series is an empirically compiled list where materials are arranged from top to bottom depending on their relative ability to lose or gain electrons, beginning with the most positively charged material and ending with the material carrying the most negative charge. Table 18.2 shows several triboelectric series reported by different researchers. Although these series do not agree with each other completely, there are some similarities. For example, wool and nylon fibers typically appear at the positive end of the series, cellulose fibers in the middle, and the synthetic fibers other than nylon at the negative end.

According to the triboelectric series shown in Table 18.2, the polarity of static charge generated on fibers can be determined. For example, when wool fibers contact cotton fibers, wool acquires positive charge and cotton negative charge because cotton has better ability to gain electrons than wool. On the contrary, the same cotton fibers acquire positive charge when contacting polyethylene fibers because cotton has a greater tendency to lose electrons as compared to polyethylene.

The contact-induced charge separation does not directly involve relative motion of the two contact materials. However, motion certainly can enhance the formation of static charges. In many cases, rubbing two polymer fibers produce temperature gradients. Hot spots often develop due to the friction effect, and charges can move from hot spot to cold surrounding area.

The contact-induced charge separation is the main cause of static charges during the processing and consumer use of polymer fibers. However, other static charge generation mechanisms, such as pressure-induced charge separation (i.e., piezoelectric effect), also play important roles. Pressure-induced charge separation is determined by the ability of polymer fibers to generate static charges in response to applied mechanical stress or strain. The nature of the pressure-induced charge separation is closely related to the formation of electric dipole moments in fibers. The electric dipole moments can either be induced in crystal lattice sites with asymmetric charge surroundings or can be carried directly by molecular groups. The dipole density or polarization can be calculated for crystals by summing up the dipole moments per unit cell volume. The change of polarization under a mechanical stress or strain can either be caused by the re-configuration of the dipole-inducing surrounding or by the re-orientation of molecular dipole moments under the influence of the external stress or strain. As a result, pressure-induced charge separation can occur when there is a variation in the polarization strength, polarization direction, or both, depending on: (*i*) the orientation of polarization within the crystal, (*ii*) crystal symmetry, and (*iii*) the applied mechanical stress. Although the change in polarization appears as a variation of surface charge density upon the crystal faces, pressure-induced charge separation is not caused by the change in charge density on the surface, but by the change of dipole density in the bulk. The pressure-induced charge separation often is observed in natural fibers, such as wool and silk. In synthetic fibers, polyvinylidene fluoride (PVDF) exhibits piezoelectricity several times greater than other polymer fibers.

Like stress or strain, heating also can generate a separation of charges in polymer fibers. This is so-called heat-induced charge separation (i.e., pyroelectric effect). The atomic or molecular properties of heat and pressure response are closely related. Therefore, heat-induced charge separation also is a mechanism that is

Table 18.2. Triboelectric Series.

Lehmick 1949	Henry 1953	Ballou 1954	Hersh and Montgomery 1955	Henniker 1962	Adams 1987
More Positive (+)					
Glass	Platinum	Wool	Wool	Nylon 11	Nylon
Human hair	Formvar	Nylon	Nylon	Nylon 6,6	Wool
Nylon yearn	Filter paper	Silk	Viscose	Wool, knitted	Silk
Nylon polymer	Cellulose acetate	Silk	Cotton	Silk, wove	Paper
Wool	Cellulose triacetate	Cordura®	Silk	Polyethylene glycol	Cotton
Silk	Polyethylene	Human skin	Acetate	Cellulose acetate	Wood
Viscose	Aluminum	Fiber glass	Lucite®	Cotton, woven	Hard rubber
Cotton	Polystyrene	Cotton	Polyvinyl alcohol	Polystyrene	Acetate, rayon
Paper	Copper	Glass	Dacron®	Polyisobutylene	Polyester
Ramie	Nature rubber	Ramie	Dynel®	Polyvinyl butyral	Styroform®
Steel		Dacron®	Velon®	Natural rubber	Orlon®
Hard rubber		Chromium	Polyethylene	Polyacrylonitrile	Saran®
Acetate		Orlon®	Teflon®	Polyethylene	Polyethylene
Synthetic rubber		Polyethylene		Polyvinyl chloride	Polypropylene
Orlon®					Polyvinyl chloride
Polyethylene					Teflon®
More Negative (-)					

Sources: Lehmicke, D.J., *American Dyestuff Reporter*, 38, 853–855, 1949.; Henry, P.S.H., *British Journal of Applied Physics Supplement No. 2*, 4, S31-S36, 1953.; Ballou, T.W., *Textile Research Journal*, 24, 146–155, 1954.; Hersh, S.P., et. al., *Textile Research Journal*, 25, 279–295, 1955.; Henniker, J., *Nature*, 196, 474, 1962.; Adams, C. K. *Nature's Electricity, Tab Books, Blue Ridge Summit*, 1987.

related to the change of dipole density or polarization in fibers. All pyroelectric materials also are piezoelectric.

Charge-induced charge separation (i.e., electrostatic induction) is another important mechanism for the static charge generation. In insulating polymer fibers, although the electrons are bound to atoms and are not free to flow between atoms, they can move within the atoms. For example, if a positively charged object is brought near a polymer fiber, the electrons in each atom in the fiber are attracted toward the charged object and move to the side of the atom facing the charge, while the positive nucleus is repelled and moves slightly to the opposite side of the atom. Since the negative charges now are closer to the external object than the positive charges, their attraction is greater than the repulsion of the positive charges, resulting in a small net attraction toward the inducing charge. This effect is microscopic, but since there are so many atoms, it could add up to significant static charges.

18.2.3 ANTISTATIC TREATMENTS

The basic principle for addressing the static charging problem of polymer fibers is to increase either the ionic or electronic conductivity of the fibers. As discussed in section 18.1.2, the introduction of water molecules can increase the fiber conductivity by providing transport carriers to facilitate the migration of ions in moisture-absorbed fibers. Therefore, humidity control is a common practice in many fiber processing facilities. Spraying a mist of water or aqueous solution to the local surrounding of the fibers also is a common practice. Humidifiers also can be added to the central heating and air conditioning system. However, even for hydrophilic natural polymer fibers such as cotton, wool, and silk that are capable of absorbing large amount of water molecules, their conductivities still may not be sufficient in some occasions. In addition, when the relative humidity is reduced, these hydrophilic fibers become highly insulating again and static charges can be built up easily. Therefore, it often is necessary to introduce antistatic functionality to polymer fibers, depending on the intended use.

The application of antistatic agents is the most common approach to obtain antistatic polymer fibers. Most of the known antistatic agents are hydroscopic compounds that can improve the ionic conductivity of polymer fibers by ensuring the presence of water molecules and dissolved ions. Antistatic agents can be ionic or nonionic; however, ionic agents generally are more effective. Nonionic agents serve mainly as vehicles for carrying ions of other sources, such as impurities. Ionic agents typically are ionic group-containing molecules that can establish their functionality without relying on other ion sources. Both ionic and nonionic agents typically are hygroscopic, and they need water to realize their antistatic functionality. In this case, the main roles of water molecules are to: (*i*) lower the activation energy for the ionization of ionic groups, (*ii*) increase the number of the resultant ions, and *iii*) facilitate the transportation of ions. Many researchers believe that, for maximum efficiency, the water must be present as a continuous phase, preferably on the surface, rather than in the bulk. Therefore, most antistatic agents are applied on the surface of polymer fibers to increase the surface conductivity rather than the volumetric conductivity. However, in some stages of processing, antistatic agents can be absorbed into the polymer fibers and they are no longer just on the surface. In addition, internal antistatic agents that are added to the bulk of the polymer also are used in some applications.

In addition to ionic conductivity, antistatic polymer fibers also can be prepared by enhancing the electronic conductivity. As discussed in section 18.1.3, electronically conductive polymer fibers can be obtained by: (*i*) dispersing conductive carbon or metal particles into synthetic polymers before or during fiber spinning, (*ii*) coating the fiber surface by a thin layer of electronically conducting materials such as silver, copper, aluminum, or gold, and (*iii*) producing fibers directly from electrically conductive polymers. The advantages of these methods are that the resultant antistatic properties are durable and do not relay on the presence of water molecules. However, the conductive component added typically is either black or colored, and affects the appearance of the final product.

18.2.4 UTILIZATION OF STATIC CHARGING

There are applications in which the static charging phenomenon of polymer fibers can be utilized. One such example is filtration. Polymer fibers have large surface areas and often are used to make dust filters or masks. Statically charging the polymer fibers in these filters and masks can significantly increase their capability to capture the dust particles.

Another application that takes advantage of static charges is in the production of spunbond fibers. Spunbonding is a process for making nonwoven fabrics by depositing as-spun filaments directly onto a collecting belt in a uniform random manner, followed by bonding the fibers. During that process, the as-spun fibers tend to clump together, leading to poor uniformity. This problem can be solved by charging the fibers prior to the deposition on the collecting belt. Statically charged fibers repel one another, and as a result, the obtained nonwovens have better uniformity.

REFERENCES

[1]   Adams, C. K. *Nature's Electricity, Tab Books, Blue Ridge Summit*, 1987.

[2]   Ballou, T.W., "Static Electricity in Textiles", *Textile Research Journal*, 24, 146–155, 1954.

[3]   Elias, H.G., *An Introduction to Polymer Science*, VCH Publishers, 1997.

[4]   Henniker, J., "Triboelectricity in Polymers", *Nature*, 196, 474, 1962.

[5] Henry, P.S.H., "Survey of Generation and Distribution of Static Electricity", *British Journal of Applied Physics Supplement No. 2*, 4, S31–S36, 1953.

[6] Hersh, S.P., and Montgomery, D.J., "Static Electrification of Filaments. Experimental Techniques and Results", *Textile Research Journal*, 25, 279–295, 1955.

[7] Holme, I., McIntyre, J.E., and Shen, Z.J., "Electrostatic Charging of Textiles", *Textile Progress*, 28, 1–85, 1998.

[8] Kumar, D., and Sharma, R.C., "Advances in Conductive Polymers", *European Polymer Journal*, 34, 1053–1060, 1998.

[9] Lehmicke, D.J., "Static in Textile Processing", *American Dyestuff Reporter*, 38, 853–855, 1949.

[10] Morton, W.E., and Hearle, J.W.S., *Physical Properties of Textile Fibres*, Fourth Edition, Woodhead Publishing Limited, 2008.

[11] Pionteck, J., and Wypych, G., *Handbook of Antistatics*, Chemtec Publishing, 2007.

[12] Rebouillat, S., and Lyons, M.E.G., "Measuring the Electrical Conductivity of Single Fibres", *International Journal of Electrochemical Science*, 6, 5731–5740, 2011.

[13] Saito, S., Sasabe, H., Nakajirza, T., and Yada K., "Dielectric Relaxation and Electrical Conduction of Polymers as a Function of Pressure and Temperature", *Journal of Polymer Science: Part A-2*, 6, 1297–1315 (1968).

[14] Schindler, W.D., and Hauser, P.J., *Chemical Finishing of Textiles*, Woodhead Publishing Ltd, Cambridge, 2004.

[15] Smith, F.S., and Scott, C., "The Electrical Conductivity of Poly(ethylene terephthalate) in the Temperature Range 180–290°C", *British Journal of Applied Physics*, 17, 1149–1154, 1966.

[16] Sperling, L.H., *Introduction to Physical Polymer Science*, 4th Edition, John Wiley & Sons, Inc., 2006.

[17] Uchida, E., Utama, Y., and Ikada, Y., "Antistatic Properties of Surface-Modified Polyester Fabrics", *Textile Research Journal*, 61, 483–488, 1991.

[18] Valko, E.I., and Tesoro, G.C., "Polyamine Resins for Finishing of Hydrophobic Fibers", *Textile Research Journal*, 29, 21–31, 1959.

[19] Warner, S.B., *Fiber Science*, Prentice Hall, 1995.

PROBLEMS

(1) What is the difference between electronic and ionic conductivities?

(2) Describe the electronic band structure of polymer fibers.

(3) What is the conductivity-temperature relationship for polymer fibers?

(4) What are the main approaches to obtain electrically conductive polymer fibers?

(5) Why can static charges be generated easily on polymer fibers?

(6) What are the potential problems if static charges are generated on polymer fibers?

CHAPTER 19

Frictional Properties of Fibers

Frictional properties of fibers are important because they affect the processing, structure and properties of all fiber-based products. For example, friction is the force that holds the fibers together in yarns and fabrics. If there is not sufficient friction, the strength and structural integrity of yarns and fabrics will be lost. However, if the friction is too high, it could cause equipment failure, fiber surface damage, and even fiber breakage. In addition to these two examples where friction is clearly an advantage or a disadvantage, there are many other properties of fiber-based products that are affected by friction. Examples are the wear resistance of fibers and fabrics, the draping behavior of fabrics, the formation of nonwovens, etc. This chapter addresses the basic principles associated with the frictional properties of polymer fibers.

19.1 BASIC CONCEPTS

19.1.1 AMONTONS' LAW

Friction is the force that resists the motion or attempted motion of one surface against another. Figure 19.1 shows the loading force applied to move one surface over another, the normal force pressing the two surfaces together, and the resultant friction force. To understand the friction of materials, it is important to establish the relationship between these forces.

About 500 years ago, Leonardo da Vinci recognized two basic laws of friction:

- The friction force is independent of the contact area between two surfaces.
- The friction force is proportional to the normal force between the two surfaces in contact.

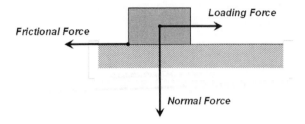

Figure 19.1. Schematic of loading force, normal force, and the resultant frictional force.

These two laws were later rediscovered by Amontons in 1699 and are expressed mathematically by using the so-called Amontons' law:

$$F = \mu N \tag{19.1}$$

where F is the externally applied loading force, N the normal force, and μ the coefficient of friction.

The friction behavior of polymer fibers does not follow the Amontons' law. The deviations from the Amontons' law will be discussed in sections 19.3 and 19.4. Despite the deviations, the Amontons' law lays the foundation for understanding the friction behavior of many fibers.

19.1.2 STATIC FRICTION VS. KINETIC FRICTION

It is also important to point out the distinction between static friction and kinetic friction. Static friction is the force that must be overcome to begin sliding. Static friction force is equal and opposite to the applied loading force up to a maximum static friction force, and no acceleration or movement occurs below the maximum force. According to the Amontons' law, static frictional force is proportional to the normal force pushing the two surfaces together:

$$F_{s,max} = \mu_s N \tag{19.2}$$

where $F_{s,max}$ is the maximum static friction force, and μ_s the coefficient of static friction. On the other hand, kinetic friction is the force resisting continued sliding. Kinetic frictional force is opposite to the direction of motion, and is also proportional to the normal force:

$$F_k = \mu_k N \tag{19.3}$$

where F_k is the kinetic friction force, and μ_k the coefficient of kinetic friction. For most materials, the kinetic friction coefficient is independent of the sliding speed and is smaller than the static friction coefficient.

When two objects are in contact and a loading force is applied to slide one object again the other, the relationship between the friction force and the applied loading force will determine whether the object will slide or not move at all. Figure 19.2 shows the friction forces generated while sliding an object against a flat surface under different conditions. At all these conditions, the normal force does not change since the mass of the object remains constant. When the object is at rest and there is no applied force, the friction force (F_A) is zero since there is no attempted motion (Figure 19.2A). When an external force is applied to push the object to the verge of sliding, a friction force (F_B) is generated to resist the attempted motion (Figure 19.2B). In this case, F_B is equal to the $F_{s,max}$ described in Equation 19.2. The object starts to slide when the applied force is greater than F_B. The resultant friction force (F_C) is determined by the kinetic friction coefficient and normal force, as described by Equation 19.3. F_C is smaller than F_B since the kinetic friction coefficient is smaller than the static friction coefficient. At this condition, the sliding speed of the object continues to increase since the applied force is greater than F_C (Figure 19.2C). To keep a constant speed, the applied force must be reduced so it is equal and opposite to the friction force (F_D) (Figure 19.2D). If the applied force continues to decrease and becomes smaller than the friction force (F_E), the object starts to slow down (Figure 19.2E). Both F_D and F_E are determined by Equation 19.3, and they are equal to F_C since the kinetic friction coefficient is independent of the sliding speed. Therefore, under these five sliding conditions, the friction forces follow the following order: $F_B > F_C = F_D = F_E > F_A = 0$.

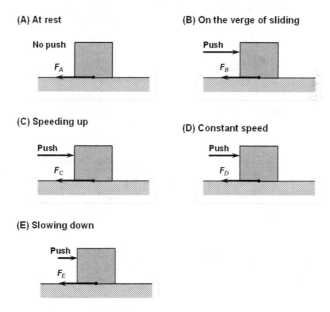

Figure 19.2. Friction forces under different sliding conditions.

19.2 NATURE OF FRICTION

Friction is a complicated phenomenon and is not fully understood yet. One common belief is the friction force is related to the irregular structure of material surfaces. On the microscale, almost all surfaces are irregular, and true surface contacts only occur at the tips of the asperities (Figure 19.3). When a loading force is applied to slide one surface again another, considerable compressive and shear stresses are developed locally at the contacting tips. These stresses lead to the plastic deformation of contacting points. The plastic deformation is the major cause of the friction between two surfaces. In addition, the energy associated with the plastic deformation also facilitates the diffusion of atoms or molecules between the surfaces. This welding or adhesion process also contributes to the friction. Therefore, the total frictional force is the sum of two terms: the force of deformation and the force of adhesion.

The magnitude of deformation depends on the mechanical properties of the surface materials. Under a fixed normal force, the contacting tips will continue to deform until the pressure at the points of contact is reduced to the yield stress. The contacting tips then will be able to support the normal force without further deformation. The yield pressure (P_y) can be expressed:

$$P_y = \frac{N}{A} \tag{19.4}$$

where N is the normal force, and A the true contact area. Equation 19.4 can be rewritten to give the true contact area of the two surfaces:

$$A = \frac{N}{P_y} \tag{19.5}$$

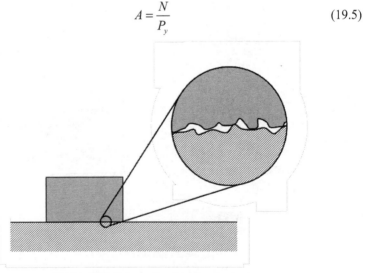

Figure 19.3. Schematic of surface contact.

Equation 19.5 indicates the true contact area is proportional to the normal force. When the deformation occurs, the generated energy allows the diffusion of atoms or molecules between the surfaces, creating welded junctions. To allow sliding, these joints must be broken by shear stress. To resist the shear stress, the friction force (F) is generated and can be calculated by:

$$F = \tau^* A \tag{19.6}$$

where τ^* is the shear strength of the weaker material of the two surfaces. Substituting Equation 19.5 into Equation 19.6 gives:

$$F = \frac{\tau^*}{P_y} N \tag{19.7}$$

Since both τ^* and P_y are constants, Equation 19.7 is the Amontons' law with:

$$\mu = \frac{\tau^*}{P_y} \tag{19.8}$$

Therefore, the coefficient of friction is determined by the yield pressure and shear strength of the weaker material.

19.3 FIBER-ON-FIBER FRICTION

19.3.1 FRICTION COEFFICIENT

The friction properties between fibers are important. The friction between fibers is essential to keep the strength and integrity of yarns and nonwovens. Experimental research has found marked deformation and welding at points of contact on damaged fiber surfaces. This demonstrates the fiber-on-fiber friction force is the sum of the force of deformation and the force of adhesion. Table 19.1 shows typical static and kinetic friction coefficients of polymer fibers. Like most other materials, the static friction coefficients of fibers are greater than their kinetic counterparts. The difference between the static and kinetic friction coefficients affects the feel of the fibers. Fibers with large differences have coarse, crunchy feel. Sometimes, the large difference between the static and kinetic friction coefficients causes the "stick-slip" motion. For rayon and nylon fibers, their friction coefficients are independent of the direction of sliding. However, when wool fibers are involved, the friction becomes directional due to the presence of scales on the wool fiber surface.

Table 19.1. Static and kinetic friction coefficients between fibers.

	Static Friction Coefficient, μ_s	Kinetic Friction Coefficient, μ_k
Nylon-on-nylon	0.47	0.40
Rayon-on-rayon	0.35	0.26
Wool-on-wool		
with scales	0.13	0.11
against scales	0.61	0.38
fibers in same direction	0.21	0.15
Wool-on-rayon		
with scales	0.11	0.09
against scales	0.39	0.35
Wool-on-nylon		
with scales	0.26	0.21
against scales	0.43	0.35

Source: Olofsson, B., et. al., *Textile Research Journal*, 20, 467–476, 1950.

19.3.2 FACTORS AFFECTING THE FRICTION COEFFICIENT

Many factors affect the friction coefficient of polymer fibers. Friction coefficients shown in Table 19.1 are just some typical values. They can be used to provide some basic information on fiber-on-fiber friction, but they cannot be expected to have validity in all circumstances.

One important factor that affects the fiber-on-fiber friction is the normal force. According to the Amontons' law, the friction coefficient should be a constant and is independent of the normal force. However, the fiber-on-fiber friction does not obey the Amontons' law. Figure 19.4 shows the effect of normal force on the friction coefficient between fibers. The friction coefficient of fibers decreases with increase in normal force. This behavior may be explained by the elastic deformation of surface asperities on fibers. The relationship between fiber-on-fiber friction force and normal force can be described by using an empirical equation:

$$F = aN^n \tag{19.9}$$

where a and n are constants. The n value depends on the type of fiber and direction of sliding, generally ranging from 3/4 to 1.

As discussed in section 19.1.2, the friction coefficient of most materials is independent of the sliding speed. However, polymer fibers are different. The friction coefficient of polymer fibers is affected by the sliding speed. In general, at low speeds, a decrease in friction coefficient can be observed as the speed increases, but at high sliding speeds, the friction coefficient increases with increase

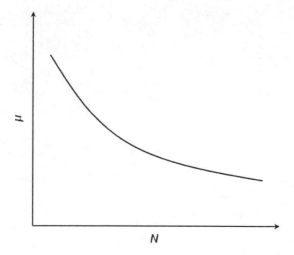

Figure 19.4. Effect of normal force on the friction coefficient between polymer fibers.

in sliding speed. This behavior is related to the viscoelastic properties and physicochemical activities of polymer fibers. It should be recognized the relationship between friction coefficient and sliding speed is affected by the test temperature. When the temperature is comparable or greater than the glass transition temperature, the friction coefficient exhibits a strong dependence on the sliding speed. However, below the glass transition temperature, the friction coefficient is less dependent on the sliding speed.

Humidity is another factor that affects the friction coefficient between fibers. Figure 19.5 shows the effect of relative humidity (% RH) on the friction coefficient between fibers. With increase in relative humidity, the friction coefficient between fibers increases. One possible reason for increased friction coefficients at higher relative humidities is that water molecules penetrate the contact points and increase the contact areas. In addition, while sliding the fibers at high relative humidities, the shear of the water surface also may contribute to the increased friction coefficient.

The friction coefficient between fibers also increases with increase in temperature. As a matter of fact, temperature effect is one of the causes for the increased friction coefficients at high sliding speeds. At very high speeds, the temperature of fibers may increase, and this could contribute to the increased friction coefficients.

19.4 FIBER-ON-OTHER-MATERIAL FRICTION

19.4.1 FRICTION COEFFICIENT

The friction of fibers on other materials also is important. For example, to convert fibers to final products, they often need pass around cylinder surfaces, such as

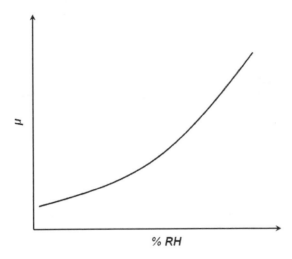

Figure 19.5. Effect of relative humidity on the friction coefficient between polymer fibers.

guides, pulleys, etc. When a fiber is pulled over a cylinder surface, a tension must be developed to overcome the friction force (Figure 19.6). The development of the tension can be described by the Capstan equation:

$$\frac{T_2}{T_1} = \exp\left(\mu\theta\right) \tag{19.10}$$

where T_1 is the incoming tension, T_2 the outgoing tension, μ the friction coefficient between the fiber and cylinder surface, and θ the angle of contact.

Figure 19.7 shows the theoretical T_2/T_1 ratios calculated using the Capstan equation. The tension on the fiber develops quickly while the fiber is being pulled over a cylinder surface. The development of fiber tension can be accelerated by increasing the contact angle or the friction coefficient. In practice, when the tension is too high, the fiber could be broken while passing over the cylinder surface. In addition, the surface of the fiber could be damaged at high friction, which in turn makes the breakage of the fiber much easier.

The Capstan equation can be rewritten to give the friction coefficient of fibers on other materials:

$$\mu = \frac{\ln\left(\dfrac{T_2}{T_1}\right)}{\theta} \tag{19.11}$$

Equation 19.11 often is used for measuring the friction coefficient of fibers on other materials. Table 19.2 shows the experimentally measured friction coefficients

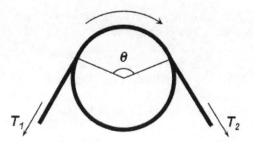

Figure 19.6. Schematic of a fiber passing over a cylinder surface.

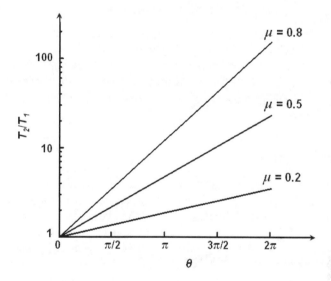

Figure 19.7. *T2/T1* ratio as a function of θ angle for a fiber being pulled over a cylinder surface with different friction coefficient μ values.

Table 19.2. Friction coefficients of fibers on steel and porcelain guides.

	Steel Guide	Porcelain Guide
Nylon	0.32	0.43
Cotton	0.29	0.32
Rayon	0.39	0.43
Acetate	0.38	0.38
Linen	0.27	0.29
Source: Buckle, H., et. al., *Journal of the Textile Institute Transactions*, 39, T199–T210, 1948.		

of fibers on steel and porcelain guides. Both steel and porcelain guides are used routinely in the industry. For most fibers shown in Table 19.2, their friction coefficients on porcelain guide are greater than those on the steel guide. This suggests the damage to fiber surface and the wear of the guide will be greater when the porcelain guide is used to pass fibers. However, the friction coefficient values vary with many experimental conditions, such as normal force, sliding speed, humidity, temperature, etc., and hence the data reported in Table 19.2 may not be valid in many circumstances. In addition, lubricants often are applied to both steel and porcelain guides, and this changes the friction coefficients significantly, which will be discussed in section 19.5.

19.4.2 FACTORS AFFECTING THE FRICTION COEFFICIENT

Factors that affect the fiber-on-other-material friction coefficient include but are not limited to normal force, sliding speed, humidity, and temperature. With a few exceptions, the effects of these factors on fiber-on-other-material friction are the same as those on fiber-on-fiber friction. Normally, the friction coefficient of fibers on other materials increases with increase in normal force, sliding speed, humidity, and temperature.

19.5 LUBRICATION

While sliding one dry surface over another, the surface asperities rub against each other, leading to damage or wear of the surfaces. This can be addressed by introducing a third material (i.e., lubricant) between the two contacting surfaces. The lubricant tends to fill the gaps between the asperities and acts as a fluid bearing layer to allow smoother movement of the two surfaces. A good lubricant for fibers is a material that has relatively low shear strength and adheres strongly to the fiber surface. In addition, the lubricant also should be thermally stable since the energy generated during high speed processing could lead to high temperatures.

Two most important types of lubrication conditions for polymer fibers are: boundary lubrication and hydrodynamic lubrication. The boundary lubrication occurs when the amount of lubricant is not sufficient to mask the asperities on the surface. In this case, the lubricant acts by forming a thin layer on the surface and preventing the adhesion of the two surfaces at the contact points. This significantly reduces the force of adhesion, and the force of deformation becomes the main source of friction. In boundary lubrication, the heat developed by the local deformations often causes a condition, called stick-slip. In addition, since there are fewer contacts between the two surfaces, the force needed to shear the lubricant layer itself also makes important contribution to the friction. The hydrodynamic lubrication occurs when a greater amount of lubricant is present and forms a relatively thick film between the surfaces. In this case, the friction mainly results from the viscous resistance to the flow of the lubricant.

The coefficient of friction between lubricated surfaces can be described by the following equation:

$$\mu = f\left(u\eta / P\right) \tag{19.12}$$

where u is the relative speed of the two surfaces, η the viscosity of the lubricant, and P the normal pressure (or load) on the surface. Figure 19.8 shows friction coefficient between lubricated surfaces. At low speeds (or high loads), the lubricant film cannot mask the surface asperities and boundary lubrication dominates. The resultant friction coefficient decreases with increased speed or decreased load. At high speeds (or low loads), the lubricant can mask the surface asperities and hydrodynamic lubrication dominates. In this case, the friction coefficient increases with increased speed or decreased load. From Figure 19.8, it also can be concluded that to reduce friction coefficient, the key is to reduce boundary friction at low speeds and reduce the hydrodynamic friction at high speeds.

The effect of friction coefficient on the damage or wear of lubricated surfaces is complex. A higher friction coefficient does not always means a higher wear rate of the surface. For example, the friction coefficient of fibers in the hydrodynamic lubrication condition can be very high at high speeds. However, the wear rate of the fiber surface in the boundary lubrication condition still can be much higher than that in the hydrodynamic lubrication condition even if the friction coefficient of the boundary lubrication is lower. This is because in a boundary lubrication condition, the asperities of the two surfaces contact each other and can be broken off by shear. On the other hand, the two surfaces do not have direct contact in the hydrodynamic lubrication condition.

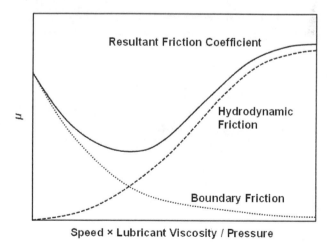

Figure 19.8. Friction coefficient between two lubricated surfaces.

REFERENCES

[1] Braun, O.M., and Naumovets, A.G, "Nanotribology: Microscopic Mechanisms of Friction", *Surface Science Reports*, 60, 79–158, 2006.

[2] Brostow, W., Deborde, J.L., Jaklewicz, M., and Olszynski, P., "Tribology with Emphasis on Polymers: Friction, Scratch Resistance and Wear", Journal of Materials Education, 24, 119–132, 2003.

[3] Buckle, H., and Pollitt, J., "An Instrument for Measuring the Coefficient of Friction of Yarns Against Other Materials", *Journal of the Textile Institute Transactions*, 39, T199-T210, 1948.

[4] Kilic, G.B., and Sular, V., "Frictional properties of Cotton-Tencel Yarns Spun in Different Spinning Systems", Textile Research Journal, 82, 755–765, 2012.

[5] Mogahzy, Y.E.E., and Gupta, B.S., "Friction in Fibrous Materials: Part II: Experimental Study of the Effects of Structural and Morphological Factors", *Textile Research Journal*, 63, 219–230, 1993.

[6] Morton, W.E., and Hearle, J.W.S., *Physical Properties of Textile Fibres*, Fourth Edition, Woodhead Publishing Limited, 2008.

[7] Myshkin, N.K., and Kovalev, A.V., "Adhesion and Friction of Polymers", in *Polymer Tribology*, Editors Sinha, S.K., and Briscoe, B.J., World Scientific, 2009.

[8] Olofsson, B., and Gralen, N., "Measurement of Friction between Single Fibers V. Frictional Properties of Viscose Rayon Staple Fibers", *Textile Research Journal*, 20, 467–476, 1950.

[9] Olofsson, B., "Measurement of Friction Between Single Fibers VI. A Theoretical Study of Fiber Friction", *Textile Research Journal*, 20, 476–480, 1950.

[10] Schwarz, U.D., Zworner, O., Koster, P., and Wiesendanger, R., *Physical Review B*, 56, 6987–6996, 1997.

[11] Shooter, K.V., and Tabor, D., "The Frictional Properties of Plastics", *Proceedings of the Physical Society. Section B*, 65, 661–671, 1952.

[12] Warner, S.B., *Fiber Science*, Prentice Hall, 1995.

PROBLEMS

(1) Describe the Amontons' law.

(2) Compare static friction with kinetic friction. Which one is greater?

(3) What is the nature of friction?

(4) Discuss how you would expect the friction coefficient of a polymer fiber to vary with:

    (i)   Normal force
    (ii)   Sliding speed
    (iii) Temperature
    (iv) Humidity

(5) Compare hydrodynamic lubrication with boundary lubrication.

CHAPTER 20

Optical Properties of Fibers

When light encounters a fiber, it is either transmitted, reflected or absorbed, depending on the structure of the fiber and the wavelength of the light. The transmission, reflection and absorption of light determine the visual appearance of an individual fiber. The appearance of fiber assembles then is the result of the combined effects of individual fibers, and also is affected by the arrangements of fibers. In addition, optical properties of fibers provide a convenient measure of many structural characteristics, especially the molecular orientation. Theoretical treatment of optical properties of fibers is complex. This chapter discusses the practical aspects of the optical properties of fibers.

20.1 POLARIZATION AND LIGHT

Polarization refers to the separation of charge, either momentarily or permanently. There are four mechanisms of polarization (Figure 20.1).

- Electronic polarization arises from the temporary distortion of electron clouds with respect to the nuclei with which they are associated, upon the application of an external electric field. Electronic polarization can occur to all materials and also is called atom or atomic polarization. Electronic polarization induces dipole moments.
- Ionic polarization occurs in materials that have ionic characteristic. These ionic materials have internal dipoles, but these built-in dipoles cancel each other and are unable to rotate by themselves. During ionic polarization, the external electric field displaces the cations and anions in opposite directions, leading to net dipole moments.

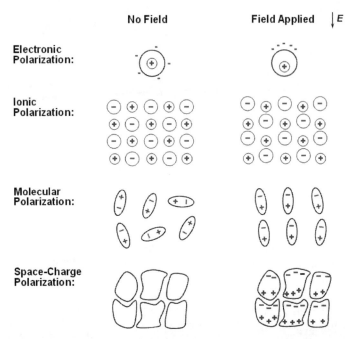

Figure 20.1. Schematic of electric, ionic, molecular and space-charge mechanisms.

- Molecular polarization occurs in polar molecules that can rotate freely. In thermal equilibrium, these natural dipoles are randomly oriented. The external electric field aligns the dipoles to some extent and induces a polarization of the material.
- Space-charge polarization, also known as interface polarization, involves the redistribution of ionically charged layers. In many cases, surfaces, grain boundaries, interphase boundaries of materials may be charged. The charged layers contain dipoles that may become oriented to some degree in an external electric field and leads to the polarization.

Light basically is an electromagnetic wave, which attempts to polarize the material as it passes through. When light travels, it typically propagates as a transverse wave, i.e., the electric field of the wave is perpendicular to the wave's direction of travel. Since the frequency of the waves of visual light is very high (400–790 trillion Hz), only the polarization of the electron clouds around the nuclei of atoms is fast enough to respond to the electric field of the light. As a result, the optical properties of materials are determined by the electronic polarization mechanism. The polarization of larger-scale charges, such as the permanent dipoles, cannot take place fast enough, and hence ionic, molecular and space-charge polarization mechanisms are not activated when light passes the materials.

20.2 REFRACTIVE INDEX AND BIREFRINGENCE

20.2.1 REFRACTIVE INDEX

The velocity of light often changes with the medium through which the light is transmitting. This property can be used to give the most fundamental definition of refractive index (n), which is the ratio of the velocity of light in a vacuum (v_{vacuum}) to the velocity of light in the medium (v_{medium}):

$$n = \frac{v_{vacuum}}{v_{medium}} \qquad (20.1)$$

Since light travels slower in a medium than in a vacuum, the refractive index typically is greater than 1. One consequence is the direction of light is refracted or bent while passing from one medium to another (Figure 20.2). As a result, an alternative definition of refractive index is:

$$n = \frac{\sin \theta_i}{\sin \theta_r} \qquad (20.2)$$

where θ_i is the angle of incidence, and θ_r the angle of refraction.

Refractive index is a basic optical property of fibers that is directly related to other optical properties. In general, the refractive index of fibers varies with temperature and wavelength. The standard conditions for refractive index measurement involve the use of specific wavelength (589 nm) at a specific temperature (20°C).

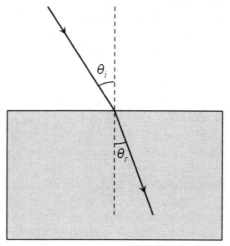

Figure 20.2. Refraction of light in a medium.

The refractive index of fibers also is affected by the fiber density. This is because electronic polarizability increases when the number of electrons per unit volume increases. For many fibers, the relationship between refractive index and fiber density (ρ) can be expressed by Gladstone and Dale's law:

$$\frac{n-1}{\rho} = constant \tag{20.3}$$

Most fibers are anisotropic and the refractive index value is directional. When the average refractive index is used, the constant in Equation 20.3 is around 0.3570.

A similar relationship can be obtained between the refractive index (n_m) and volume (v_m) of a mixture of different components:

$$v_m (n_m - 1) = v_1 (n_1 - 1) + v_2 (n_2 - 1) + v_3 (n_3 - 1) + \dots \tag{20.4}$$

where v_1, v_2, v_3, ... and n_1, n_2, n_3, ... are the refractive indices and volumes of the individual components. This relationship can be used to describe the effect of moisture on the refractive index of fibers. The refractive index of water is 1.333, and hence the effect of moisture on the refractive index can be described by:

$$v_{MR} (n_{MR} - 1) = v_0 (n_0 - 1) + 0.333 MR \tag{20.5}$$

where v_0 is the volume of 1 gram of dry fiber, v_{MR} the volume of the sample fiber at a fractional moisture regain of MR, and n_0 and n_{MR} the refractive indices of the same fiber when it is dry and moisturized, respectively. The refractive index values of most fibers are greater than that of water, and hence they decrease with increase in moisture regain. Figure 20.3 shows schematically the effect of moisture on the average refractive index of fibers. For some fibers, an increase in refractive index is observed at low moisture regains and this probably is caused by the filling up of voids or defects in the fibers by water.

20.2.2 BIREFRINGENCE

When light is transmitted through a fiber, the change of velocity is associated with the electronic polarization. In general, the electrons in the inner shells are not easily displaced, and hence only the outer electrons, which are involved in the covalent bonds, are affected by light waves. Figure 20.4 shows the electronic polarization process while the electric field is applied on a covalent bond through different directions. The electronic polarization is the greatest when the electric field is applied along the direction of the covalent bond. In isotropic polymer materials, the covalent bonds are arranged randomly in all directions, and hence the refractive index is identical in all directions and is the sum of the polarizabilities

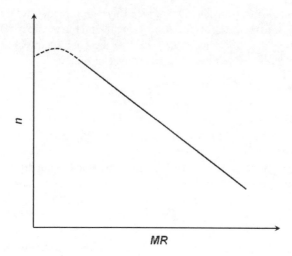

Figure 20.3. Effect of moisture regain on the refractive index of fibers.

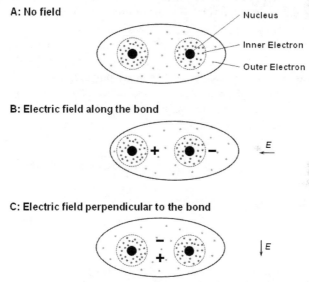

Figure 20.4. Schematic of electronic polarization of two atoms linked by a covalent bond. (A) Electron distribution around the atoms without the presence of electric field, (B) polarization while applying an electric field along the covalent bond, and (C) polarization while applying an electric field perpendicular to the covalent bond.

of all covalent bonds. However, polymer fibers are anisotropic and the polymer chains are largely aligned along the fiber axial direction. As a result, the refractive index of oriented polymer fibers is directional.

Most oriented fibers can be characterized by two principal refractive indices, one parallel to the fiber axis, n , and one perpendicular to the fiber axis, $n_\perp$. Here, the subscripts and $\perp$ indicate the vibration direction of the light waves. The two principle refractive indices obey the conversation law:

$$n_{iso} = \frac{n + 2n_\perp}{3} \tag{20.6}$$

where n_{iso} is the refractive index of the unoriented, isotropic sample made from the same material.

The birefringence (Δn) of a fiber then can be defined as the difference between the two principal refractive indices:

$$\Delta n = n - n_\perp \tag{20.7}$$

Table 20.1 shows the two principal refractive indices and birefringence values of fibers. The values given in Table 20.1 are only typical examples. For example, both the refractive indices and birefringence of fibers change with increase in molecular orientation. Table 20.2 shows the effect of drawing on the refractive indices and birefringence values of polypropylene fibers. With increase in draw ratio, the birefringence of polypropylene fibers increases due to the increased molecular orientation. In practice, the measurement of birefringence is an important method for studying the molecular orientation in polymer fibers.

The birefringence of polymer fibers is associated to the orientation of the crystal axes in the crystalline phase and the orientation of the individual polymer chains or chain segments in the amorphous phase. As a result, the birefringence of a polymer fiber can be described as:

$$\Delta n = V_c \Delta n_c + (1 - V_c) \Delta n_a \tag{20.8}$$

where Δn_c is the birefringence of the crystalline phase, Δn_a the birefringence of the amorphous phase, and V_c the volumetric degree of crystallinity. The birefringence of crystalline and amorphous phases can be written as:

$$\Delta n_c = \Delta n_{c,intri} f_c \tag{20.9}$$

and

$$\Delta n_a = \Delta n_{a,intri} f_a \tag{20.10}$$

where $\Delta n_{c,intri}$ is the intrinsic, or maximum possible, birefringence of the crystalline phase when all polymer chains are perfectly oriented along the filament axis, $\Delta n_{a,intri}$ the intrinsic, or maximum possible, birefringence of the amorphous phase,

Table 20.1. Refractive indices and birefringence of fibers.

Fiber	n	$n_\perp$	Δn
Synthetic Polymer Fibers			
Polyethylene	1.550	1.510	0.040
Polypropylene	1.526	1.490	0.036
Nylon	1.582	1.519	0.063
Polyester	1.720	1.540	0.180
Acrylic (Orlon®)	1.500	1.500	0.000
Acrylic (Terylene®)	1.520	1.524	−0.004
Kevlar	2.267	1.606	0.662
Natural Polymer Fibers (including regenerated fibers)			
Cotton	1.578	1.532	0.046
Ramie	1.596	1.528	0.068
Flax	1.596	1.528	0.068
Wool	1.553	1.542	0.010
Silk	1.591	1.538	0.053
Rayon	1.539	1.519	0.020
Acetate	1.476	1.470	0.006
Triacetate	1.474	1.479	−0.005
Non-Polymer Fibers			
Glass	1.547	1.547	0.000

Source: Hamza, A.A., et. al., *Journal of Optics A: Pure and Applied Optics*, 9, 820–827, 2007.; Heyn, A.N.J., *Textile Research Journal*, 22, 513–522, 1952.; Kumar, S., *Indian Journal of Fiber and Textile Research*, 16, 52–64, 1991.; Preston, J.M., *Modern Textile Microscopy*, Emmott, 1933.; Preston, J.M., *Transactions of the Faraday Society*, 29, 65–71, 1933.

Table 20.2. Refractive indices and birefringence of polypropylene fibers prepared with different draw ratios.

Draw Ratio	n	$n_\perp$	Δn
6:1	1.518	1.494	0.024
7:1	1.521	1.493	0.028
8:1	1.523	1.492	0.031
9:1	1.524	1.491	0.033
10:1	1.526	1.490	0.036
11:1	1.527	1.489	0.038

Source: Hamza, A.A., et. al., *Journal of Optics A: Pure and Applied Optics*, 9, 820–827, 2007.

f_c the orientation factor of the crystalline phase, and f_a the orientation factor of the amorphous phase. Substituting Equations 20.9 and 20.10 into Equation 20.8 gives:

$$\Delta n = V_c \Delta n_{c,intri} f_c + \left(1 - V_c\right) \Delta n_{a,intri} f_a \tag{20.11}$$

In this equation, the Δn, V_c, $\Delta n_{c,intri}$, $\Delta n_{a,intri}$ and f_c values can be either measured experimentally or calculated theoretically. Only the f_a value is difficult to measure directly or calculate by other means. Therefore, Equation 20.11 often is used to calculate the f_a value, which is an important property of fibers. High f_a is beneficial for improving some of the mechanical properties, but it could cause large thermal shrinkage and poor dye penetration.

Both Equations 20.8 and 20.11 work for dry fibers. When fibers absorb a large amount of moisture, the birefringence may be greater than the value given by these two equations. This is because these two equations only consider the orientation of polymer chains in the crystalline and amorphous phases. Research has shown that when non-spherical particles are dispersed with a preferred orientation in a medium of different refractive index, a birefringence of greater than zero can be observed even if both the particles and the medium are isotropic. This is called form birefringence. For dry fibers, the difference between the refractive indices of the crystalline and amorphous phases is relatively small and the contribution of form birefringence is negligible. When fibers absorb moisture, the water molecules mainly enter the amorphous phase and change its refractive index. Therefore, in wet fibers, the refractive index difference between the crystalline and amorphous phases become larger and the form birefringence starts to make contribution to the total fiber birefringence. The effect of form birefringence become significant only when the moisture regain is large, e.g., greater than 15%.

20.3 REFLECTION AND LUSTER

When the light falls on a fiber, part of the light is reflected. The amount of light reflected and how it is reflected are important optical properties of fibers. The amount of light reflected can be estimated by:

$$R = \left(\frac{n-1}{n+1}\right)^2 \tag{20.12}$$

where R is the reflectivity or the fraction of light reflected, and n the refractive index. Figure 20.5 shows three major types of surface reflection. Light may be reflected specularly, leaving the surface with an angle $\theta_r = \theta_i$ (Figure 20.5A), or reflected diffusively, with equal intensity in all directions (Figure 20.5B). Most real surfaces show a combination of specular and diffuse reflections (Figure 20.5C).

The luster of a single fiber is determined by total visual appearance of these reflections from the fiber surface.

The reflection of flight from a fiber surface is affected by how it is incident upon the fiber. Figure 20.6 shows the surface reflection when the light falls on a smooth, cylinder-shape fiber along two different directions. When the light is incident upon the fiber along the longitudinal direction, it can be predominantly reflected at a constant angle as long as the fiber surface is sufficiently smooth. However, when the light falls across the fiber on the transverse direction, it is reflected at various angles. This is an important feature of the surface reflection on fibers. However, many fibers do not have smooth surface or circular cross-section. Rough surface and irregular cross-sectional shapes increase the diffuse reflection. Fibers with rough or irregular cross-sectional shapes, such as wool and cotton, are not lustrous even when the light is incident along the fiber longitudinal direction. Lustrous fibers are those with smooth surface and regular cross-sectional shape, such as silk and some synthetic polymer fibers.

In addition to the primary reflection from the outer surface of the fiber, light can reflected from the internal surfaces. Figure 20.7 shows the primary and secondary reflections from a cylinder-shape fiber. When light falls on the surface of the fiber, some of it is transmitted through the fiber. A portion of the transmitted

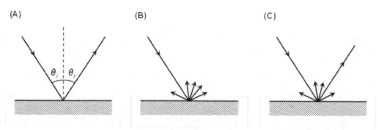

Figure 20.5. Types of surface reflection. (A) Specular reflection, (B) diffuse reflection, and (C) combination of specular and diffuse reflections.

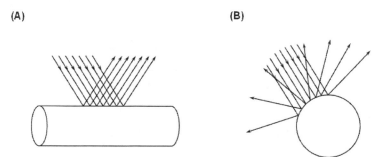

Figure 20.6. Reflection of light from the surface of a smooth, cylinder-shape fiber. Light is incident upon the fiber along: (A) the longitudinal direction, and (B) the transverse direction.

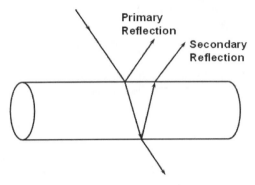

Figure 20.7. Primary and secondary reflections.

light can be reflected from the internal surfaces and join the light reflected from the outer surface. This is called secondary reflection. The secondary reflection is enhanced in fibers that have hollow tunnels (e.g., lumen), cavities or particulate fillers (e.g., TiO_2). Figure 20.8 shows the secondary reflection on these fibers. Hollow tunnels, cavities and particulate fillers scatter the transmitted light and cause apparent diffuse reflection. This effect masks the specular reflection and can be used to produce delustered fibers.

20.4 ABSORPTION AND DICHROISM

When light falls on a fiber, it is transmitted, reflected, or absorbed. Sections 20.2 and 3 discussed the transmission and reflection of light, respectively. This section addresses the absorption of light by fibers.

The absorption of light is the result of the interaction between the electromagnetic waves and the electron clouds in the fiber. The color of a fiber is determined by the selective absorption of light wavelengths (or frequencies). For example, a yellow, opaque fiber has a yellow color because it absorbs all wavelengths in the visual spectrum except yellow, and the yellow light is reflected. A yellow, transparent (or translucent) fiber is yellow when viewed in transmission because it allows yellow light to be transmitted while absorbing other wavelengths in the spectrum.

The absorption of light in a fiber obeys the Lambert's law:

$$I = I_0 \exp(-kx) \tag{20.13}$$

where I is the intensity of light after passing for a distance x through a fiber, I_0 the intensity of the incident light, and k the absorption coefficient.

Polymer fibers are semicrystalline, and they typically are translucent. Most of them are either colorless or slightly colored in neutral shades. In order to produce color, fibers often are dyed. The absorption coefficient k of a dyed fiber is

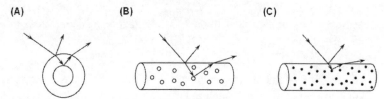

(A) **(B)** **(C)**

Figure 20.8. Secondary reflection on fibers with (A) hollow tunnel, (B) cavities, or (C) particulate fillers.

proportional to the density or concentration of the dye molecules added to the fiber. The Lambert's law then can be rewritten to give the Beer-Lambert equation:

$$I = I_0 \exp(-ck'x) \qquad (20.14)$$

where c is the concentration of dye molecules, and k' the extinction coefficient or absorption per unit of dye concentration.

For a dyed fiber, the absorption of light by dye molecules may vary with the direction of polarization of the light. This effect is called dichroism and it often leads to differences in the depth of shade or even in actual color. For dichroism to occur in a dyed fiber, the dye molecules must have an asymmetrical structure so that the absorption of light can vary with the direction of polarization. In addition, the dye molecules must be absorbed onto polymer chains with a particular angle and the polymer chains need be oriented. When polarized light is used to examine a dyed fiber that exhibits dichroism, the following intensity ratio often is assessed:

$$\frac{\log(I \,/\, I_0)}{\log(I_\perp / I_0)} = \frac{k}{k_\perp} = \theta \equiv \text{dichroic ratio} \qquad (20.15)$$

where I and $I_\perp$ are the intensities of the light polarized along the longitudinal and transverse directions of the fiber, respectively, and k and $k_\perp$ are the corresponding absorption coefficients. The dichroic ratio, θ, is independent of the concentration of dye molecules and can be used to assess the orientation in fibers. In general, the dichroic ratio increases with increasing orientation in fibers.

REFERENCES

[1] Duckett, K.E., and Cheng, C.C., "The Detection of Cotton Fiber Convolutions by the Reflection of Light", *Textile Research Journal*, 42: 263–268, 1972.

[2] Duckett, K.E., and Tripp, V.W., "X-Ray and Optical Orientation Measurements on Single Cotton Fibers", *Textile Research Journal*, 37, 517–524, 1967.

[3] El-Dessouky, H.M., Mahmoudi, M.R., Lawrence, C.A., Yassien, K.M., Sokkar, T.Z.N., and Hamza, A.A., "On the Physical Behavior of Isotactic Polypropylene Fibers Extruded at Different Draw-Down Ratios. I. Optical Properties and Cold-Drawing", *Polymer Engineering and Science*, 49, 2216–2224, 2009.

[4] Fouda, I.M., El-Farahaty, K.A., and El-Tonsy, M.M., "Optical Anisotropy in Mohair Fibers", *Textile Research Journal*, 59: 506–512, 1989.

[5] Fouda, I.M., and Seisa, E.A., "Birefringence and Orientation Parameters of Cold-Drawn Viscose Fibers", *Journal of Applied Polymer Science*, 106, 1768–1776, 2007.

[6] Hamza, A.A., "A Contribution to the Study of Optical Properties of Fibers with Irregular Transverse Sections", *Textile Research Journal*, 50, 731–734, 1980.

[7] Hamza, A.A., and Abd El-Kader, H.I., "Optical Properties and Birefringence Phenomena in Fibers", *Textile Research Journal*, 53, 205–209, 1983.

[8] Hamza, A.A., Belal, A.E., Sokkar, T.Z.N., El-Bakary, M.A., and Yassien, K.M., "Interferometric Detection of Structure Deformation Due to Cold Drawing of Polypropylene Fibres at High Draw Ratios", *Journal of Optics A: Pure and Applied Optics*, 9, 820–827, 2007.

[9] Hamza, A.A., and El-Farahaty, K.A., "Optical Properties and Geometrical Parameters of Poly(p-phenylene Terephthalamide) Fibers", *Textile Research Journal*, 56, 580–584, 1986.

[10] Hamza, A.A., Fouda, I.M., El-Farhaty, K.A., and Badawy, Y.K., "Production of Polyethylene Fibers and their Optical Properties and Radial Differences in Orientation", *Textile Research Journal*, 50: 592–596, 1980.

[11] Hamza, A.A., and Sokkar, T.Z.N., "Optical Properties of Egyptian Cotton Fibers", *Textile Research Journal*, 51: 485–488, 1981.

[12] Heyn, A.N.J., "Observations of the Birefringence and Refractive Index of Synthetic Fibers with Special Reference to Their Identification", *Textile Research Journal*, 22, 513–522, 1952.

[13] Kumar, S., "Advances in High Performance Fibers", *Indian Journal of Fiber and Textile Research*, 16, 52–64, 1991.

[14] Lynch, L.J., "A Study of the Relationship Between Geometry and Light Scattering Profiles of Single Wool Fibers", *Textile Research Journal*, 44: 446–448, 1974.

[15] Lynch, L.J., and Thomas, N., "Optical Diffraction Profiles of Single Fibers", Textile Research Journal, 41, 568–572, 1971.

[16] Morton, W.E., and Hearle, J.W.S., *Physical Properties of Textile Fibres*, Fourth Edition, Woodhead Publishing Limited, 2008.

[17] Preston, J.M., *Modern Textile Microscopy*, Emmott, 1933.

[18] Preston, J.M., "Relations between the Refractive Indices and the Behaviour of Cellulose Fibres", *Transactions of the Faraday Society*, 29, 65–71, 1933.

[19] Rudolf, A., and Smole, M.S., "Structure–Properties Relations of the Drawn Poly(ethylene terephthalate) Filament Sewing Thread", *Journal of Applied Polymer Science*, 110, 2641–2648, 2008.

[20] Warner, S.B., *Fiber Science*, Prentice Hall, 1995.

[21] Wei, W., Qiu, L., Wang, X.L., Chen, H.P., Lai, Y.C., Tsai, F.C., Zhu, P. and Yeh, J.T., "Drawing and Tensile Properties of Polyamide 6/Calcium Chloride Composite Fibers", *Journal of Polymer Research*, 18, 1841–1850, 2011.

[22] Yeh, J.T., Lin, S.C., Tu, C.W., Hsie, K.H., and Chang, F.C., "Investigation of the Drawing Mechanism of UHMWPE Fibers", *Journal of materials Science*, 43, 4892–4900, 2008.

PROBLEMS

(1) What type of polarization mechanism is involved when the light encounters a fiber? Why?

(2) What is refractive index? How does the fiber density affect the refractive index of a fiber?

(3) What is birefringence? Why is birefringence so important in fiber science?

(4) Compare specular reflection with diffuse reflection.

(5) What are the possible approaches to produce delustered fibers?

(6) What is dichroism?

Index

About the Author

 Professor *Xiangwu Zhang* received his B.S. in Polymer Materials and Engineering in 1997 and Ph.D. in Materials Science and Engineering in 2001, both from Zhejiang University, China. Following his graduation from Zhejiang University, Zhang joined the Center for Electrochemical Systems and Hydrogen Research at Texas A&M University as a Postdoctoral Research Associate in 2001. During 2002–2006, he was a Postdoctoral Research Associate in the Department of Chemical and Biomolecular Engineering at North Carolina State University. He joined the faculty in the Department of Textile Engineering, Chemistry, and Science at North Carolina State University in 2006. Zhang's research interests focus on nanostructured and multifunctional polymer, composite, fiber, and textile materials with an emphasis on practical applications: (*i*) energy storage and conversion, (*ii*) chemical and biological protection, and (*iii*) composites. His research encompasses both fundamental materials studies such as synthesis and physical characterization, as well as system design and fabrication. Widely published, he is frequently an invited speaker at major conferences in his field of expertise. Zhang is an inaugural University Faculty Scholar and has received the Alumni Association Outstanding Research Award and Outstanding Teacher Award from North Carolina State University.

Zhang currently serves as the President and Executive Committee Chair of the NCSU Chapter of Sigma Xi, the Scientific Research Society. Zhang is an active member of the Minerals, Metals & Materials Society (TMS), American Association of Textile Chemists and Colorists (AATCC), the Fiber Society, the American Society of Mechanical Engineers (ASME), the American Chemical Society (ACS), Materials Research Society (MRS), and the Electrochemical Society (ECS). Zhang is also an Executive Editor, Associate Editor or Editorial Board Member of Advances in Nanoparticles, Journal of Energy Storage and Conversion, Journal of Membrane Science & Technology, Journal of Nanoparticles, Journal of Textile Science and Engineering, Textiles and Light Industrial Science and Technology, Global Journal of Physical Chemistry, and International Journal of Nano Science, and Nano Engineering and Nanotechnology.